Unit 3
Weather

Gas Laws and Phase Changes

Teacher Guide
Preliminary Edition

Angelica M. Stacy, Jan Coonrod,
and Jennifer Claesgens

Acknowledgments:
Living by Chemistry has been developed at the Lawrence Hall of Science, University of California, Berkeley. This material is based upon work supported by the National Science Foundation grant No. ESI-9730634. Any opinions, findings, and conclusions or recommendations expressed in this material are those of the authors and do not necessarily reflect the views of the National Science Foundation or the Regents of the University of California.

The authors would like to thank Sally Rupert, Nicci Nunes, and Daniel Quach for contributions to the development of the Weather Unit. David R. Dudley contributed the cartoons and sketches of materials interspersed throughout the Unit.

Cover Photo Credits:
Weather map: F. Hirdes/Masterfile
Earth/crepuscular rays: PictureQuest
Hot air balloon, thermometer: Steve Allen/PictureQuest
Sun and storm clouds: StockTrek/PictureQuest

Published by Key Curriculum Press
Key Curriculum Press
1150 65th Street
Emeryville, CA 94608
510-595-7000
editorial@keypress.com
www.keypress.com

Printed in the United States of America
10 9 8 7 6 5 4 3   08 07 06 05 04

ISBN 1-55953-708-6

Weather – Contents

Introduction

Teaching and Learning with *Living by Chemistry*

Humans develop ways of understanding the world around them based on their experiences. Learning is a personal interpretation of experience, and each person has to assimilate new information into an existing framework of understanding – one that is quite individual. So, every lesson in the *Living by Chemistry* (LBC) curriculum begins by activating student's prior understanding of and knowledge about a subject. Students *can* accumulate facts and information, but true understanding comes when they actively make sense of the new information that you give them or tell them directly, restructuring their existing ideas to accommodate it.

Using this curriculum you'll rarely ask students to accept any piece of information on faith alone, as scientific fact. They'll look for patterns in evidence and examples, and you'll encourage them to think and to come to their own conclusions. You'll notice that nomenclature and formal definitions are frequently introduced *after* students have explored, scrutinized, and developed a concept. At first, you might find it difficult to restrain yourself from telling the students the "facts" - what chemists seem to "know" to be true. Nevertheless, it is important for your success and theirs that you simply guide the inquiry and avoid preempting it, allowing the lessons to unfold and students' native curiosity to motivate them. We hope you'll agree that engaging students in an ongoing mental process is more likely to lead to true understanding. It also reflects more authentically the mindset and practice of real scientists.

The LBC approach requires your students to be active thinkers. Some students who have been successful in school by getting information passively (through lecture or assigned reading) may be uncomfortable with the new LBC approach at first. They have a formula for success – absorb the information, accept it as fact, and repeat it back to the instructor – but perhaps they don't have an understanding of the concepts Their success as students may dip at first or they might have trouble getting used to the fact that "the rules have changed". Eventually these students will become attuned to the new approach and will welcome the new challenges and the opportunity to share their ideas. On the other hand, with the LBC curriculum you'll ask students to think, ask questions, and understand. Students who have experienced only mediocre or partial success may begin to excel. As they are challenged to become more active participants in the classroom, they'll be encouraged to share their ideas and theories. They'll find that "wrong" or offbeat answers are not only greeted favorably, but become useful fodder for discussion.

In the long run, we have found that both groups of students benefit more from this approach, both in chemistry class and in their daily lives. A deeper understanding, rather than just a surface knowledge of chemistry, provides a substantial foundation for learning down the road. Developing critical thinking and problem-solving skills benefits all students in all facets of their lives. Being able to support their answers with evidence and to advance their own reasoning are skills they will need for eventual success at the college level and in the job world. Students who use the LBC curriculum testify that they are learning thinking and problem solving skills that they can apply in other classes and disciplines.

For ultimate success with this curriculum, your patience with the learning process and your trust in it will be indispensable. At first, this approach may seem to take a bit more time and may seem to start a little slower. In actuality students are probably learning more in less time. For instance, you may be skeptical that the students will indeed discover the appropriate patterns in structural formulas, which chemists refer to as functional groups. How much easier it seems to just point them out rather than take the time to let the students deduce them! Nevertheless, our experience shows, and field-test teachers confirm, that students not only *can* do these things, but that they retain and comprehend more as a result of having gone through the process. The scaffolding approach to learning, in which you guide students from what they know already to what you want them to learn, allows them to function at the cutting edge of their development.

Living by Chemistry begins with the basics. We don't assume that your students come into your classroom with any exposure to chemistry or its concepts. At first glance, introducing rudimentary concepts may seem detrimental to a student who has had some background in chemistry. Nevertheless, the LBC approach is different enough that a student with prior knowledge is actually learning new things in new ways about a potentially old topic. Many students with exposure to chemistry come in with chemistry vocabulary and some ideas – they are often able to arrive at the "correct answer" to a question. But experience has taught us that most of these students do not understand the concepts behind the words. They may use the word "molecule" or "bond" but may not have an accurate conceptual understanding to accompany the word. With this curriculum you'll even the playing field by bringing everyone along, from your poorest students to your most gifted ones, and build a common foundation of understanding.

Finally, your role in the classroom changes as you work with the curriculum. Student-centered curriculum is precisely that— centered on the learner. The activities in *Living by Chemistry* are based in guided inquiry. You are their guide. Students complete an activity every day, often working in pairs or teams of four. As your students inquire and explore, you'll develop a more dynamic, in-the-present instruction style. Sometimes you'll feel that you have a little less control in the classroom as ideas fly around the room. Many times the exploratory process will generate questions you can't answer right away. Both of these are likely possibilities with this curriculum. But feel secure in the knowledge that these are some of the signs of a fertile, successful learning environment. It is up to you to foster this active curiosity and to make the classroom a safe place not only for new ideas and interesting hypotheses but also for wild ideas and shaky hypotheses, as well as routine inaccuracies, misconceptions, and simplistic questions. Students using the LBS curriculum are grateful for the group input, reporting that they benefit from a wider variety of strategies and approaches to a problem, rather than a single approach presented by an instructor. Eventually, your classroom may seem to run itself. As students work cooperatively on the challenges you set for them, you will be free address the individual needs of different learners.

Overview of Unit Structure and Lesson Design

Living by Chemistry is a full-year high school chemistry curriculum that meets state and national standards. The entire curriculum consists of six units organized around content. A single contextual theme runs throughout each unit, enhancing students' understanding of the chemistry content. The context provides a real-world foundation for the chemistry concepts and holds the students' interest.

Each unit consists of 25–30 lessons of 50-minute duration each. These daily lessons are clustered into 4 or 5 investigations. Each investigation addresses a piece of the content that students need for a full understanding of the context-based question asked at the beginning of the unit.

The lessons follow a standard format designed to support a guided inquiry approach to teaching and learning. The main parts are Exploring the Topic, Activity, Making Sense Discussion, and Check-in. Here are the goals of these instructional components.

 Exploring the Topic: The main goal of this section is to activate students' current thoughts, beliefs, and understanding on a specific topic. Upon starting class, you immediately engage students in an exercise, one that focuses them on the main goal of the lesson and generates interest. We call this exercise the ChemCatalyst. Once the students have answered the question individually, a class discussion ensues. This discussion is an opportunity for you to find out what your students think. We recommend that you listen to student ideas and ask for explanations, without judgment.

 Activity: Each lesson has an activity to allow students to work with the day's ideas and gather further information about the topic. The activities are quite varied, and include experiments, card sorts, worksheets with problems, model building, etc. Generally, you'll have the students work in small groups. You circulate from group to group, offering evidence, and guiding students to refine their ideas. We recommend that you avoid giving your students answers. Instead give them a chance to think and build their own understanding.

 Making Sense Discussion: The main goal of this part of the lesson is to assist students in formalizing their understanding. This is a chance to engage the class as a whole in processing the activity, with the goal of illuminating some new chemistry concepts, ideas, tools, or definitions. We recommend that you get the class to provide evidence for the key ideas, using information gathered in the activity.

 Check-in: A question is posed to provide both you and your students with a quick assessment of their grasp of the day's concepts.

The lesson structure supports the investigative process: students are engaged with the ChemCatalyst, they explore their ideas in the Activity, and they explain and elaborate on their ideas in the Making Sense Discussion. Evaluation and monitoring of understanding is embedded throughout.

One common question is: How much time does this take? First of all, the preparation for each class is different. Instead of spending time creating a lesson, you will be spending time setting up activities. During the class, instead of lecturing, you will be mainly interacting with students and guiding their explorations. Finally, hands-on and minds-on learning may seem slow at first. However, because students retain and understand the ideas more fully, the amount you can cover increases as the year progresses. We believe it is possible to surpass state and national standards.

Teacher's Materials and Kit

The *Living by Chemistry* curriculum comes with a student guide, a detailed teacher's guide, and a kit with supplies that are not typically found in a chemistry classroom. The teacher's guide has step-by-step instructions for each lesson. Here are some highlights of what is contained in these materials:

- ChemCatalyst and Check-in questions

- Student worksheets for each lesson

- Sample questions to ask students in discussions along with typical student responses

- Pages to photocopy onto transparencies for use in class discussions

- Detailed descriptions of the set-up for each lesson

- Supplies that cannot be purchased in a store

- A list of supplies that are not included

Conclusion

Our preliminary field-test results suggest that student performance improves with the *Living by Chemistry* curriculum. One of the most gratifying comments that we hear frequently from teachers is that they find many more students participating, including those who were not participating previously. We hope your experience with the curriculum meets these expectations.

The *Living by Chemistry* Development Team

Weather Unit – Topics Covered

Covered in depth

Mole/number conversions

Gas pressure

Random motion of gas particles

Gas laws

STP

Temperature scales

Absolute zero

Kinetic theory of gases

Ideal gas law

Temperature and heat

Prerequisites for the Weather Unit

Periodic table, atomic number, atomic mass

Weather Unit – Kit Supplies

Kit Inventory List

<u>Lab Ware</u>
8 **squirt bottles**
16 1.5-mm **capillary tubes** closed at one end
16 small **glass vials**
16 **rubber stoppers** with hole
16 **50-mL syringes** without caps
2 **50-mL syringes** with screw caps
3-ft clear **tubing**
24-ft flexible **tubing**
10 plastic **pipettes**

<u>Other supplies</u>
16 permanent **markers**
8 non-permanent **markers**
16 12-inch transparent **rulers**, marked in inches and cm
32 small **rubber bands**
Laminated **index card**

330 party **balloons**[R]
320 short **straws** to fit snugly in tubing
Food coloring[R]
Long **matches**[R]
2 clear plastic **cups**

400 mL **rubbing alcohol**
16 **oven mitts**
8 vials **mineral oil**
1 cup **potting soil**
2 cups **sand**

[R]: Key has provided enough of these items for 10 classes, but they are consumable and will need to be replaced after 2–3 years.

Weather Unit – Other Materials Needed

Common labware, lab supplies, chemicals, and other easily obtainable materials have not been included in this kit. They are listed below.

32 pairs **safety goggles** (1 per student)
16 250-ml **Erlenmeyer flasks**
1000-mL **Erlenmeyer flask**
16 25-ml **graduated cylinders**
8 **graduated cylinders** (preferably 250 ml or 500 ml)
8-16 **buckets** or large beakers
16 100-ml **beakers**
2 400-ml **beakers**
24 250-ml **beakers**
16 plastic **pipettes** or droppers (optional)
4-6 **tongs** (optional)
16 **test tubes**
16 **test tube holders**
16 **thermometers** (Celsius scale)
Ring stand and clamp
Large shallow **tub** to catch spills
Flasks, stoppers, glass tubing, and rubber tubing (if vacuum pump is unavailable)
8 **scale balances**
8 **hot plates**
Vacuum dessicator or a side-arm flask with a stopper
Funnel
Wooden or stiff plastic **ruler**

Vacuum pump (recommended)
Bathroom **scale** (1 mandatory, more optional)
Styrofoam **cooler** or ice chest
Hammer
2–4 5-gallon **cylindrical containers** (such as plastic flowerpots)
Desk **lamp** with high intensity bulb
17 2-liter **plastic bottles** with caps
2–3 empty aluminum **soda cans**
2 sheets of **newspaper**

8 plastic **garbage bags** (5 gallon size)
8 **twist ties**
Rock salt
Vaseline (optional, to seal stopper)
Marshmallows
2–3 **hard boiled eggs** (for lesson III-4)
Nitrogen gas or air, enough for 1 balloon (for lesson IV-2)
Helium balloon (for lesson IV-2)
Carbon dioxide gas, from dry ice or the reaction of baking soda and vinegar
        (for lesson IV-2)
Ice (for lessons I-1, I-4, II-2, II-4)
5–7 pounds **dry ice** (for lesson I-4)

Lesson-By-Lesson Lab Guide

An attempt has been made to provide the chemicals and specialized items needed for each lab. However, common labware, lab supplies, and other easily obtainable materials have not been included in this kit. They are listed in the "Other materials needed" column.

For consumable items, one kit contains enough materials for ten classes of 32 students. Please note that Bunsen burners can be substituted for hot plates, but hot plates are safer to use.

Lesson I-1: Weather or Not

Materials provided in kit	Other materials needed
16 party balloons	32 safety goggles (1 per student)
16 oven mitts	16 250-ml Erlenmeyer flasks
	8–16 25-mL graduated cylinders
	8 hot plates
	8–16 buckets or large beakers of ice
	Tap water

Students work in pairs. Each pair needs an Erlenmeyer flask and a balloon. Other equipment can be shared between two pairs of students.

Lesson I-2: Raindrops Keep Falling...

Materials provided in kit	Other materials needed
8 squirt bottles	16 100-mL beakers
16 12-inch transparent rulers	16 25-ml graduated cylinders
	Plastic pipettes or droppers (optional)

Students work in pairs. Each pair needs a graduated cylinder and a ruler. Other equipment can be shared between two pairs of students.

Lesson I-3: Having a Meltdown

Materials provided in kit	Other materials needed
8 squirt bottles	8 25-mL graduated cylinders
	Scales
	Tap water

Lesson I-4: It's Sublime...

Materials provided in kit	Other materials needed
8 oven mitts	32 safety goggles (1 per student)
	5-7 pounds of dry ice
	1 Styrofoam cooler or ice chest
	1 hammer
	8 plastic garbage bags (5 gallon size)
	8 twist ties
	Scales
	2-4 5-gallon cylindrical containers
	Several ice cubes (for demo)
	2 400-ml beakers (for demo)
	1 hot plate (for demo)
	4-6 tongs (optional)

Students work in teams of four students. Check your phone directory for dry ice vendors. Five pounds is more than enough for five classes. The hammer is needed to break the dry ice into smaller pieces. Students will use the 5-gallon cylindrical containers to measure the volume of the carbon dioxide gas.

Lesson II-1: Hot Enough

Materials provided in kit	Other materials needed
16 small glass vials (2 or 4-dram size)	32 safety goggles (1 per student)
16 rubber stoppers with a hole	24 250-ml beakers
16 clear plastic straws	8 hot plate
Food coloring	Ice cubes
16 12-inch transparent rulers (metric)	Vaseline (optional, to seal stopper)
16 permanent markers	

Students work in pairs. Each pair will need a small glass vial, a rubber stopper with a hole that fits tightly on the glass vial (or a septum with a hole), and a straw that fits tightly into the hole in the stopper. They can share hot plates, markers, and beakers of boiling water, room temperature water, and ice water with another pair.

Lesson II-2: Full of Hot Air

Materials provided in kit	Other materials needed
16 1.5-mm capillary tubes closed on one end	32 safety goggles (1 per student)
32 small rubber bands	8 hot plates
Food coloring	16 test tubes
16 12-inch transparent rulers (metric)	16 test tube holders
16 permanent markers	16 thermometers (Celsius scale)
Few mL mineral oil	8 small beakers or vials (for oil)
	16 250-mL beakers
	8 hot plates
	Tap water
	Ice
	Rock salt

Students work in pairs. Each pair will need a test tube, a test tube holder, a capillary tube, a thermometer, two small rubber bands, and a permanent marker. They can share hot plates, beakers of boiling water, and beakers with an ice water/rock salt mixture with another pair.

Lesson II-4: It's Only a Phase

Materials provided in kit	Other materials needed
16 Oven mitts	32 safety goggles (1 per student)
	16 250-mL beaker
	16 ice cubes (kept below 0°C)
	16 thermometers
	8 hot plates
	Ring stand and clamp to hold the thermometer (optional)

Students work in pairs. Each pair will need a beaker, a thermometer, and an ice cube. If at all possible, the ice cube should be below 0°C (removed directly from a freezer before use). They can share hot plates with another pair.

Lesson II-6: Hot Cement

Materials provided in kit	Other materials needed (for demo)
50 g potting soil (for demo)	Desk lamp with high intensity bulb (for demo)
2 clear plastic cups (for demo)	Tap water
	2 thermometers (for demo)

Lesson III-1: Balancing Act

Materials provided in kit	Other materials needed
12 party balloons	2-3 safety goggles
2 50-ml syringes	1 2-liter plastic bottle
3 feet of clear tubing	1 hot plate
1 clear plastic cup	2-3 empty aluminum soda cans
1 laminated card to fit over mouth of plastic cup	1 large shallow tub to catch spills
	Tap water
	1 pair of tongs
	Vacuum pump (recommended)
	Vacuum dessicator or a side-arm flask with a stopper
	Flasks, stoppers, glass tubing, and rubber tubing if vacuum pump is unavailable
	Marshmallows (mini if using syringe)

Lesson III-2: Feeling Under Pressure

Materials provided in kit	Other materials needed
2 party balloons (for demo)	32 safety goggles (1 per student)
2 cups of sand (for demo)	1 funnel
16 50-mL syringes (without caps)	Bathroom scale (one mandatory, more if available)
2 50-mL syringes with screw caps	

Pairs of students need a 50-mL syringe (without caps). The bathroom scale and the syringe that is capped will be used for a demonstration. If more bathroom scales are available, then more students can participate.

Lesson III-4: Egg in a Bottle

Materials provided in kit	Other materials needed
1 oven mitt	1 1000-mL Erlenmeyer flask (for demo)
	2-3 hard boiled eggs, shelled (for demo)
	1 hot plate (for demo)

Lesson IV-1: Tower of Air

Materials provided in kit	Other materials needed
	2 sheets of newspaper (for demo)
	1 wooden or stiff plastic ruler (for demo)

Lesson IV-2: Lighter Than Air

Materials provided in kit	Other materials needed
3 party balloons (for demo)	Nitrogen gas or air (for demo)
	Helium gas (for demo)
	Carbon dioxide gas – can be generated from the reaction of baking soda and vinegar (for demo)

Lesson IV-3: More Than a Trillion

Materials provided in kit	Other materials needed
	16 sets of 24 small pieces of paper – index cards or small Post-its work well, or students can tear regular sheets of paper into 24 pieces

Lesson IV-4: Take a Breath

Materials provided in kit	Other materials needed
8 pieces of 3-ft flexible tubing	8 2-L plastic soda bottles with caps
32 short straws to fit snugly in tubing (straws can be cut)	8 graduated cylinders (preferably 250 mL or 500 mL)
8 non-permanent markers	Tap water
	8 containers for water (~5-L size)

Students work in teams of four. Each team needs a 2-L plastic bottle and a piece of 3-ft flexible tubing. Each students needs his or her own straw (or piece of a straw) to use as a clean mouthpiece.

Lesson IV-5: Up in the Clouds

Materials provided in kit	Other materials needed
Long matches	8-16 2-L plastic soda bottles with caps
	Dry 2-L plastic soda bottle with cap
	Tap water
	Hot water (~80°C)

Students can work in pairs or teams of four depending on how many plastic soda bottles are available. The dry 2-L bottle can be shared among the whole class or each team can have their own.

Lesson IV-6: Rain in the Forecast

Materials provided in kit	Other materials needed
50-mL rubbing alcohol	Tap water
8-10 plastic pipettes	8-10 droppers (optional)

To order new kits, contact:
Key Curriculum Press
1150 65th Street
Emeryville, CA 94608
(800) 995-6284   www.keypress.com

To report errors or problems, please call us or send an e-mail to editorial@keypress.com

Weather © UC Regents, LHS Living by Chemistry, 2003.

 **Key Curriculum Press**

Living By Chemistry

Unit Feedback Form

Unit 3: <u>Weather</u>

Your feedback is valuable to us, even if you do not answer every question. Once you have filled out this form, please fold it and drop it in the mail. We'll pay the postage. Thank you!

Was it easy for you and your students to understand the objectives of this unit? _____

1. Do you think that the unit met all of its objectives? _____

_____

_____

2. Rate the difficulty of this unit. ☐ Too difficult ☐ Too easy ☐ About right

   Comments: _____

_____

3. Was too much or too little time spent on any topic? Please comment: _____

   <u>Too much:</u> _____

   <u>Too little:</u> _____

4. What topics were *not* included in this unit, but should have been in order to satisfy your state or district standards? _____

_____

5. What kinds of material did you add to this unit? _____

_____

6. Compared to your previous curriculum, did students learn concepts more thoroughly or less thoroughly with this unit?

   ☐ More thoroughly ☐ Less thoroughly ☐ About the same

   Please comment: _____

   What criteria did you use to answer this question? _____

_____

7. How would you describe your overall experience with the unit?

   ☐ very positive ☐ positive ☐ fair ☐ negative ☐ very negative

   Comments: _____

_____

8. What changes would you make to this unit? _____

_____

9. What activities or lessons were most successful? Why? _____

Submitted by: _____ Date: _____

May we contact you to further discuss your experiences? Yes ☐ No ☐

If yes, please include the best way to reach you:

Phone _____ E-mail_____

Please detach page, fold on lines and tape edge.

BUSINESS REPLY MAIL
FIRST CLASS   PERMIT NO. 338   OAKLAND, CA

POSTAGE WILL BE PAID BY ADDRESSEE

KEY CURRICULUM PRESS
1150 65TH STREET
EMERYVILLE CA 94608-9740

Attention Editorial: *Living by Chemistry*

 **Key Curriculum Press**

Living by Chemistry
Unit 3: Weather

Correction/Comment Form

Please help us correct and improve *Living by Chemistry*. If you find mistakes in the Teacher Guide or Student Guide, use this form to let us know. If you have further comments or suggestions about the materials, we'd like to hear those as well.

Once you've filled out this form, all you have to do is fold it and drop it in the mail. We'll pay the postage. Thank you!

Your Name _____

School _____

School Address _____

City/State/Zip _____

Phone _____

Teacher Guide:

Page _____ Comment _____

Page _____ Comment _____

Page _____ Comment _____

Page _____ Comment _____

Page _____ Comment _____

Page _____ Comment _____

Student Guide:

Page _____ Comment _____

Page _____ Comment _____

Page _____ Comment _____

Page _____ Comment _____

Page _____ Comment _____

Page _____ Comment _____

Do you have any general comments about *Living by Chemistry,* or any suggestions for improving the student or teacher material? (Please use the Unit Feedback Form if you wish to give more extensive feedback.)

_____

_____

_____

Please detach page, fold on lines and tape edge.

BUSINESS REPLY MAIL
FIRST CLASS   PERMIT NO. 338   OAKLAND, CA

POSTAGE WILL BE PAID BY ADDRESSEE

KEY CURRICULUM PRESS
1150 65TH STREET
EMERYVILLE CA 94608-9740

Attention Editorial: *Living by Chemistry*

Unit 3: Weather

Investigation I: Locating Matter

Contents of Investigation I   *Page*

Investigation I Summary:

Locating Matter

Investigation I consists of five lessons. Together they introduce the topic of weather to the class and open the door to the study of physical change. The first lesson engages students in performing an experiment in which they inflate a balloon with water vapor, and directly observe the movement of matter caused by physical change. This is followed by measurement of the height of rainfall and a discussion of precision in measurement in the second lesson. In the third lesson, students convert from mass of snowfall to mass of rainfall by using the density of rain and snow. Students measure the large change in density when dry ice sublimes in the fourth lesson. The location of water on the planet based on its density and how the movement of water drives weather is consider in the final lesson. The investigation ends by interpreting a map of average rainfall in the United States.

Students are immediately involved in thinking about the weather on the first day. They consider the words used in weather reports and how meteorologists forecast weather. The mathematics students will need to explore the topic is introduced in this investigation as students consider what it means that two quantities are proportional to one another. The relationship between weather and mass, volume, density, and phase change are emphasized.

Lesson 1 – Weather or Not. This lesson introduces students to the weather context. After considering what is included in a weather forecast, students perform an activity in which they inflate and deflate a balloon by changing water from a liquid to a gas and back again. Students consider how the volume, temperature, pressure, number of molecules, and concentration of molecules affect the balloon. These variables are important in weather reporting, and are the focus of the Weather Unit. The discussion comes to a close as students consider how water moves around the planet.

Lesson 2 – Raindrops Keep Falling… The students begin their explorations of weather by considering how rainfall is measured. Students learn about precision in measurement and significant figures by considering which container would make a better rain gauge – a beaker or a graduated cylinder. Next, students consider how to keep track of the rain that falls during a storm by measuring the height and volume of water in a graduated cylinder. Students graph volume vs. height for different amounts of water, and discuss how both increase with increasing rainfall. The proportionality between volume and height is introduced. This lesson serves to scaffold slowly some of the math concepts that will be of use to students in later classes of the Weather Unit. (In an optional experiment, students explore why meteorologists report height rather than volume when reporting rainfall.)

Lesson 3 – Having a Melt Down. Now that students have experience measuring volume of rainfall, they are asked to consider how volume of snowfall is related to volume of rainfall by the mass, and more specifically by the density. Students design their own experiment to measure the mass and volume of different amounts of water, and then graph the data they acquire. Density is introduced and related to the slope of the line. Students then use differences in density between rain and snow to predict how much snow there will be in the mountains for a given amount of rainfall at lower elevations.

Lesson 4 – It's Sublime. The exploration into phase changes continues as students explore the change in density when solid carbon dioxide sublimes to form carbon dioxide gas. Using dry ice, students will collect rough quantitative data relating the mass and volume of solid CO_2 to the volume of the same amount of CO_2 as a gas. Students will gain convincing evidence of the magnitude of the difference between the density of a solid and the density of a gas.

Lesson 5 – Waterworld. The investigation comes to a close with a discussion of the relocation of water from the Earth's surface to the atmosphere and back again. Students first compare the densities of several substances to look for general trends. They then consider how the density of water changes as water converts from liquid to vapor to clouds and to rain and snow. They consider how motions of molecules are involved in moving water molecules from the liquid to the upper reaches of the atmosphere and then back again.

BEFORE CLASS...

LESSON 1 – Weather or Not

Key Ideas:

Weather can be seen as an interaction between the sun (a heat source) and the water on our planet. Meteorologists track the movement of moisture around our planet. The Earth's atmosphere and its soil also play critical roles in this dynamic interplay. This unit will investigate the relationships between phase, density, volume, temperature, and amounts of matter. This is the chemistry of physical change.

What Takes Place:

This lesson opens the entire unit and introduces the context of weather to the class. Students work with a flask, a small amount of water, and a balloon to explore the changes in volume that occur when water changes phase from liquid to gas and back again. Phase changes of water and the associated movement of water are linked to changes in the weather.

Materials: (per team of 2 students)

- 250 mL Erlenmeyer flask
- 25 mL graduated cylinder
- Medium-sized party balloon
- 5 mL of water
- Hot plate
- Oven mitt
- Bucket or large beaker with ice and water
- Student worksheet
- Water bottle (optional)

Investigation I – Locating Matter

LESSON 1 – Weather or Not

This lesson introduces students to the weather context. After considering what is included in a weather forecast, students perform an activity in which they inflate and deflate a balloon by changing water from a liquid to a gas and back again. Students consider how the volume, temperature, pressure, number of molecules, and concentration of molecules affect the balloon. These variables are important in weather reporting, and are the focus of the Weather Unit. The discussion comes to a close as students consider how water moves around the planet.

Exploring the Topic   (5–10 min)

1. Introduce the ChemCatalyst exercise. (Transparency)

Display the following transparency for students to complete individually.

Below are a picture and weather report of a hurricane off the coast of Florida in the United States.

FORECAST FOR THE MIAMI AREA: The tenth depression of the season in the Atlantic has become Hurricane Jan. The center of Jan is southeast of Florida. The maximum sustained winds are near 120 miles per hour. The estimated minimum central pressure is 28.5 inches. Skies over Miami are mostly cloudy. The temperature is 35°C / 95°F with 90% humidity. Jan is expected to drop as much as 10 inches of rain in the southern part of Florida with rising temperature and humidity.

- What are hurricanes and what do you think causes them?
- What is weather? What causes weather?
- How do meteorologists predict things like hurricanes?

2. Discuss the ChemCatalyst exercise.

Use the discussion to get a sense of students' initial ideas.

Discussion goals:
Assist students in sharing their initial ideas about weather. They may wish to share their experiences with extreme weather.

Sample questions:
What is a hurricane? What do you think causes hurricanes?
What is weather?
What causes weather?
What is the most extreme weather you've ever experienced?
How do meteorologists predict the weather?
What role does weather play in the survival of our planet?
What things do you need to know about in order to forecast the weather?
What do you think chemistry has to do with weather?

Points to cover:
Weather can be seen as an interaction between the sun (a heat source), the water on the planet, the Earth's surface, and the atmosphere of the planet. This unit will explore the chemistry of weather and will seek to answer the question: "What causes the weather?"

A hurricane is a tropical storm over the ocean with winds of at least 74 miles per hour. Listen to students' ideas about weather, but do not judge their responses at this point.

3. Explain the purpose of today's activity.

If you wish you can write the main question on the board.

Points to cover:
Tell students that today they will be concentrating on the movement of water around the planet and how this causes changes in weather. The guiding question is: "What causes water to 'cycle' or move around on the planet?"

Activity – Weather or Not   (15 min)

4. Introduce the activity. (Worksheet)

Pass out the worksheet to individual students. Ask students to work in pairs.

Materials: (for each team of two students)
250 mL Erlenmeyer flask

25 mL graduated cylinder
Medium-sized party balloon
5 mL of water
Hot plate
Oven mitt
Bucket or large beaker with ice and water

Procedure:
1. Place about 5 mL of water into a 250 mL Erlenmeyer flask.
2. Place the open end of a balloon over the mouth of the Erlenmeyer flask.
3. Heat the flask on a hot plate until the water boils. Do not boil all the water away. (The hot plate setting should be about 4.)
4. After several minutes, use a towel or oven mitt to remove the flask from the hot plate.
5. Hold the flask standing upright in ice water.
6. Reheat and re-cool as desired to observe.

Optional additional investigation:
Repeat the procedure given above, except reverse steps 2 and 3: Once the water is boiling, remove the flask with an oven mitt from the hot plate. Put the balloon on the flask (be careful, the glass is very hot!) Once the balloon is attached, put the flask back on the hot plate.

Answer the following questions:

1. What did you observe when the flask was heated? (The balloon inflated as the water boiled, some of the water became gaseous. Some water also drips down the sides of the flask.)

2. What did you observe when the flask was cooled? (The balloon deflated. In the optional investigation, the balloon inflated inside the flask.)

3. Why did the balloon get so large? (When the water is converted from liquid to vapor, the water molecules move around more and inflate the balloon.)

4. What happens to the water molecules as the flask is cooled? What evidence do you have to support your answer? (The water molecules change from gas to liquid when the flask cools. The balloon deflates and moisture drips down the inside of the flask.)

5. Water droplets come together to form clouds in the atmosphere at an altitude of about 2,000 meters. Do you think the air in the atmosphere becomes hotter or colder as the altitude increases? Explain using evidence from this experiment. (When the flask was cooled, the gaseous water became liquid droplets. Since water molecules are changing from gas to liquid when clouds are formed, it must be colder 2000 meters up in the atmosphere.)

6. Gaseous water is also called water vapor. Humidity is the measure of the amount of water vapor in the air. As the temperature of the air increases, what do you think happens to the humidity? Explain your thinking. (The humidity increases because more water becomes a gas at higher temperatures.)

7. A meteorologist would say the pressure of the air inside the heated flask is greater than the pressure of the air inside the cooled flask.

    a) What evidence do you have that the pressure inside the heated flask is greater? (The balloon inflates.)

    b) What do you think air pressure measures? (Air molecules push on things. The air molecules in the flask push the rubbery material of the balloon to cause it to inflate.)

Making sense question

Based on this experiment, explain what causes water to "cycle" around the planet?

If you finish early…

Do the optional experiment. Explain your observations. (When the balloon is put on the flask *after* the water is boiling, it inflates inside the flask upon cooling. This is because the "air" in the flask was mostly water vapor when the balloon was put on. Upon cooling, the water molecules condense. Since much of the "air" was water vapor, the volume of air decreases significantly when the water molecules condense upon cooling.)

Making Sense Discussion   (10–15 min)

Major goals: The goal of this discussion is to assist students in explaining their observations. They should begin to articulate how water molecules move around as they change from phase to phase when water is heated and cooled. The effect of a gas/liquid phase change on the volume of water should also be explored. The concept of physical change is introduced as the theme of the Weather Unit.

5. Discuss the students' findings.

Discussion goals:
Focus the discussion on the students' observations, and their explanations of what happened during the activity.

Sample questions:
    Why do you think the balloon inflated when the flask was heated? (air in the flask expanded when it was heated, water became a gas and expanded)
    Explain where the water molecules are located when the flask is hot. (They are in the air; in the balloon, and some in the flask.)

Do you think the number of water molecules changed when the temperature changed? Explain your thinking. (The number of molecules did not change. The system is closed, no new molecules are introduced and no molecules can escape.)

Why do you think the balloon deflated when it was cooled? (Gaseous water molecules became liquid and moved out of the balloon. Air and water molecules contracted because they stopped moving so fast.)

Explain what happens to the amount of space or volume occupied by the water molecules as they change from liquid to gas and back again. (The volume of the water molecules increases when the water becomes a gas, and decreases again when it changes back to a liquid.)

Explain where the water molecules are located when the flask is cold. (Most of them are liquid and are therefore in the bottom of the flask.)

Is it "raining" in the cold flask? Explain your thinking. (Yes, what is happening in the flask is similar to rain. The gaseous water is condensing and becoming water droplets.)

What do we mean when we say that water "cycles" on the planet?

Points to cover:

As the water in the flask is heated, the balloon inflates. This observation is evidence that the water molecules are moving from the liquid water up into the air to push the stretchy material of the balloon out. Water vapor and liquid water are two different **phases** of water – gas and liquid. Since the balloon inflates, we can also conclude that the **phase change** from liquid to gas is associated with a large volume change. Water in the gas phase takes up more space than water in the liquid form as is apparent from the change in balloon volume in this activity. The gaseous water molecules are heated and are therefore moving quickly and pressing out on the skin of the balloon. The changing of water from liquid to gas is given a specific name - **evaporation**.

As the water and air in the flask and balloon are cooled, the balloon deflates. In addition, water droplets can be seen on the inside of the flask. This observation is evidence that the water molecules are moving from gas to liquid when the flask is cooled, thereby reducing the air volume and deflating the balloon. The changing of water from gas to liquid is called **condensation.**

Evaporation is the changing of a substance from the liquid phase to the gas phase. **Condensation** is the changing of a substance from the gas phase to the liquid phase.

Gas, liquid, and solid are three different **phases** of matter. A **phase change** refers to the conversion of a liquid to a gas or a solid, or vice versa.

---

6. Discuss physical change.

Inform the class that they have been exploring one type of physical change today.

Discussion goals:
Assist the class in defining physical change.

Sample questions:
What do you think the term *physical change* means in chemistry?
How are phase changes associated with changes in volume?
When the water in the flask was heated, the air pressure in the sealed container increased. What does this mean?
How could you decrease the number of water molecules in the air right now?

Points to cover:
Chemists talk about physical changes and chemical changes of matter. A phase change (from gas to liquid to solid or vice versa) is one type of **physical change** that matter goes through. A physical change is one in which the form or temperature of something is changed without changing the chemical make-up of the substance. The most common physical changes we will encounter in chemistry are changes in phase, temperature, pressure, volume, and/or changes in the number of molecules of a substance.

> A **physical change** is one in which the form or temperature of a substance is changed without changing its chemical make-up.

One question on the worksheet talked about humidity. **Humidity** is a measure of the amount of water vapor (or gaseous water) in the air. A change in humidity is a physical change because it represents a change in the number of molecules in a given space. Humidity will be discussed in greater detail later in the Weather Unit.

7. Relate today's activity to the Weather Unit.

Use this discussion to begin to flesh out the context that will drive the investigation into matter.

Discussion goals:
Assist students in thinking about the movement of water on the planet and what forces affect the water cycle.

Sample questions:
How does the sun affect the location of the water on our planet? (by evaporating liquid water)

What do you think causes water vapor in the air to fall as rain? (cold air, since water condenses and becomes rain, it must be cold high up in the sir)

Why do clouds form high up in the air rather than closer to the earth's surface? (it is colder higher up in the atmosphere)

Does the humidity of the air change when the temperature changes? (as it gets warmer, the humidity of the air increases because water evaporates)

Describe how water moves from the ocean to the clouds and back to earth as rain.

How do you think wind affects the water cycle?

What evidence do you have that the phase changes of water might be an important factor in the weather?

Points to cover:

The phase changes of water are intimately connected with changes in weather. Water moves around our planet as it changes from one phase to another. Phase changes cause the transport of water from oceans into the atmosphere and then back to the earth as rain. These phase changes are associated with temperature changes. The sun is our planet's heat source, and is responsible for the temperature changes we observe on the planet. The regular movement of water around the planet in this manner is called the **water cycle.**

The Weather Unit is set up to explore how physical change causes weather on our planet. Investigation I explores the relationship between the location of water and it's phase, volume, and density. In referring to the *location* of water we are talking about where water is on the planet (in the oceans, in the atmosphere, in the snowpack, etc.). Thus, *location* also refers to what phase water is in – liquid, gas or solid. Later in the unit we will explore other physical changes and their effects on the weather, in more detail.

Check-in   (5 min)

8. Complete the Check-in exercise.

Put the following exercise on the board for students to answer individually..

- Using what you learned today about the movement of water, explain what causes rain on the planet Earth.

9. Discuss the Check-in exercise.

Get a sense of the level of understanding by asking students to defend their choices.

Discussion goals:

Make sure that students understand the relationship between air temperature, phase, and rain.

Suggested questions:

Explain what causes rain.

Water evaporates into the air when it is heated by the sun. When it cools down again the water becomes a liquid (condenses) and forms water droplets (clouds and rain). Students may also mention that as the altitude increases, the temperature of the atmosphere decreases.

10. Wrap-up

Assist the students in summarizing what was learned in the class.

- Weather is an interaction between the sun (a heat source), the water on the planet, the Earth's surface, and the Earth's atmosphere.
- Water moves around through phase changes.
- Phase changes affect the volume of substances.

Homework

11. Assign homework.

Use the homework provided with the curriculum or assign your own.

Homework – Investigation I – Lesson 1

1. Snow is a solid form of water. Explain why you think snow and ice are so different if they are both forms of solid water.

2. When you take a shower, the mirror in the bathroom becomes "fogged up". Explain what is happening.

3. Do other planets have weather? Explain why or why not.

4. If water evaporates into the air from the ocean, why doesn't it rain over the ocean all the time? Why does it rain over land sometimes?

Transparency

ChemCatalyst: Below are a picture and a weather report of a hurricane off the coast of Florida in the United States.

FORECAST FOR THE MIAMI AREA: The tenth depression of the season in the Atlantic has become Hurricane Jan. The center of Jan is southeast of Florida. The maximum sustained winds are near 120 miles per hour. The estimated minimum central pressure is 28.5 inches. Skies over Miami are mostly cloudy. The temperature is 35°C / 95°F with 90% humidity. Jan is expected to drop as much as 10 inches of rain in the southern part of Florida with rising temperature and humidity.

Weather or Not

Name: _____

Date: _____Period _____

Purpose: In this activity you will heat and cool water in a flask with a balloon attached. Your observations will help you determine what makes the water "cycle."

Materials
250 mL Erlenmeyer flask
25 mL graduated cylinder
Medium sized party balloon
5 mL of water
Hot plate
Oven mitt
Ice

Procedure:
1. Place about 5 mL of water into a 250 mL Erlenmeyer flask.
2. Place the open end of a balloon over the mouth of the Erlenmeyer flask
3. Heat the flask on a hot plate until the water boils. Do not boil all the water away. (The hot plate setting should be about 4.)
4. After several minutes, use a towel or oven mitt to remove the flask from the hot plate.
5. Hold the flask standing upright in ice water.
6. Reheat and re-cool as desired to observe.

Optional additional investigation:
Repeat the procedure given above, except reverse steps 2 and 3: Once the water is boiling, remove the flask from the hot plate with an oven mitt. Put the balloon on the flask (be careful, the glass is very hot!) Once the balloon is attached, put the flask back on the hot plate.

Answer the following questions:
1. What did you observe when the flask was heated?

2. What did you observe when the flask was cooled?

3. Why did the balloon get so large?

4. What happens to the water molecules as the flask is cooled? What evidence do you have to support your answer?

5. Water droplets come together to form clouds in the atmosphere at an altitude of about 2,000 meters. Do you think the air in the atmosphere becomes hotter or colder as the altitude increases? Explain using evidence from this experiment.

6. Gaseous water is also called water vapor. Humidity is the measure of the amount of water vapor in the air. As the temperature of the air increases, what do you think happens to the humidity? Explain your thinking.

7. A meteorologist would say the pressure of the air inside the heated flask is greater than the pressure of the air inside the cooled flask.

    a) What evidence do you have that the pressure inside the heated flask is greater?

    b) What do you think air pressure measures?

Making sense:
Based on this experiment, explain what causes water to "cycle" around the planet?

If you finish early…
Do the optional experiment. Explain your observations.

BEFORE CLASS...

LESSON 2 – Raindrops Keep Falling...

Key Ideas:

Meteorologists measure rainfall in inches or millimeters. These are both measures of height. Rainfall is not measured in volume. But, the volume of a container is proportional to its height. As rainfall increases, both height and volume increase. The height of rainfall is the same in any rain gauge. The volume depends on the area of the base of the rain gauge (volume = area of base x height). The precision of a rain gauge depends on the number of gradations that have been marked on it to measure inches and/or mL.

What Takes Place:

In this activity students consider how to keep track of rainfall by measuring mL (volume) and inches (height) of water in a rain gauge. They begin by exploring the difference in precision between a beaker and a graduated cylinder to determine which instrument would make a better rain gauge. They then measure the height of rain for different volumes of water in a rain gauge, and are asked to plot these data on a graph. The graph allows students to see the proportional relationship between the height of rain and the volume of rain that falls. (In an optional experiment, students determine that the height of rain that falls in a storm is the same for all rain gauges, whereas the volume depends on the diameter of the rain gauge.)

Materials: (per team of 2 students)
- Student worksheet
- 25 mL graduated cylinder
- 100 mL beaker
- 12 inch ruler
- Water bottles (use plastic pipettes or droppers if you do not have water bottles)

Investigation I – Locating Matter
LESSON 2 – Raindrops Keep Falling…

The students begin their explorations of weather by considering how rainfall is measured. Students learn about precision in measurement and significant figures by considering which container would make a better rain gauge – a beaker or a graduated cylinder. Next, students consider how to keep track of the rain that falls during a storm by measuring the height and volume of water in a graduated cylinder. Students graph volume vs. height for different amounts of water, and discuss how both increase with increasing rainfall. The proportionality between volume and height is introduced. This lesson serves to scaffold slowly some of the math concepts that will be of use to students in later classes of the Weather Unit. (In an optional experiment, students explore why meteorologists report height rather than volume when reporting rainfall.)

Exploring the Topic   (5–10 min)

1. Introduce ChemCatalyst exercise. (Transparency)

Show the transparency with the following exercise for students to complete individually.

A map showing annual rainfall in the United States in 2002 is shown below/

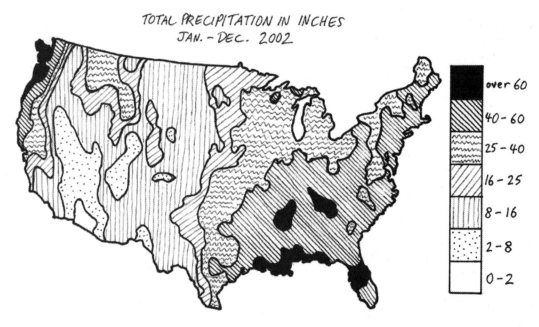

- How much rain fell where you live?
- How is rainfall measured?
- What type of instrument or container is used to measure rainfall?

2. Discuss the ChemCatalyst exercise.

Use the discussion to get a sense of students' initial ideas.

<u>Discussion goals</u>
Discuss different ways that you might keep track of rainfall.

Sample questions:
What is the annual rainfall where you live?
How do meteorologists keep track of rainfall? What instruments do they use?
Describe how you would measure inches of rainfall. What kind of container would you use?
Describe how you would measure volume of rainfall in mL. What kind of container would you use?
Do both height and volume increase as more rain falls? Why or why not?
How is volume different from height?

A rain gauge is a cylindrical container used to measure the height of rainfall in inches of water. The height of water in a container is measured with a ruler. Scientists prefer to use centimeters (cm) or millimeters (mm) to measure height, but since rainfall is reported in inches in the United States, we will use inches. In other countries rainfall is measured in millimeters. Volume is another way to keep track of rainfall. In general, volume depends on the area over which the rainfall was measured, whereas height does not.

3. Explain the purpose of the activity.

If you wish you can write the main question on the board.

Points to cover:
Meteorologists report the amount of rain that falls each day. Height and volume are two ways of keeping track of amounts of water. Tell students that in this lesson they will be gathering information to address the question: "How do meteorologists keep track of rainfall"

Activity – Raindrops Keep Falling...   (15 min)

4. Introduce the activity.

Tell students that they will begin by examining the use of a beaker and a graduated cylinder as rain gauges.

Materials (for each pair of students):
25-mL graduated cylinder
100-mL beaker
12-inch ruler
Water bottles (plastic pipettes or droppers can be used if you do not have water bottles)

Part 1: Measuring volume – How precise is the instrument?

Procedure:

Measure 20 mL of water in the beaker then pour it into the graduated cylinder.

1. Is 20 mL in the beaker the same as 20 mL in the graduated cylinder? (no, because the precision is not the same) What is the volume in the graduated cylinder?

2. What does each line represent on the graduated cylinder? (0.1 mL) What does each line represent on the beaker? (Somewhere around 10 mL, depending on the beaker)

3. If you need to measure 15 mL of water, should you use a beaker or a graduated cylinder? Explain. (The graduated cylinder, because it is difficult to tell where 15 mL is on the beaker.)

4. The beaker is designed to measure a maximum of 80 mL of liquid, while the graduated cylinder is designed to measure a maximum of 25.0 mL of liquid. Why do you think a decimal place is included on the graduated cylinder and not the beaker? (The extra digit beyond the decimal point indicates that the graduated cylinder is more precise and can measure volumes as closely as one tenth of a milliliter.)

5. Which is more precise, the beaker or the graduated cylinder? (The graduated cylinder is more precise because it has more measured divisions.)

6. Which would make a better rain gauge – the beaker or the graduated cylinder? Explain why. (The graduated cylinder because it is more precise.)

Part II: Measuring rainfall – Keeping track of rainfall with inches and mL

Procedure:

A rain gauge is a cylindrical container used to measure the height of rainfall. Use the 25 mL graduated cylinder as a rain gauge. Put exactly 5.0 mL of water into the rain gauge. Use a water bottle to put the last few drops in to get exactly 5.0 mL measured to the bottom of the meniscus. Measure the height as carefully as possible. Record the height in the table. Repeat for 10.0, 15.0, and 20.0 mL of water. Graph the results. (A sample data set is shown below. The exact numbers depend on the diameter of the graduated cylinder.)

You may need to remind students how to read a meniscus.

Height (inches)	0 in	7/8 in	1 7/8 in	2 7/8 in	3 7/8 in
Volume (milliliters)	0 mL	5 mL	10.0 mL	15.0 mL	20.0 mL

Plot these points on the graph. Draw a line through the points. Use a ruler and make sure your line passes through, or near, as many of your data points as possible. (The data the students collect may not lie on a straight line. Tell students to draw the best straight line through the points.)

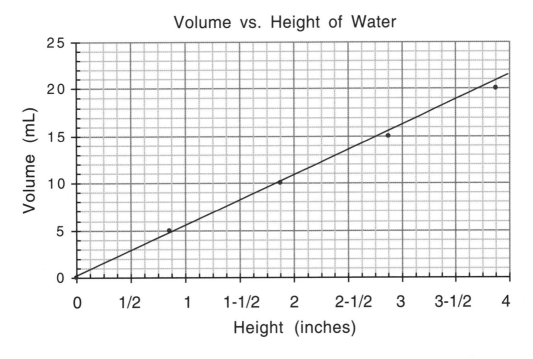

Answer the following questions:

1. Why don't all of the data points lie exactly on the line you drew? (errors in measurement)

2. If the height of the water is exactly 1-3/4 inches, can you determine this using your ruler? Why or why not? (yes, the ruler has markings to 1/16 inches)

3. Use the graph to predict the volume of 1-3/4 inches of rain.

4. Use the data table to predict the volume of 4 inches of rain.

5. Explain how you would predict the volume of 10 inches of rain.

6. Why do you think scientists use graphs?

Making sense question

Meteorologists can keep track of the amount of rainfall by measuring either the volume or the height of rainfall in a rain gauge.

• If the amount of rainfall increases, do both the volume and height of water in the rain gauge keep track of this increase? Explain your thinking.

• What does the precision of measuring height and volume depend on? Is there a difference in the precision of measuring height or volume? Explain your thinking.

If you finish early...

Put 2 inches of water in the 100 mL beaker and 2 inches in the 25 mL graduated cylinder. Determine the volume of water in the beaker and the graduated cylinder.

- If 2 inches of rain fall in a storm, what height in inches will you measure in the beaker? In the graduated cylinder?

- If you use a beaker for a rain gauge, and the weather station uses a graduated cylinder, will both instruments give the same volume? The same height in inches?

- If a large washtub, a dog's water dish, and a graduated cylinder were left outside during a rainstorm, would the three containers all have the same volume of water in them after the storm? Explain why or why not.

- Why do meteorologists prefer to measure the height of rainfall?

Making Sense Discussion   (15 min)

Major goals: One goal of this discussion is to introduce students to significant figures, and to explore precision in measurement. A second goal is to introduce to the idea of proportional relationships. Students should grasp that the volume of water in a cylindrical container is directly proportional to its height. This proportionality makes it possible to predict the volume of rainfall if you know the inches of rainfall for a given rain gauge, and vice versa. (Optional discussion: Meteorologists report the height of rainfall in inches because the height does not depend on the area over which the measurement is made, whereas the volume does.)

Note: We have opted to measure height in inches in this lesson because inches are used to report the height of rainfall in the United States.

5. Discuss precision in measurement.

The following table shows what readings you would get if you measured exactly ten milliliters of liquid in four different pieces of glassware. Put the table on the board for the discussion.

Glassware	# of decimal places	reading: 10 ml of liquid	number of significant figs
Beaker	0	10 mL	2
Erlenmeyer Flask	0	10 mL	2
Graduated Cylinder	1	10.0 mL	3
Graduated Pipette	2	10.00 mL	4

Discussion goals

Discuss differences in the precision of a volume measurement using different pieces of equipment.

Sample questions:

What makes the graduated cylinder more precise than the beaker?

Which piece of glassware in the lab do you think measures liquids most accurately? (graduated pipette is precise to 0.01 mL)

A graduated pipette has markings every tenth of a milliliter. To how many decimal places could a volume be read using this piece of glassware?

Your backyard rain gauge reads 1.5 inches of rain overnight, while a nearby weather station reports 1.53 inches. Why do you think these two numbers are different?

What could cause the weather station's data to be more precise than yours?

Points to cover:

Different pieces of measurement equipment have different types of markings. Some have very few markings (like a beaker) and others have many markings (like a graduated cylinder and a graduated pipette). **Significant figures** are the numbers one can read off of an instrument or piece of equipment, <u>plus one more estimated number</u>. The more significant figures, the more precise the measurement is.

A graduated cylinder has markings every milliliter, so a measurement can be estimated to a tenth of a milliliter. The beaker has markings every 10 milliliters, so you can only estimate a measurement to a whole number of milliliters. With a graduated pipette, you can estimate to a hundredth of a milliliter. For example, if you read the following graduated cylinder (draw it on the board), you would estimate that it has 53.6 mL of liquid in it. The five and three are read directly off the container, but the 6 is estimated. This number (53.6) has three significant figures.

Significant figures are the numbers one can read off of an instrument or piece of equipment, <u>plus one more estimated number.</u> The glassware or instrument being used in a measurement determines how many significant figures can be recorded.

Your students may be wondering why the word precision is being used instead of accuracy. It is important to distinguish between precision and accuracy. Precision is related to the number of significant figures in a measurement. Accuracy is related to the degree to which the measurement matches a standard. You can have a very precise measurement that is inaccurate. For example, if the markings on the graduate cylinder have the wrong spacing, the measurement would still be precise, but inaccurate.

6. Discuss proportional relationships.

Discussion goals:
Assist the students in sharing their ideas about the relationship between volume and height of rainfall.

Sample questions:
   What happens to the height of rainfall as the volume of rain measured increases? (the height increases with the volume – in direct proportion to the volume)
   How can you use the graph to predict the volume of 2 1/2 inches of rain?
   How can you use the data table to predict the height in inches of 40 mL of rain?
   What does it mean that the volume of rainfall is proportional to its height?
   If the amount of rainfall increases, do both the volume and height of water in the rain gauge keep track of this increase? Explain your thinking.

Points to cover:
During a rainstorm, both the volume and height of rainwater in a rain gauge increase. Therefore, either volume or height can be used to keep track of rainfall.

When the volume of rainfall is plotted vs. the height of rainfall in a certain rain gauge, the result is a straight line that passes through the origin (0, 0). Whenever a graph of two variables results in a straight line that passes through the origin (0, 0), the two variables are **proportional** to each other. Thus, the volume of rainfall in a specific rain gauge is proportional to the height of the rainfall. When two variables are proportional to one another, it is possible to use a graph of volume vs. height to predict the volume of rainfall if you know the height, and vice versa.

Two quantities are **proportional** if a graph of the two variables results in a straight line that passes through the origin (0, 0).

Proportional relationships are discussed further in the next lesson, when these ideas will be related to the slope of the line and the idea that the ratio of the two variables doesn't change for a given situation.

7. Discuss why meteorologists report height of rainfall.

Discussion goals:
Assist the students in sharing their ideas about why meteorologists choose to report the height of rainfall rather than the volume of rainfall.

Sample questions:

If a large washtub, a dog's water dish, and a graduated cylinder are left outside during a rainstorm, will the three containers all have the same height of water in them after the storm? Explain why or why not.

Will all three containers have the same volume of water? Explain why or why not.

If you use a beaker for a rain gauge, and the weather station uses a graduated cylinder, will both instruments give the same volume? The same height?

Why do you think meteorologists prefer to measure the height of rainfall?

Points to cover:

Volume is not a particularly good measurement to use for rainfall because the volume of rain collected in a rain gauge is dependent on the diameter of the container being used, not on the size of the actual rainstorm. After a storm a container with a larger diameter will naturally have more water in it than one with a smaller container. This makes volume variable depending on the diameter of the container used. In contrast, the height of rain collected in a rain gauge is not dependent on the diameter of the container being used. A rainstorm that drops one inch of rain in one container drops one inch of rain in any other container. Thus, meteorologists report rainfall in inches. If they report volume, they would all need to choose a rain gauge with the identical diameter in order to compare measurements.

Meteorologists around the world report the height of rainfall in mm. It is only in the United States that the height of rainfall is reported in inches.

Check-in   (5 min)

8. Complete the Check-in exercise.

Write the following question on the board for the students to complete individually.

- Suppose you find that 1.0 inch of rainfall in a graduated cylinder has a volume of 4.0 mL. What volume would you measure for 2.0 inches of rainfall?

  A) 4 mL   B) 4.0 mL   C) 4.00 mL   D) 8 mL   E) 8.0 mL   F) 8.00 mL

  Explain your thinking.

9. Discuss the Check-in exercise.

Get a sense of the level of understanding by asking students to defend their choices.

<u>Discussion goals:</u>
Make sure that students understand the relationship between volume and height, and the correct number of significant figures to use in reporting the volume measurement.

Suggested questions:

How is volume related to height?

How accurately can you measure volume in a graduated cylinder?

The correct answer is E because as the height doubles, the volume doubles. The graduated cylinder has markings to the mL, so you can estimate to tenths of mL.

10. Wrap-up

Assist the students in summarizing what was learned in this class.

- Precision differences in measurements are a result of the glassware or instrument that is used.
- Significant figures are defined as all of the numbers that can be read directly from an instrument, plus one estimated number.
- The volume of water in a cylindrical container is directly proportional to the height of the water.
- Graphs of two variables that are proportional always lead to a straight line through the origin.

Homework

11. Assign the following for homework.

Use the homework provided with the curriculum or assign your own.

Homework – Investigation I – Lesson 2

1. a) What is the volume measured in each graduated cylinder?

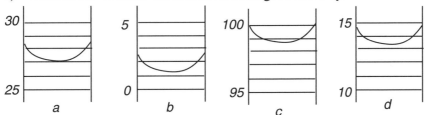

b) How many significant figures are being read? Explain.

2. Look at a ruler that is marked in both inches and centimeters. Make a graph of centimeters to inches so that the *y*-axis is centimeters and the *x*-axis is inches.
   a) Convert 12 inches to centimeters.
   b) How many inches is 10 centimeters?
   c) How many inches is 1 centimeter?

3. Consider the following three rain gauges. Imagine that they are placed next to each other at a weather station during a heavy rainstorm.

   A is two inches in diameter, B is four inches in diameter, C is 6 inches in diameter.

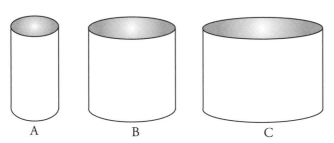

Volume = (area of base) x (height)

Area of base = πr^2

After an hour of rain the rain gauges hold the following volumes:
Rain gauge A: 6.28 in^3 Rain gauge B: 25.12 in^3 Rain gauge C: 56.52 in^3

a) Complete the following table.

	Volume (inches^3)	Area (inches^2)	Height (inches)	$\dfrac{Volume}{Area}$
A	6.28	3.14	2	
B	25.12	12.56		
C	56.52	28.16		

b) Plot a graph with volume on the y-axis and height on the x-axis. Are volume and area for a cylinder proportional to one another?

c) After the storm there are two inches of rain in the first rain gauge. How many inches of rain are in the other two rain gauges? Explain.

Transparency

ChemCatalyst: Annual rainfall in the United States

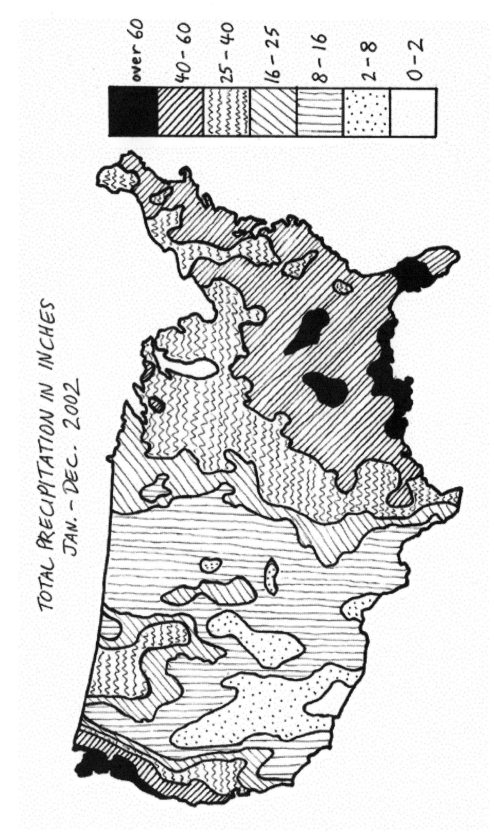

TOTAL PRECIPITATION IN INCHES
JAN. – DEC. 2002

over 60
40 – 60
25 – 40
16 – 25
8 – 16
2 – 8
0 – 2

- How much rain fell where you live?
- How is rainfall measured?
- What type of instrument or container is used to measure rainfall?

Raindrops Keep Falling…

Name: _____

Period: ____Date: _____

Purpose: This lesson introduces you to precision in measurement and allows you to explore measuring rainfall in inches and milliliters.

Part 1: Measuring volume – How accurate is the instrument?

Procedure:
Measure 20 mL of water in the beaker then pour it into the graduated cylinder.

1. Is 20 mL in the beaker the same as 20 mL in the graduated cylinder? What is the volume in the graduated cylinder?

2. What does each line represent on the graduated cylinder? What does each line represent on the beaker?

3. If you need to measure 15 mL of water, should you use a beaker or a graduated cylinder? Explain.

4. The beaker is designed to measure a maximum of 80 mL of liquid, while the graduated cylinder is designed to measure a maximum of 25.0 mL of liquid. Why do you think a decimal place is included on the graduated cylinder and not the beaker?

5. Which is more precise, the beaker or the graduated cylinder?

6. Which would make a better rain gauge – the beaker or the graduated cylinder? Explain why.

Part II: Measuring rainfall – Keeping track of rainfall with inches and mL

Procedure:
A rain gauge is a container used to measure the height of rainfall in inches of water. Use the 25 mL graduated cylinder as a rain gauge. Put exactly 5.0 mL of water into the rain gauge. Use a water bottle to put the last few drops in to get exactly 5.0 mL measured to the bottom of the meniscus. Measure the height as carefully as possible. Record the height in the table. Repeat for 10.0, 15.0, and 20.0 mL of water. Graph the results.

Height (inches)	0 inches				
Volume (milliliters)	0 mL	5 mL	10.0 mL	15.0 mL	20.0 mL

Plot these points on the following graph. Draw a line through the points. Use a ruler and make sure your line passes through, or near, as many of your data points as possible.

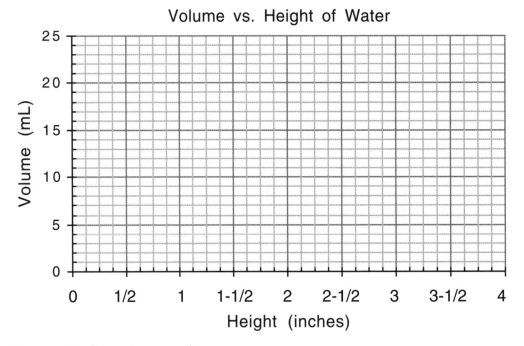

Volume vs. Height of Water

Answer the following questions:
1. Why don't all of the data points lie exactly on the line you drew?

2. If the height of the water is exactly 1 3/4 inches, can you determine this using your ruler? Why or why not?

3. Use the graph to predict the volume of 1 3/4 inches of rain.

4. Use the data table to predict the volume of 4 inches of rain.

5. Explain how you would predict the volume of 10 inches of rain.

6. Why do you think scientists use graphs?

Making sense questions
Meteorologists can keep track of the amount of rainfall by measuring either the volume or the height of rainfall in a rain gauge.

- If the amount of rainfall increases, do both the volume and height of water in the rain gauge keep track of this increase? Explain your thinking.

- What does the precision of measuring height and volume depend on? Is there a difference in the precision of measuring height or volume? Explain you thinking.

If you finish early…
Put 2 inches of water in the 100 mL beaker and 2 inches in the 25 mL graduated cylinder. Determine the volume of water in the beaker and the graduated cylinder.

- If 2 inches of rain fall in a storm, what height in inches will you measure in the beaker? In the graduated cylinder?

- If you use a beaker for a rain gauge, and the weather station uses a graduated cylinder, will both instruments give the same volume? The same height in inches?

- If a large washtub, a dog's water dish, and a graduated cylinder were left outside during a rainstorm, would the three containers all have the same volume of water in them after the storm? Explain why or why not.

- Why do meteorologists prefer to measure the height of rainfall?

BEFORE CLASS...

LESSON 3 – Having a Melt Down

Key Ideas:
Scientists measure the volume of winter snowfall to predict the amount of water that will be available for consumption the rest of the year. However, three milliliters of snow is not equivalent to three milliliters of rain. These two different forms of water have very different densities. Density is proportional to both mass and volume, so if we know the density of snow we can calculate the volume of water obtained when a given volume of snow melts.

What Takes Place:
Before the activity students consider a graph showing the relationship between the volume of snow and its mass. They explore the idea that snow and liquid water have different densities. Then they design a procedure to measure the volume and mass of different amounts of water. Finally, they use their data to calculate volume of rainwater obtained when a given volume of snow melts.

Materials: (per team of 4 students)
- Student worksheet
- 25 mL graduated cylinder
- Scale
- Water bottle (small dropper or plastic pipette if water bottles are not available)

Investigation I – Locating Matter
LESSON 3 – Having a Meltdown

Now that students have experience measuring volume of rainfall, they are asked to consider how volume of snowfall is related to volume of rainfall by the mass, and more specifically by the density. Students design their own experiment to measure the mass and volume of different amounts of water, and then graph the data they acquire. Density is introduced and related to the slope of the line. Students then use differences in density between rain and snow to predict how much snow there will be in the mountains for a given amount of rainfall at lower elevations.

Exploring the Topic   (5–10 min)

1. Introduce ChemCatalyst exercise.

Write the following exercise on the board for students to complete individually.

* Meteorologists measure the snowpack in the mountains to predict the amount of water that will fill the lakes and reservoirs. Do you think that 3 milliliters of snow is the same as 3 milliliters of rain? Explain your reasoning.

2. Discuss the ChemCatalyst exercise.

Use the discussion to get a sense of students' initial ideas.

Discussion goals:
Assist the students in sharing their ideas about the comparison between milliliters of rain and milliliters of snow.

Sample questions:
Is three milliliters of snow the same as three milliliters of rain?
Why is it important to measure snowpack in the mountains?
How is snow different from rain? How is it the same?
Do 10 grams of snow have the same mass as 10 grams of water? Explain.
If you measure 20 milliliters of snow and it melts, what happens to the volume? (decreases) The mass? (stays the same)

Listen to student's ideas about rain and snow, without judgment. Some students will recognize that snow is not packed very tightly, and has a lot of air within the volume it occupies so it occupies less volume once it has melted. When snow melts into water, the mass of the original snow is equal to the mass of the water that is recovered.

3. Compare mass and volume of snow. (Transparency)

Display the transparency with the following graph to the class.

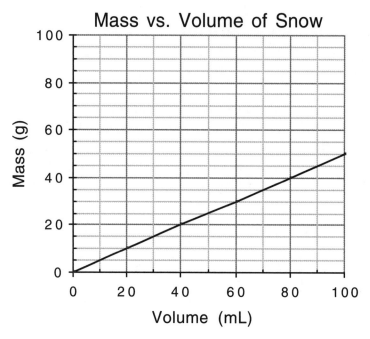

Mass vs. Volume of Snow

Discussion goals:

Assist students in sharing their initial ideas about mass and volume, and how they are related to one another.

Sample questions:

According to the graph what is the mass of 20 mL of snow? What is the mass of 40 mL of snow? (For these data the mass is always equal to half of the volume.)

What is the ratio of the mass of snow to its volume? (1/2)

The **slope** is the change in y divided by the change in x. What is the slope of the line? (.5 or 1/2)

How does the mass of snow vary with volume?

Will the same volume of water have more or less mass than the snow? Explain your thinking. (The water will have more mass than the snow because the snow is lightly packed and full of air.)

How do you think a similar graph for water will compare? Will it be a straight line? Will it have the same slope? (straight line, different slope)

Points to cover:

The **density** (D) of a substance is mass (m) per unit volume (V). The formula is D = m/V. The units of density are typically g/mL.

The **slope** of the line is the change in mass divided by the change in volume (change in y divided by change in x). Since one point on the line is the origin (0,0), the change in mass divided by the change in volume is just the ratio of mass to volume for any point on the line. Therefore, you can determine the density by finding the ratio of y/x.

> The **slope** of a line is the change in y divided by the change in x. For a line that goes through the origin (0, 0), the slope is simply any value of y divided by the corresponding value of x.

> The **density** of a substance is the slope of the line for a graph of mass vs. volume.

At this point, listen to students' ideas. Give them a chance to express their notions of the relationship between mass and volume for water and snow.

4. Explain the purpose of the activity.

If you wish you can write the main question on the board.

Points to cover:
Tell students that they will be measuring the mass of different volumes of water in order to determine how mass and volume are related for liquid water. The relationship between mass and volume is key in relating rainfall to snowfall. Tell students they will be trying to answer the following question: "How can you convert from volume of snowfall to volume of liquid water"?

Activity – Having a Meltdown   (15 min)

5. Explain the procedure and pass out the worksheets. (Worksheet)

Tell students that they will be constructing a graph of mass vs. volume of water using a graduated cylinder. They will collect at least 4 data points. (Allow the students to design the procedure. They will need to measure the weight of the graduated cylinder empty so that they can subtract the empty weight from the weight of the cylinder with water.)

Materials: (for each team of four students)
25-mL graduated cylinders
Scale
Water bottle (small dropper or plastic pipette if water bottles are not available)

Instructions:
Work with your group to determine the relationship between mass and volume for liquid water. Use a 25-mL graduated cylinder to determine the mass of 4 different volumes of water. Design your own procedure.

Make sure that students remember to subtract the mass of the empty graduated cylinder to get just the mass of the water.

1. Describe your procedure on a separate sheet of paper. Be as specific as possible.

2. Record the mass of the water plus the graduated cylinder, the mass of the water, the volume of the water, and the mass/volume ratio in the table below.

Mass of the graduated cylinder empty: _____

Measured			Calculated
Mass of water plus graduated cylinder (g)	Mass of water (g)	Volume of water (mL)	Mass/volume (g/mL)
	5.5	5.5	1.0
	10.2	10.2	1.0
	15.7	15.7	1.0
	25.0	25.0	1.0

3. Plot the data on a graph with mass on the y-axis and volume on the x-axis.

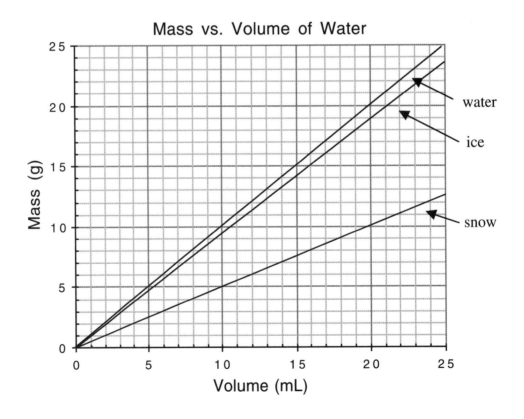

Weather © UC Regents, LHS Living by Chemistry, 2003.

Use your graph to answer the following questions:

1. What do you notice about the ratio of the mass of water to its volume? (They are the same. The ratio is 1/1)

2. The ratio of mass to volume is called **density.** Determine the density of water in g/mL. (1.0 g/mL)

3. The slope of the line is equal to the change in y divided by the change in x ($\Delta y/\Delta x$). Show that the slope is equal to the density.

4. Use your graph to show that the density is constant for different volumes of water. (Any point on the line has the same ratio of mass/volume.)

5. If you collected 3 mL of loosely packed snow in the graduated cylinder would it weigh the same as 3 mL of water? Why or why not? (The snow will weigh less than the water because loosely packed snow has a smaller density than water.)

6. The density of ice is 0.92 g/mL. Plot mass vs. volume for ice on the same graph that you made for water. How does the slope of the line for ice compare with water? (The slope is less steep because the density is smaller.)

7. If you collected 3 mL of ice in the graduated cylinder would it weigh the same as 3 mL of rainwater? Why or why not? (The ice will weigh less than the water because ice has a smaller density than water.)

8. Plot mass vs. volume for snow on the same graph for snow with a density of 0.5 g/mL.

9. If rain is denser than snow, do you expect more or less milliliters of rain compared with snow? Explain. (If rain is denser, it takes up less volume compared with snow, so there will be fewer milliliters of rain for the same mass of snowfall.)

10. If you collect 20 mL of snow from the mountains, what volume of water does the snowpack hold? Assume that the snow has a density of 0.5 g/mL. Use the formula D = m/V or use your graph. (10 mL of water)

Making sense question
Explain how you can relate volume of snow to volume of rain.

If you finish early…
Both snow and rain consist of water molecules, but rainwater is denser that snow. How can the densities be different if they are both made of water molecules? (It depends on how the water molecules themselves are packed together. Moreover, in the case of snow, there is a lot of air packed in between the ice crystals.)

Making Sense Discussion (15 min)

Major goals: The goal of this discussion is to provide students with an opportunity to become proficient at working with ratios and proportional analysis. In the process students gain practice using density to convert between mass and volume. Ultimately they practice converting volume of snow into volume of rain.

6. Explore the relationship between mass and volume.

On the board, make a list of different ways students come up with to determine the mass of water for a given volume.

Discussion goals:
Assist students in making connections between the different ways of expressing the relationship between mass and volume.

Sample questions:
Describe the graph of mass vs. volume for liquid water. (It is a straight line that goes through zero with a slope of 0.5)
Is the ratio of m / V always the same for liquid water? Provide evidence to support your answer.
What are the slopes of the three lines on your graph?
How can you determine the mass of water for a given volume?
How can you determine the mass of snow for a given volume?

Points to cover:
The mass and volume of water, snow, and ice are all **proportional** to one another. This means that their ratio is always the same. When the mass of one of these substances is multiplied by two, the resulting volume is also multiplied by two (and vice versa). If the mass is multiplied by three, the volume is also multiplied by three. Likewise when the mass is divided in half, the volume is also divided in half.

When you graph quantities that are proportional to one another, you get a straight line that goes through the origin. The slope of the line for these graphs is the ratio of mass to volume. In the case of $y = m$ and $x = V$, the slope is m / V (the density).

Given this information, there are two ways you can determine the mass of water for a given volume.

- Use the graph. Find the volume and read off the mass.
- Use the equation: $m_1 / V_1 = \text{slope} = m_2 / V_2$

7. Discuss density.

Discussion goals:
Assist students in relating the definition of density to the slope of the line for a graph of mass vs. volume.

Sample questions:
How do the graphs for ice, water, and snow differ? How are they the same? (they have different slopes, different steepness, each is a straight line going through the origin)
What is constant in each graph?
Is the constant for ice the same as the constant for water? Explain.
Which is denser, snow or rainwater? Explain.
How do the graphs show that ice and water do not have the same density?
Will the same volume of water have more or less mass than the snow? Explain your thinking.
Will the same mass of water have more or less volume than the snow?

Points to cover:
The graphs for ice, snow, and water are all straight lines through the origin, but the lines have different slopes. The slope of the line in a graph of mass vs. volume is equal to the density of the substance. For a given substance at a given temperature, the density doesn't change. In other words, you can have different amounts of a substance, but the ratio of m / V is always stays the same.

Please note that all snow is not of the same density. In our early example the snow had a density of 0.5 g/mL. Some snow may be more or less dense than this snow.

8. Introduce proportional and dimensional analysis.

Write the following sample problems on the board and have students solve them before discussing:

Example Problem I:
Imagine you have a box that is 5.0 mL in volume. What mass of ice will just fill this box?

Points to cover:
One way to solve this problem is to read the answer off your graph for ice. In addition there are two main mathematical methods that are used to convert between two different measurements: **proportional analysis** and **dimensional analysis**. Both lead to the same answer. In the case of proportional analysis you are using the idea that the ratio of the mass and volume always stays the same for a given situation and that this ratio is equal in value to the slope of the line. For a particular substance, m / V is always the same, thus:

$$m_1 / V_1 = \text{slope} = m_2 / V_2$$

We set up proportional analysis problems by multiplying both sides by the same quantity (as shown in the box on the left below).

In the case of dimensional analysis you are using the idea that if you have 5.0 mL of a substance and the ratio of grams to milliliters in that substance is always 0.92 g/mL then all you have to do is multiply these two numbers together in order to solve for grams. The units of milliliters will cancel out, leaving you with the number of grams. (This method is shown in the box on the right.)

Proportional Analysis	**Dimensional Analysis**
$\dfrac{0.92 \text{ g}}{1 \text{ mL}} = \dfrac{x}{5.0 \text{ mL}}$ $x = (0.92)(5.0) = 4.6 \text{ g}$	$\left[5.0 \text{ mL} \right] \left[\dfrac{0.92 \text{ g}}{1 \text{ mL}} \right] = 4.6 \text{ g}$

Example Problem II:
You have 20 grams of snow with a density of 0.50 g/mL. What volume does this snow occupy (how many milliliters)?

Proportional Analysis	**Dimensional Analysis**
$\dfrac{0.5 \text{ g}}{1 \text{ mL}} = \dfrac{20 \text{ g}}{x \text{ mL}}$ $x = (20)\left(\dfrac{1}{0.5}\right) = 40 \text{ mL}$	$\left[20 \text{ g} \right] \left[\dfrac{1 \text{ mL}}{0.5 \text{ g}} \right] = 40 \text{ mL}$

9. Convert milliliters of snow to milliliters of rain.

Write math steps on the board as they are discussed.

Discussion goals:
Assist students in thinking about how to convert milliliters of snowfall to milliliters of rainfall given the density of rain and snow.

Sample questions:
   You have the same mass of rain and snow. Will the volume occupied by the rain and snow be the same or different? Explain.
   If you have 100 mL of snow, how would you determine the volume of the same amount of rain?

Points to cover:
The denser the precipitation that falls (whether it be snow, sleet, rain, or ice), the fewer number of milliliters will be measured. In order to figure out what

volume of water is represented by a certain volume of snow, it will take two mathematical steps. First you must find out the mass of the snow. This will be identical to the mass of the water (only the volume of these two substances is different). After you calculate the mass of the water it is easily converted to volume using the density of liquid water.

Example Problem III: If you have 100 mL of snow, what volume of water do you have? (You must first find out what mass of snow you have and then convert that to volume of water.)

Step 1: Proportional Analsysis	Step 1: Dimensional Analysis
$\dfrac{0.5\ g}{1\ mL} = \dfrac{x\ g}{100\ mL}$ x = (0.5) (100 mL) = 50 grams	$\left[100\ mL \right] \left[\dfrac{0.5\ g}{1\ mL} \right] = 50\ grams$
Step 2: Proportional Analsysis	Step 2: Dimensional Analysis
$\dfrac{1\ g}{1\ mL} = \dfrac{50\ g}{x\ mL}$ x = (1) (50) = 50 mL	$\left[50\ mL \right] \left[\dfrac{1\ g}{1\ mL} \right] = 50\ mL$

Check-In   (5 min)

10. Complete the Check-in exercise.

Write the following question on the board for the students to complete individually.

- You have equal masses of snow and rain. Which has a greater volume? Explain your thinking.
- What is the mass of 14 mL of rainwater?

11. Discuss the Check-in exercise.

Get a sense of the level of understanding by asking students to defend their choices.

Discussion goals:
Make sure that students understand the relationship between density, mass, and volume.

Suggested questions:
Which is denser, snow or rain?
For the same mass, which has a greater volume?

What is the mass of 14 mL of rainwater? (14 grams because water has a density of 1.0 g/mL)

Since snow is less dense than rain, it will occupy a larger volume for a given mass.

12. Wrap-up

Assist the students in summarizing what was learned in this class.

- Density a measure of the mass of a substance per unit of volume.
- If the ratio between two quantities is constant then a graph of these two quantities will be a line that passes through the origin.
- Water can have different densities depending on whether it is snow, ice or liquid (rain).
- When a substance changes phase (from solid to liquid to gas) it changes density.

Homework

13. Assign the following for homework.

Use the homework provided with the curriculum or assign your own.

Homework – Investigation I – Lesson 3

Write a lab report. Include the following: provide a title, state the purpose, describe your procedure, show your data, include a graph, and provide a conclusion that answers the question: "How can you convert from volume of rainfall to volume of snowfall?" The question should be answered with words, graphs, and with mathematical formulas.

1. Suppose you have a box with a volume of 17.5 mL.

    a. If you fill this box with ice (solid water), what will be the mass of H_2O? (The density of ice is 0.92 g/mL.)

    b. If you fill this box with liquid water, what will be the mass of H_2O? (The density of water is 1.0 g/mL.)

2. Suppose that you have a box that is full and contains 0.5 grams of a substance.

    a. What is the volume of the box if the substance inside it is corn oil? (The density of corn oil is 0.92 g/mL.)

    b. What is the volume of the box if the substance inside is lead? (The density of lead is 11.35 g/mL.)

Having a Meltdown

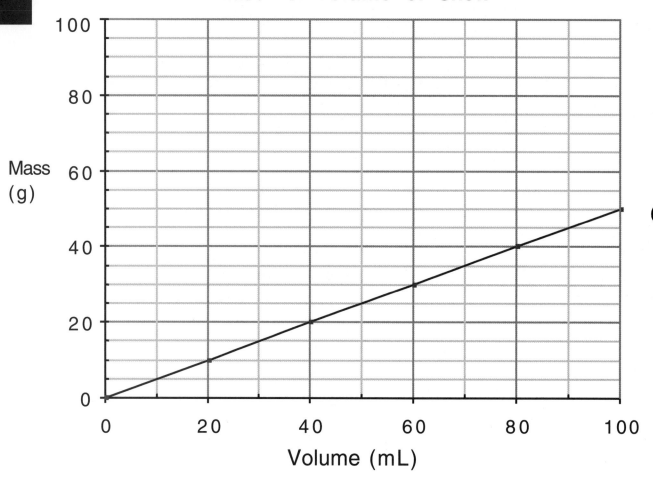

Mass vs. Volume of Snow

Weather © UC Regents, LHS Living by Chemistry, 2003.

Having a Meltdown

Name: _____
Period: _____Date: _____

Purpose: This activity allows you to relate volume of snowfall with volume of rainfall by using the density of snowfall and rainfall.

Instructions:
You will be working in a team of 4 students to determine the relationship between mass and volume. Use a 25-mL graduated cylinder to determine the mass of 4 different volumes of water. Design your own procedure.

1. Describe your procedure on a separate sheet of paper. Be as specific as possible.

2. Record the mass of the water plus the graduated cylinder, the mass of the water, the volume of the water, and the mass/volume ratio in the table below.

Mass of the graduate cylinder empty: _____

Measured			Calculated
Mass of water plus graduated cylinder (g)	Mass of water (g)	Volume of water (mL)	Mass/volume (g/mL)

3. Plot the data on a graph with mass on the y-axis and volume on the x-axis.

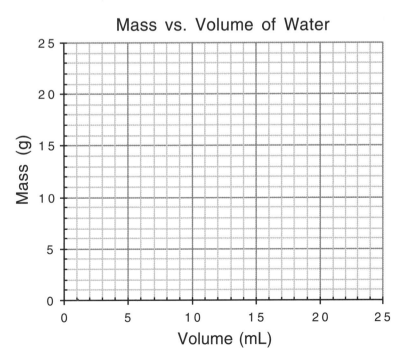

Answer the following questions:

Use your graph to answer the following questions:

1. What do you notice about the ratio of the mass of water to its volume?

2. The ratio of mass to volume is called **density.** Determine the density of water in g/mL.

3. The slope of the line is equal to the change in y divided by the change in x ($\Delta y/\Delta x$). Show that the slope is equal to the density.

4. Refer to the graph to show that the density is constant for different volumes of water.

5. If you collected 3 mL of loosely packed snow in the graduated cylinder would it weigh the same as 3 mL of water? Why or why not?

6. Plot mass vs. volume for ice on the same graph that you made for water. The density (ratio of m / V) of ice is 0.92 g/mL. How does the slope of the line for ice compare with water?

7. If you collected 3 mL of ice in the graduated cylinder would it weigh the same as 3 mL of rainwater? Why or why not?

8. Plot mass vs. volume for snow on the same graph for snow with a density of 0.5 g/mL.

9. If rain is denser than snow, do you expect more or less milliliters of rain compared with snow? Explain.

10. If you collect 20 mL of snow from the mountains, what volume of water does the snowpack hold? Assume that the snow has a density of 0.5 g/mL. Use D = m/V or use your graph.

Making Sense Question
Explain how you can relate volume of snow to volume of rain.

If you finish early...
Both snow and rain consist of water molecules, but rainwater is denser that snow. How can the densities be different if they are both made of water molecules?

BEFORE CLASS…

LESSON 4 – It's Sublime

Key Ideas:

When substances change phase (from solid to liquid to gas or vice versa), they also change in density. When solid carbon dioxide (CO_2) changes phase it goes directly from a solid to a gas. This type of phase change is called sublimation. When carbon dioxide gas sublimes there is a dramatic change in density. Solid CO_2 is also called "dry ice" because it sublimes (and does not melt).

What Takes Place:

At the beginning of class teams of students will quickly weigh a sample of dry ice and place it in a garbage bag to sublime. This step is completed before the ChemCatalyst in order that the dry ice have enough time before the end of class to sublime completely. A demonstration comparing an ice cube and dry ice on a hot plate follows the ChemCatalyst. Students complete some questions before finally measuring the volume of their bags of CO_2 gas.

Set-up:

Before class, acquire 5–7 pounds of dry ice (suppliers are listed in your local phone directory). You may wish to break up the dry ice into manageable chunks before class with a hammer.

You will need to place volume markings on the side of a cylindrical container (about 5 gallon size), such as a trashcan. The volume of a cylinder $= \pi r^2 h$. Determine the radius in cm, so that you can determine the height in cm that corresponds to various volumes in cm^3 = mL up to ~20,000 mL. Students will use these containers to measure the volume of bags filled with gaseous carbon dioxide.

Materials:
- Student worksheet
- Several cubes of ice
- Hot plate
- 5–20 grams of dry ice per team of students
- Styrofoam cooler or ice chest
- Scale
- 6–8 Medium plastic garbage bags – five-gallon size
- 6–8 Twist ties
- 6–8 Oven mitts (or tongs)
- 2–4 Five-gallon buckets or other cylindrical receptacle

Investigation I – Locating Matter
LESSON 4 – It's Sublime

The exploration into phase changes continues as students explore the change in density when solid carbon dioxide sublimes to form carbon dioxide gas. Using dry ice, students will collect rough quantitative data relating the mass and volume of solid CO_2 to the volume of the same amount of CO_2 as a gas. Students will gain convincing evidence of the magnitude of the difference between the density of a solid and the density of a gas.

Exploring the Topic   (10–15 min)

1. Set up the laboratory activity.

Tell students they will be setting up a laboratory investigation at the beginning of class.

Points to cover:
Explain to students that they will need to weigh a chunk of dry ice and then get it into a garbage bag as quickly as possible. Make sure each team of four students has a chunk of dry ice that is somewhere between 4 and 20 grams and a 5-gallon garbage bag. Explain the following procedure:

Procedure:
1. Send one team member to acquire a piece of dry ice. **(Use gloves – dry ice can cause frostbite.)**
2. Quickly find the mass of the solid. (The mass changes continuously as the dry ice sublimes. In order to get a good estimate of the mass of the dry ice that goes into the bag, the students need to get the dry ice into the bag quickly after weighing it.)
3. Remove all of the air from a five-gallon garbage bag.
4. Place the dry ice in the deflated bag and close the top with a twist tie so that it does not leak.

The students are setting up the laboratory experiment at the beginning of class because it will take about 20-30 minutes for the dry ice to sublime. Once it has sublimed completely, they will measure the mass as part of the activity.

2. Introduce the ChemCatalyst exercise.

Write the following exercise on the board for students to complete individually.

Show students a beaker with a piece of dry ice and another beaker with an ice cube (frozen water).

- Describe the differences between the two.
- Why do you think one is called "dry" ice?

3. Discuss the ChemCatalyst question.

Use the discussion to get a sense of students' initial ideas.

Discussion goals:
Assist students in sharing their observations about the differences between dry ice and water ice.

Sample questions:
  How does dry ice differ from a normal ice cube?
  What do you think the "smoke" is?
  What is "normal" ice made of?
  What is dry ice made of?

Many students will know that dry ice is frozen carbon dioxide gas. Try to focus them on describing what they observe as well as what they know or can infer.

4. Demonstrate sublimation.

Suggested demonstration:
Have an ice cube and a piece of dry ice handy. Set up a hotplate at the front of the class. Turn it on to about medium heat. Ask students to predict what will happen if you put the ice on the hot plate. Do it and ask students for their observations. Then have them predict what will happen if you put dry ice on the hot plate. Use an oven mitt (or tongs, if you prefer) to place the dry ice on the hot plate. Ask students for their observations.

Sample questions:
  What do you predict will happen when the ice is put on the hot plate?
  What do you observe?
  What do you predict will happen when the dry ice is put on the hot plate?
  What do you observe?
  Why do you think it is called "dry" ice?

Points to Cover:
Ice melts into a liquid upon heating, and then into steam. Dry ice doesn't "melt" into a liquid upon heating, and hence it is called "dry" ice. When a solid goes into a liquid it is called melting and when a liquid goes into a gas it is called evaporation. When a solid goes directly into a gas without forming a liquid it is called **sublimation.**

It is possible to observe **sublimation** for several substances. One of these is solid CO_2, carbon dioxide. Solid carbon dioxide is also known as dry ice. Dry ice turns into a vapor at a temperature of $-78°C$. Thus room temperature is quite warm to a piece of dry ice. Iodine is another solid that sublimes directly to a gas.

The term sublime is also used to describe the reverse process of the gas changing directly to the solid again upon cooling. Iodine gas condenses directly to a crystalline solid upon striking a cool surface. In this way pure crystals of iodine are prepared. It turns out that *nearly everything will sublime* given the appropriate conditions, some of which are quite extreme.

There is another special case of more commonplace sublimation – it involves water, H_2O, and the weather. Sublimation occurs when water vapor rising in the atmosphere is suddenly cooled below the freezing point of water. Frost and snowflakes are thus formed by water changing directly from the gaseous to the solid state!

5. Explain the purpose of the activity.

If you wish you can write the main question on the board.

Points to cover:
Tell students they will be exploring changes in volume and changes in density that occur upon sublimation. They will be answering the question, "How different are the densities of a solid and a gas of the same substance?"

Activity – It's Sublime   (15 min)

6. Explain the remaining part of the activity.

Tell students that there are two parts to this activity. First they will complete a set of questions. Second, they will find the volume of the gas that has been produced in their garbage bags.

[Note to the teacher: Make sure students gather the volume measurement at least 10 minutes before the end of class. The dry ice should sublime for about 20-30 minutes prior. The carbon dioxide vapor will be ~800 times the volume of the solid CO_2. The density of solid carbon dioxide is 1.56 g/cm^3. The density of carbon dioxide gas is 0.0019 g/cm^3.]

Materials:
5–20 grams of dry ice per team of students
Styrofoam cooler or ice chest
Scale
6–8 Medium plastic garbage bags – five-gallon size
6–8 Twist ties
6–8 Oven mitts
2–4 Five-gallon buckets or other cylindrical receptacle (Note: 5 gallons ~19
   liters) – put volume markings on the side of the container

Part I: Answer the following questions:

1. Your bag is expanding. How is the density of the carbon dioxide changing as it sublimes? Explain. (The density is decreasing because the same amount of mass is occupying more volume.)

2. Look at the graph below comparing the mass vs. the volume of CO_2 (s) and CO_2 (g). What do the lines tell you about the two substances? (The slope of the line for the solid is much steeper than the slope for the gas.)

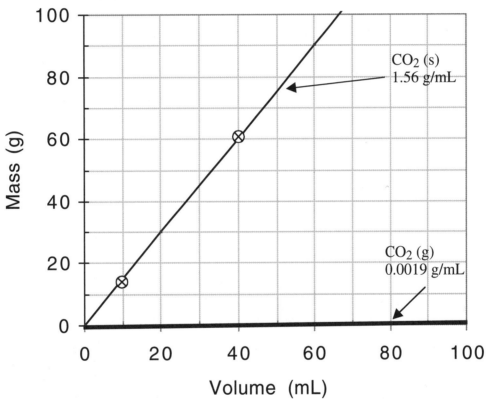

3. The formula for density is $D = m/V$. Use the graph for CO_2 (s) to show that the ratio m/V is the same for $V = 20$ mL and $V = 60$ mL. (The mass of CO_2 (s) with a volume of 20 mL is 30 g, so $m/V = 1.5$ g/mL. The mass of CO_2 (s) with a volume of 60 mL is 90 g, so $m/V = 1.5$ g/mL.)

4. Two points are marked on the line. Is the density the same for both points? Why or why not? (The density is the same. All the points on the line are in the same ratio, which is the slope of the line. This ratio also corresponds to the density.)

5. The sketches below show four models of what might happen when solid carbon dioxide sublimes to carbon dioxide gas. The circles represent molecules of carbon dioxide.

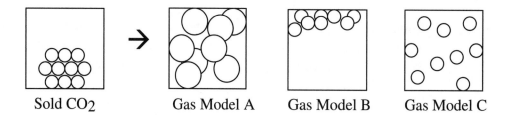

Sold CO_2 Gas Model A   Gas Model B   Gas Model C

a) Explain why Model A is incorrect. (Molecules do not change size.)

b) What evidence do you have from your dry ice experiment that would suggest that Model B is incorrect? (The bag was pushed out in all directions, not just at the top.)

c) How does Model C explain why the density of carbon dioxide gas is so small? (It shows space between the molecules.)

Part II: Finish the laboratory experiment

Procedure:
Once the solid is gone, compress the bag into a cylindrical wastebasket. Record the volume occupied by the bag of gas.

Sample data:

Mass of $CO_2(s)$ (g)	Volume of CO_2 solid (mL)	Volume of CO_2 gas (mL)
5.0 g	3.3 mL	2500 mL
8.2 g	5.3 mL	4200 mL
12.7 g	8.5 mL	6500 mL
etc.	etc.	etc.

Answer the following questions

1. In this lab you measured the mass of CO_2 (s) that you started with. Use the information given on the graph to calculate the volume of the CO_2 (s) you started with. Show your work.

2. Determine the density of gaseous CO_2 using the data from your experiment. Compare it to the value given above on the graph.

Making Sense:
If you sublime 1 mL of CO_2 (s), what volume will the gas occupy? (About 800 mL)

How many times larger than the volume of the solid carbon dioxide is the volume of the carbon dioxide gas? (about 800 times larger)

Making Sense Discussion   **(15 min)**

Major Goals: One goal of this discussion is to assist students in looking at density from a particulate point of view. Students should gain more practice working with graphs of mass vs. volume and determining density. Finally, students should begin to see the large volume change and density change that occur when there is a phase change from a solid (or liquid) to a gas.

7. Discuss particle views.

Make sketches of particle views as they are discussed.

Discussion goals:
Assist students in using particle views to explain the difference in density between solid and gas.

Sample questions:
Which model (A, B, or C) on the worksheet was the most accurate drawing of what happened on a particulate level to the carbon dioxide?
How can you explain the large increase in volume when carbon dioxide sublimes?
It is much easier to compress gases than solids. Is this consistent with your particle view?
Given what you know about gas density, how can you improve Model C? (spread the gas molecules even further apart)

8. Discuss the mass and density of carbon dioxide gas.

Discussion goals:
Inquire about the mass and density of carbon dioxide gas and carbon dioxide solid.

Sample questions:
You determined the mass of the $CO_2(s)$. Is it the same as the mass of the $CO_2(g)$? Why or why not? (Did any CO_2 escape from the bag?)
Why does the gas feel as if it weighs very little compared with the solid? (because it is spread out over a larger area)
What density did you calculate for $CO_2(g)$ using your own data?
How many times larger is the volume of $CO_2(g)$ compared with $CO_2(s)$? (~1,000 times larger)
How many times smaller is the density of $CO_2(g)$ compared with $CO_2(s)$? (~1,000 times smaller)

What happens to the density of a substance when it changes phase? (the density changes too)

Make sure that students understand that the gas has the same mass as the solid even though it feels as if it weighs very little.

Check-in   (5 min)

9. No Check-in for this laboratory activity.

10. Wrap-up

Assist the students in summarizing what was learned in this class.

- Sublimation occurs when a substance goes directly from a solid phase to a gas phase (or vice versa).
- The density of a gas is about 1/1000 the density of the same solid.

Homework

11. Assign the following for homework.

Use the homework provided with the curriculum or assign your own.

Homework – Investigation I – Lesson 4

1. What is the volume of 6.4 grams of solid CO_2? (density = 1.56 g/mL)

2. What is the mass of 3.5 liters of gaseous CO_2? (density = 0.0019 g/mL)

3. How many grams of carbon dioxide solid would you need in order to fill a 6.5 liter bag with carbon dioxide gas?

4. A person has 15 grams of dry ice and wants to fill a bag that has a volume of 8 liters with carbon dioxide gas. Is this enough dry ice to fill the bag? Explain.

5. What volume of cloud vapor (H_2O gas) would sublime in the atmosphere to form 10 mL of ice (H_2O s)?

It's Sublime

Name: _____

Period: _____ Date: _____

Part I: Answer the following questions

1. Your bag is expanding. How is the density changing when CO_2 sublimes? Explain.

2. Look at the graph below comparing the density of CO_2 (s) and CO_2 (g). How does the slope of the line showing mass vs. volume of gas compare to the mass vs. volume of the solid?

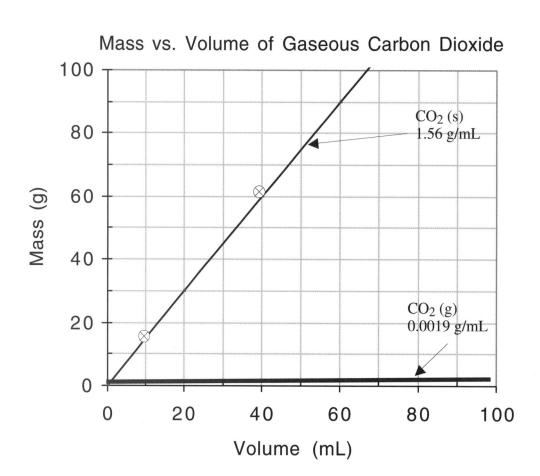

3. The formula for density is $D = m/V$. Use the graph for CO_2 (s) to show that the ratio m/V is the same for $V = 20$ mL and $V = 60$ mL.

4. Two points are marked on the line. Is the density the same for both points? Why or why not.

5. The sketches below show a model for dry ice on the left, and three possible models of what might happen when solid carbon dioxide sublimes to carbon dioxide gas. The circles represent molecules of carbon dioxide.

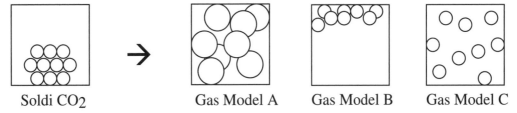

Soldi CO2   Gas Model A   Gas Model B   Gas Model C

a) Explain why Model A is incorrect.

b) What evidence do you have from your dry ice experiment that would suggest that Model B is incorrect?

c) How does Model C explain why the density of carbon dioxide gas is so small?

Part II: Complete the laboratory experiment

Procedure:
Once the solid is gone, compress the bag into a cylindrical wastebasket. Record the volume occupied by the bag of gas.

Data Table:

Mass of CO_2 (s)	
Volume of the CO_2 (g)	
Volume of the CO_2 (s)	

Answer the following questions
1. In this lab you measured the mass of CO_2 (s) that you started with. Use the information given on the graph to calculate the volume of the CO_2 (s) you started with. Show your work.

2. Determine the density of gaseous CO_2 using the data from your experiment. Compare it to the value given above on the graph.

Making Sense:
If you sublime 1 mL of CO_2 (s), what volume will the gas occupy?

How many times larger than the volume of the solid carbon dioxide is the volume of the carbon dioxide gas?

BEFORE CLASS...

LESSON 5 – Waterworld

Key Ideas:
When substances change phase (from solid to liquid to gas, and vice versa) they not only change in density and volume, but they may also change location relative to other objects or substances. Substances that are denser end up layered below substances that are less dense. The water cycle on the planet relies on this physical fact. Water evaporates from the oceans and relocates to the atmosphere as water vapor. Water vapor changes phase and becomes tiny water droplets suspended in the air as clouds. Clouds are pushed over land by prevailing winds. Water is dropped as rain and/or snow when the droplets in the clouds are large enough.

What Takes Place:
In this lesson students complete a two-part worksheet. In the first part of the activity students will explore changes in density that are associated with changes in phase. In addition, they will consider how these changes affect the location or relocation of substances on the planet. In the second part of the activity students examine a rainfall map and consider the water cycle. During the discussion, phase, volume, and density are related to the weather.

Materials:
- Student worksheet
- Handout – Density landscape

Investigation I – Locating Matter

LESSON 5 – Water World

The investigation comes to a close with a discussion of the relocation of water from the Earth's surface to the atmosphere and back again. Students first compare the densities of several substances to look for general trends. They then consider how the density of water changes as water converts from liquid to vapor to clouds and to rain and snow. They consider how motions of molecules are involved in moving water molecules from the liquid to the upper reaches of the atmosphere and then back again.

Exploring the Topic   (5–10 min)

1. Introduce ChemCatalyst exercise.

Write the following exercise on the board for students to complete individually.

Suppose a quantity of rainwater occupies a volume of 1 mL.
- What volume do you think the rainwater occupies as water vapor? Explain your thinking.
- When water changes phase what other changes take place? Name at least three changes.

2. Discuss the ChemCatalyst exercise.

Use the discussion to get a sense of students' initial ideas.

Discussion goals:
Assist students in sharing their ideas about how the volume, density, and location of water change when it changes phase from rainwater to vapor.

Sample questions:
  What happens to the volume of the water when it evaporates and becomes water vapor?
  Do you expect the volume change between liquid water and water vapor to be similar to the volume change you observed for the sublimation of dry ice? Why or why not?
  What happens to the density of water when it evaporates and becomes water vapor?
  What other changes take place when water changes density?
  Where do you expect to find water vapor?
  How is density related to the location of water on the planet?

Listen to students' ideas without judgment. Given their observations from the sublimation of dry ice in Lesson I-4 and the balloon experiment in Lesson I-1, they should expect a large increase in volume when water evaporates (~1000 times). Some students may say that it represents a bit less of a volume change than the dry ice because the water is going from liquid to gas, not solid to gas like the dry ice. In general, things that are less dense rise up into the atmosphere, while substances that are denser fall towards earth.

3. Explain the purpose of the activity.

If you wish you can write the main question on the board.

Points to cover:

Tell students they will be exploring the relationship between density and where substances are found in relationship to each other on the planet. They will be answering the question, "How are volume, density, and phase of water related to weather?"

Activity – Waterworld   (15 min)

4. Pass out worksheets.

The worksheet has two parts. In Part I, students compare the densities of various substances with their location. In Part II, students consider what factors influence the location of rainfall in the United States.

Part I: Comparing densities

Densities of various substances have been labeled in the "Density Landscape" picture.

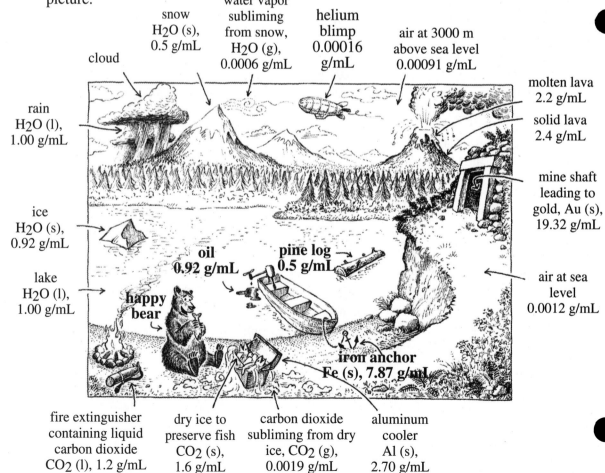

snow H_2O (s), 0.5 g/mL

water vapor subliming from snow, H_2O (g), 0.0006 g/mL

helium blimp 0.00016 g/mL

air at 3000 m above sea level 0.00091 g/mL

cloud

molten lava 2.2 g/mL

solid lava 2.4 g/mL

rain H_2O (l), 1.00 g/mL

mine shaft leading to gold, Au (s), 19.32 g/mL

ice H_2O (s), 0.92 g/mL

oil 0.92 g/mL

pine log 0.5 g/mL

lake H_2O (l), 1.00 g/mL

air at sea level 0.0012 g/mL

happy bear

iron anchor Fe (s), 7.87 g/mL

fire extinguisher containing liquid carbon dioxide CO_2 (l), 1.2 g/mL

dry ice to preserve fish CO_2 (s), 1.6 g/mL

carbon dioxide subliming from dry ice, CO_2 (g), 0.0019 g/mL

aluminum cooler Al (s), 2.70 g/mL

Use the drawing to assist you in answering the following questions:

1. How do densities of solids, liquids, and gases of the same substances compare? (The gas densities are very small, $\sim 10^{-3}$ g/cm^3. The liquid and solid densities are similar, but typically the solid is denser than the liquid. A notable exception is water evidenced by the fact that ice floats.)

2. On the basis of density, why are gases found in the atmosphere? Why is liquid water mainly on the surface of the earth on a rock layer? (Substances on the planet become layered according to their density.)

3. How are the densities for the elemental solids, aluminum, iron, and gold, related to their positions on the periodic table? (There is an increase in density with increasing atomic weight.)

4. Ice floats on liquid water. Is this consistent with the relationship between density and location? (Yes, liquid water is denser than ice.)

5. Do you expect a chunk of dry ice to float on liquid carbon dioxide? Why or why not? (The solid CO_2 will sink because it is denser.)

6. What will happen to an ice cube placed in oil? (Since ice has the same density as oil, it will neither float nor sink. As it melts, the water will sink to the bottom because it is denser.)

7. Label the places in the drawing where melting, evaporation, and condensation occur.

8. What is the volume of each of the following?

    a) 1000 g of rain (1000 mL)

    b) 1000 g of snow (assuming a density of 0.5: 2000 mL)

    c) 1000 g of ice (1087 mL)

    d) 1000 g of water vapor (1,666,667 mL)

9. What happens to the volume of the water when water vapor condenses to form clouds (clouds are droplets of liquid water)? Explain what happens to the density of the water when the volume changes. (The water volume decreases as it forms clouds. The density of the water increases as it forms clouds.)

Part II: Average rainfall

A map of average rainfall in the United States (in inches/yr) is shown below.

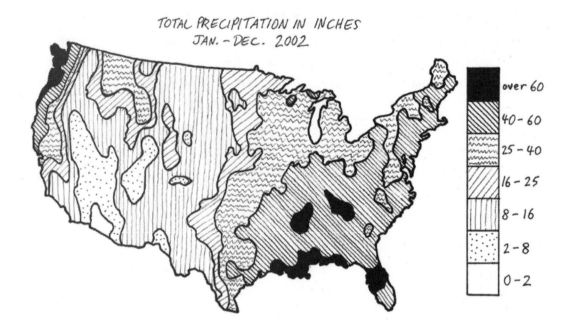

TOTAL PRECIPITATION IN INCHES
JAN. – DEC. 2002

over 60
40 – 60
25 – 40
16 – 25
8 – 16
2 – 8
0 – 2

1. Where is the average rainfall the highest in the United States? (near oceans, on the two coasts)

2. Do you think average rainfall increases if winds blow across the ocean to the land? Why or why not? (Yes, because as water evaporates from the ocean, there is more moisture in the air, which can condense as rain.)

3. Winds blow from the Pacific Ocean over the mountain ranges on the West Coast. On the western slopes of the mountains, there is a moderate amount of precipitation. The eastern slopes are much drier. Why do you think this might be?

Making sense question
How are volume, density, and phase of water related to weather?

Making Sense Discussion (15 min)

Major goals: The goal of this discussion is to tie together the concepts that have been learned over the course of this investigation. Students should come to understand that phase changes drive the water cycle and the weather on this planet. Students should understand that changes in phase also result in changes in volume and density, and that these three types of changes (phase, volume, and density) often result in the relocation of substances on the planet.

5. Discuss densities of various substances.

Discussion goals:
Assist students in articulating the differences in density between substances in the solid, liquid, and gas phases.

Sample questions:
How do the densities of solids, liquids, and gases compare?
In what way is water unusual?
As the atomic weight increases, the density typically increases. Explain why.
How is the location of a substance, either on the surface of the earth or up in the atmosphere, related to density?
How can you decide whether a substance will sink or float on water?

Points to cover:
The densities of solids and liquids of the same substance are relatively similar. In contrast, gases have considerably lower densities, about 1000 times lower. Solids tend to become less dense when they melt into a liquid, with the exception of water, which is denser as a liquid. In comparing densities of different substances in the same phase, there is a general trend towards higher densities for substances with larger atomic weights (i.e., gold is denser than iron).

Density can be used to predict whether one substance will be located above or below another substance. The denser substance will sink below the less dense substance. Since ice is less dense than water, it floats on liquid water. Since gases have very low densities they are typically found above liquids and solids. Any substance with a density lower than 1.0 g/cm^3 will float on water. Some objects, like boats or ships or Styrofoam, will float on water because they contain or trap air.

6. Discuss volume changes and the water cycle.
You may wish to show your calculations on the board to reinforce the math.

Discussion goals:
Assist students in sharing their ideas about the volume of water in different parts of the water cycle.

Sample questions:
What is the volume of 1,000 g of rainwater? (1000 mL)
What is the volume of 1,000 g of snow? (2000 mL)
What is the volume of 1,000 g of ice? (1087 mL)
What is the volume of 1,000 g of water vapor? (1,666,667 mL)
What happens to the volume of water as it goes through the water cycle?

Points to cover:
The density of water is 1.0 g/mL. So 1,000 g of rainwater occupies 1,000 mL, or 1 L. Snow is less dense than rainwater so an amount of snow occupies more volume than the same amount of rainwater. If the density of snow is 0.5 g/mL, then 1,000 g occupy 2,000 mL or 2 L. Water expands when it freezes, but just slightly. The density of ice is 0.92 g/mL so the volume of 1,000 g of ice is 1.087 mL. When water evaporates, it occupies a very large volume (like gaseous carbon dioxide); 1,000 g of water vapor occupy a space of about 1,666,667 mL. As water vapor rises, it cools off and turns into a solid (ice or snow), or a liquid (rain), and collects into clouds. The density increases and the volume occupied decreases when clouds form from water vapor.

7. Discuss factors that influence average rainfall.

Discussion goals:
Assist students in using what they know about the location and movement of water to explain variations in the average rainfall around the United States.

Sample questions:
  Where is the average annual rainfall the highest in the United States?
  How is geographic location related to average rainfall?
  Why do you think the coasts get more rainfall than the center of the country?
  Why do you think it is particularly dry on the eastern slopes of the Sierra Nevada Mountains and the Rocky mountains?

Points to Cover:
Water is transported from large bodies of water by evaporation into the air. The water vapor rises. As it gets colder up in the atmosphere the water vapor condenses to form clouds. Winds blow the clouds over land. When the water droplets get large enough, they fall as rain (or snow). The average rainfall tends to be higher in places where winds blow directly from bodies of water towards the land masses (from the Pacific Ocean and the Gulf of Mexico). It also appears that rain falls more significantly on the western slopes of mountains rather than the eastern slopes (the winds blow from the west in the United States).

Check-in   (5 min)

8. Complete the Check-in exercise.

Write the following question on the board for students to complete individually.

As water moves around the water cycle, its volume changes.

- If rainwater occupies a volume of 1 mL, what volume will it occupy when it forms water vapor?
- What is the main reason for the increase in volume during this phase change?

9. Discuss the Check-in exercise.

Get a sense of the level of understanding by asking students to defend their choices.

Discussion goals:

Check to see that students understand the differences in volume between ice, rain, and water vapor, and that they can use a particle view to explain the differences.

Suggested questions:

How does the volume of water change when rainwater evaporates? How do you know?

How can you calculate the volume occupied by water vapor when 1 mL of water evaporates completely?

What happens to the water molecules when they go from liquid to gas?

Since the density of the rainwater is 1.0 g/mL, 1 mL of water weighs 1 g. The density of water vapor is 0.0006 g/mL. Thus, 1 g of water vapor occupies a volume of 1667 mL. The volume increases because the molecules spread apart. The space between makes gases seem "thin" and as if they are not there.

10. Wrap-up

Assist the students in summarizing what was learned in this class.

- The density of a substance in the solid phase is nearly the same as its density in the liquid phase.
- The density of a substance in the gaseous phase will be much lower than its densities in the liquid and solid phases. Gases are about 1000 times less dense than liquids and solids.
- The density of a substance has a great deal to do with where that substance can be found on the planet in relationship to other substances.

Homework

11. Assign the following for homework.

Use the homework provided with the curriculum or assign your own.

Homework – Investigation I – Lesson 5

Students will need their worksheet for some of the following questions.

1. Name a common object that has:

   a) low density and small volume.

   b) low density and large volume.

   c) high density and small volume.

   d) high density and large volume.

2. One iron cube has an edge 1 cm long; a second iron cube has an edge 2 cm long.

   a) What properties of the 2 cubes are different? The same? Explain.

   b) What is the mass of each cube?

3. You are given equal masses of solid lead, iron, gold and water. Arrange these substances in order of increasing volume.

4. You are given equal volumes of solid lead, iron, gold and water. Arrange these substances in order of increasing mass.

5. Calculate the mass of each of the following (Be careful of units!!!):

   a) 10 mL of corn oil   b) 5 mL of liquid lead   c) 10 cm^3 of nitrogen

Handout

Water World

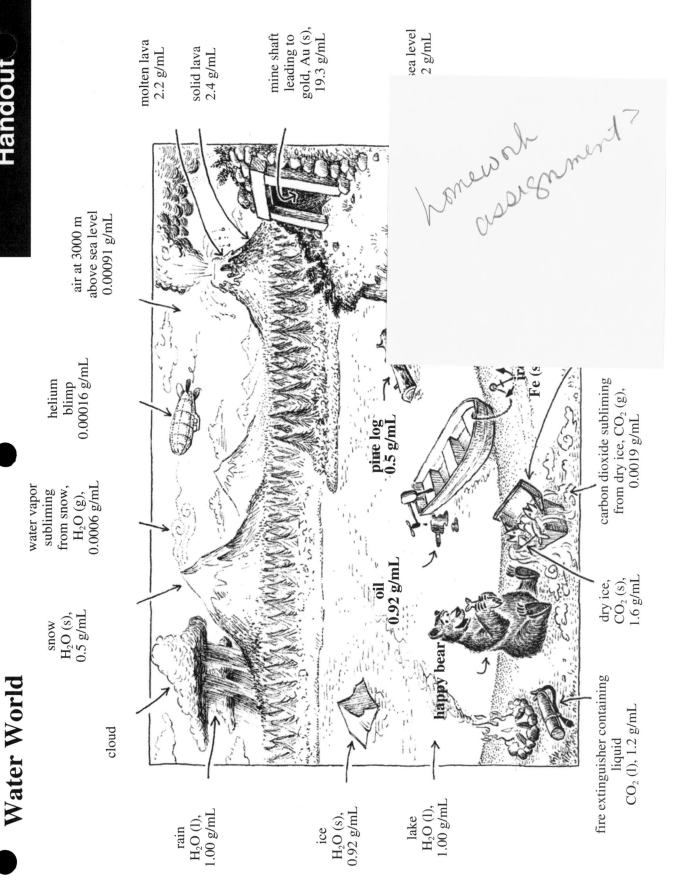

molten lava
2.2 g/mL

solid lava
2.4 g/mL

mine shaft
leading to
gold, Au (s),
19.3 g/mL

sea level
2 g/mL

air at 3000 m
above sea level
0.00091 g/mL

helium
blimp
0.00016 g/mL

water vapor
subliming
from snow,
H_2O (g),
0.0006 g/mL

snow
H_2O (s),
0.5 g/mL

cloud

pine log
0.5 g/mL

oil
0.92 g/mL

happy bear

Fe (s)

carbon dioxide subliming
from dry ice, CO_2 (g),
0.0019 g/mL

dry ice,
CO_2 (s),
1.6 g/mL

rain
H_2O (l),
1.00 g/mL

ice
H_2O (s),
0.92 g/mL

lake
H_2O (l),
1.00 g/mL

fire extinguisher containing
liquid
CO_2 (l), 1.2 g/mL

homework
assignment?

Waterworld

Name: _____

Period: _____ Date: _____

Purpose: The purpose of this lesson is to explore how phase changes are related to volume changes, density changes, and the water cycle in general.

Answer the following questions:

Part I: Comparing densities
Densities of various substances have been labeled in the Density Landscape handout.

1. How do densities of solids, liquids, and gases of the same substances compare?

2. On the basis of density, why are gases found in the atmosphere? Why is liquid water mainly on the surface of the earth on a rock layer?

3. How are the densities for the elemental solids, aluminum, iron, and gold, related to their positions on the periodic table?

4. Ice floats on liquid water. Is this consistent with the relationship between density and location? Explain.

5. Do you expect a chunk of dry ice to float on liquid carbon dioxide? Why or why not?

6. What will happen to an ice cube placed in oil?

7. Label the places in the drawing where melting, evaporation, and condensation occur.

8. What is the volume of each of the following?
    a. 1000 g of rain
    b. 1000 g of snow
    c. 1000 g of ice
    d. 1000 g of water vapor

9. What happens to the volume of the water when water vapor condenses to form clouds (clouds are droplets of liquid water)? Explain what happens to the density of the water when the volume changes.

Part III: Average rainfall

A map of average rainfall in the United States (in inches/yr) is shown below.

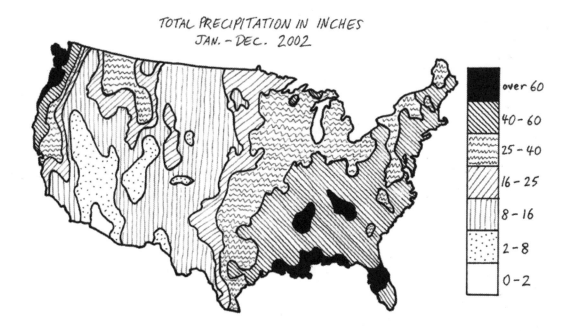

1. Where is the average rainfall the highest in the United States?

2. Do you think average rainfall increases in places where winds blow across the ocean to the land? Why or why not?

3. Winds blow from the Pacific Ocean over the mountain ranges on the West Coast. On the western slopes of the mountains, there is a moderate amount of precipitation. The eastern slopes are much drier. Why do you think this might be?

Making sense:
How are volume, density, and phase of water related to the weather?

Unit 3: Weather

Investigation II: Heating Matter

Contents of Investigation II		**Page**

Investigation II Summary:

Heating Matter

Investigation II consists of six lessons. Together they introduce heat and temperature. The first lesson gives students the opportunity to create their own thermometer, and learn how to convert between the Fahrenheit and Celsius scales. The class discovers in the second lesson that the volume of a gas changes with temperature. The proportional relationship between volume and temperature known as Charles' law is considered in the third lesson. In the fourth and fifth lessons, students turn their attention to the difference between heat and temperature as they monitor the melting and boiling of water. The investigation closes with a discussion of specific heat capacity and how this affects the weather. Students view maps of average temperatures in January and July, and consider why there are such large differences in the middle of the United States, and smaller differences on the coasts.

In Investigation I the class considered how density and phase affected the location of matter. In Investigation II, they discuss the interplay between heat from the sun and matter in driving weather. As the sun warms the land, the air warms and expands, causing it to rise. Ultimately, it is heat from the sun that causes the relocation of water, moving it from large bodies of water, up into the clouds, and back down to earth as rain and snow.

Lesson 1 – Hot Enough. The focus of the first investigation was on the relationship between phase changes of water (the water cycle) and weather. The second investigation considers the effect of heat from the sun on weather and climate. In this first lesson, temperature is examined as an important parameter in describing the effects of the sun on weather. Students investigate the use of °C (degrees Celsius) and °F (degrees Fahrenheit) in reporting temperature, and then are challenged to construct their own thermometer to measure the temperature in the room. They relate volume of a liquid to temperature, and compare °C and °F.

Lesson 2 – Full of Hot Air. Students continue to explore the effects of temperature changes on matter. In the previous lesson, students observed that liquids expand upon heating. This lesson focuses on what happens to gases upon heating. Students construct a device to measure volume changes of air trapped in a tube. They keep track of the temperature for each volume measured and plot these data on a graph. This graph of volume vs. temperature will be examined further in the next lesson. The lesson concludes with a discussion of why warm air rises.

Lesson 3 – Absolute Zero. In this lesson students will do a further analysis of the experiment they did in the previous lesson. First, they consider how to change the temperature scale so that zero volume corresponds to zero temperature. This new temperature scale, called the Kelvin scale, leads students to the proportional relationship between volume and temperature in Kelvin. This proportional relationship is known as Charles' law. Temperature is then related to motions of molecules. At higher temperatures, the molecules move faster; at absolute zero on the Kelvin scale, all motion stops.

Lesson 4 – It's Only a Phase. This lesson focuses on phase changes of water. Students measure the temperature over time as an ice cube is heated until most of the water has boiled away. They construct a graph of the data that they collected. The graph will have several plateaus on it that reflect the fact that the temperature of water during a phase change does not change. These plateaus will be explored in more depth in the following lesson.

Lesson 5 – The Heat is On. This lesson focuses on debriefing the heating curve experiment in the previous lesson. The graph of the heating curve for water has two plateaus on it, reflecting the fact that when two phases of water are present, the temperature does not change. The temperature only changes when the water has changed phase completely. These observations lead to a discussion of the differences between temperature and heat.

Lesson 6 – Hot Concrete. The focus of this investigation has been on how changes in temperature affect matter. Now students will look more generally at how heat from the sun affects weather and climate. Students begin by examining differences in average temperatures in two cities – one on the ocean and one inland. Specific heat capacity is introduced. The teacher sets up an experiment to compare the effect of heat from the sun on soil and water. On their worksheets students compare data for sand, water, air, and metal. They then apply their knowledge of specific heat capacity to understanding why certain regions of the globe have large changes in climate while others do not.

BEFORE CLASS...

LESSON 1 – Hot Enough

Key Ideas:

The sun is a driving force in the water cycle. Heat from the sun (or lack of it) causes water to change phase and move around the planet. In order to study the effect of temperature on weather, it is first important to understand how temperature is measured. A thermometer is an instrument that has been calibrated to reflect the effect of temperature on certain physical properties of another substance (usually volume). Thus thermometers can be made using many different types of substances.

What Takes Place:

In this class students create a rudimentary thermometer using a straw, vial, and rubber stopper. This instrument is placed in water of varying temperatures and the height of the liquid is marked. Finally, the students calibrate their thermometer and figure out the current temperature in the room.

Materials: (for each pair of students)
- Student worksheet
- Small glass vial (about 2-dram size)
- Stopper with one hole to fit into the vial (or a septum with a hole)
- Clear plastic straw that fits into the hole in the stopper
- Small amount of Vaseline to lubricate the stopper and the straw
- 3 250-mL beakers
- Water at room temperature with food coloring added
- Hot plate
- Ice
- Sharpie® pens to mark the straw
- Metric ruler - small

Investigation II – Heating Matter
LESSON 1 – Hot Enough

The focus of the first investigation was on the relationship between phase changes of water (the water cycle) and weather. The second investigation considers the effect of heat from the sun on weather and climate. In this first lesson, temperature is examined as an important parameter in describing the effects of the sun on weather. Students investigate the use of °C (degrees Celsius) and °F (degrees Fahrenheit) in reporting temperature, and then are challenged to construct their own thermometer to measure the temperature in the room. They relate volume of a liquid to temperature, and compare °C and °F.

Exploring the Topic   (5–10 min)

1. Introduce the ChemCatalyst exercise.

Write the exercise on the board for students to complete individually.

The weather forecast in Tokyo, Japan calls for a 60% chance of precipitation with highs reaching 30°C, while in Washington DC the weather forecast calls for a 70% chance of precipitation with highs reaching 50°F.

- Which city will be warmer? Explain your thinking.

- Do you think it will rain or snow in either of the two cities? Explain your reasoning.

2. Discuss the ChemCatalyst exercise.

Use the discussion to get a sense of students' initial ideas.

Discussion goals:
Solicit students' ideas about temperature and how a thermometer works.

Sample questions:
   What weather did you predict for the two cities? Why?
   What is the difference between °C (degrees Celsius) and °F (degrees Fahrenheit)?
   How is temperature measured?
   How does a thermometer work?
   How cold does it have to be for snow?
   Why is a liquid used in a thermometer?
   What is temperature?

Listen to students' ideas without judgment. They will be able to explore these questions further in the activity.

3. Explain the purpose of the activity.

If you wish you can write the main question on the board.

Points to cover:
Tell students they will explore how to construct a thermometer, and will examine the difference between degrees Celsius and degrees Fahrenheit. The main question is: "How is temperature measured?"

Activity – Hot Enough   (15 min)

4. Explain the procedure and pass out the worksheets. (Worksheet)

Tell students they will examine how changes in the height of a liquid can be used to create a thermometer.

Materials (for each pair of students)
Small glass vial (about 2-dram size)
Stopper with one hole to fit into the vial (or a septum with a hole)
Clear plastic straw that fits into the hole in the stopper
Small amount of Vaseline to lubricate the stopper and the straw
3 250-mL beakers
Water at room temperature with food coloring added
Hot plate
Ice
Sharpie® pens to mark the straw
Metric ruler – small

Procedure
1. Begin warming water on a hot plate in one of the beakers and keep it at a low boil. If the water level decreases, add more water.
2. Place ice water in a second beaker.
3. Place water at room temperature in a third beaker.
4. Fill the glass vial to the very top with water with food coloring added.
5. Put the straw through the hole in the stopper. The straw should stick out above the stopper about three or four inches.
6. Place the stopper with the straw on the vial. Push the stopper down so it seals the vial. You should see some water move up the straw.
7. Place the bottom of the vial into the ice water. Observe what happens.
8. Mark the level the water reaches on the straw.
9. Place the vial into the boiling water. Observe what happens.
10. Mark the level the water reaches on the straw.

Answer the following questions:

1. What do you observe when you place the vial in ice water and boiling water? (Liquid moves up in the straw when in boiling water and moves down in ice water.)

2. What happens to the density of the liquid in the vial when it is placed in the boiling water? Explain your reasoning. (As the liquid expands, the density decreases because the same mass is now in a larger volume.)

3. Consider how to determine the temperature in the room.

    a) Is the temperature in the room closer to the temperature of boiling water or ice water? Explain your reasoning. (The temperature in the room is closer to ice water because the level of the liquid in the straw is closer to the level in ice water.)

    b) Create a scale for measuring temperature by assigning numbers to the places you marked on the straw. What numbers did you choose and why? (Students can choose a variety of possibilities, for example, 0 for ice and 100 for boiling water.)

    c) By marking a scale on your straw you have created a **thermometer.** Based on your newly created temperature scale, what is the temperature in the room? Show your work. (Students can assign any arbitrary temperature to ice and boiling water, and then give a temperature for the room consistent with these markings. For example, if they choose 0 for ice and 100 for boiling water, then the temperature in the room will be about 25.)

4. Suppose you measure a height of 5.4 cm when a liquid in a tube is in ice water and a height of 7.4 cm when the same liquid is in boiling water. You decide to call the temperature of ice 32°F and the temperature of boiling water 212°F.

    a) Mark these two points on the graph. (see below)

    b) The height of the liquid at room temperature is 5.9 cm. Use the graph to determine the temperature in the room. (~75°F)

    c) If liquid in your tube reads 6.2 cm, what is the temperature in the room? (~105˚F)

    d) What height would you read on your tube for a temperature of 150˚F? (~6.7 cm)

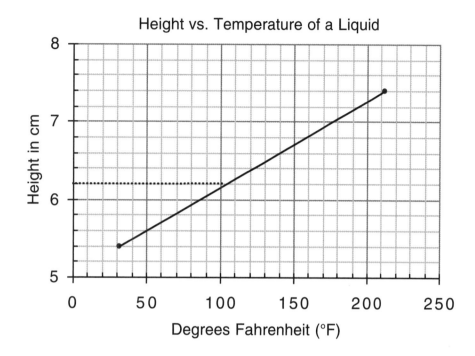

Height vs. Temperature of a Liquid

5. Imagine that you call the temperature of ice water 0°C and the temperature of boiling water 100°C. Compare this with the Fahrenheit scale.

    a) Place these two points on the graph below for the temperature of ice water and the temperature of boiling water. Draw a straight line through the two points.

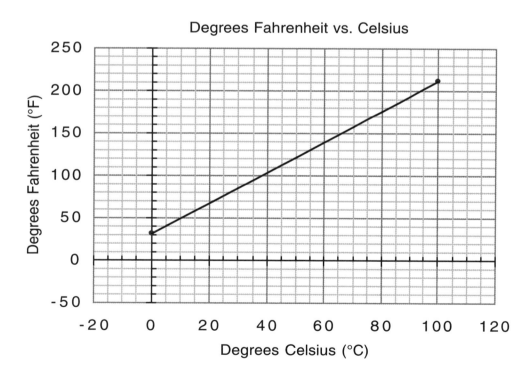

Degrees Fahrenheit vs. Celsius

b) When the temperature is 0°C, is it also 0°F? (No, at 0°C the temperature is 32°F.)

c) Which is colder 40°C or 40°F? Explain your reasoning. (40°F is colder. It is very close to the temperature of ice water on the °F scale. 40°C is between the temperatures of ice water and boiling water on the °C scale.)

d) Which is larger, °C or °F? Explain your thinking. (°C because each mark on the °C graph represents a greater change in temperature.)

e) If a weather forecast says it's 30°C in Tokyo, what temperature would it be in °F? (~85°F)

f) If a weather forecast says it's 50 °F in Washington DC, what is the temperature there in °C? (10°C)

6. The formula for converting between degrees Celsius and degrees Fahrenheit is °F = 9/5 (°C) + 32. Suppose the temperature in Spain is 35°C

a) Use the formula to convert to °F. (°F = 9/5 (35) + 32 = 95°F)

b) Double check your answer on the graph.

Making sense:
What is happening to the water in the vial to make it move up and down the straw at different temperatures?

If you finish early…
Explain why you need to measure the height for two different temperatures to define a temperature scale. Why can't you just measure the height at one temperature? (To draw a line on a graph, you need two points. If you only know one point, then you do not know how much change to expect.)

Making Sense Discussion   (15 min)

Major goals: Students should understand that most thermometers reflect changes in temperature by recording changes in volume of a liquid. They should also understand that by calibrating those changes in volume they created their own thermometer. In addition students should become more familiar with the Celsius scale and understand its mathematical relationship to the Fahrenheit scale.

5. Discuss how temperature is measured.

Discussion goals:
Solicit the students' ideas about how temperature is measured.

Sample questions:
How did you keep track of temperature in today's activity?

How does a thermometer work?

What happens to the volume of the liquid in the thermometer as the temperature increases? What about the density?

If you know the height of a liquid at two different temperatures, can you predict the temperature for a third height? Explain your thinking.

What are some possible ways to set the scale on a thermometer?

For the Fahrenheit scale - as the temperature goes up by 1 degree, does the volume always go up by the same amount? (Yes.)

Alcohol and mercury are two liquids that are often used in thermometers. Why do you think these particular liquids are chosen? (Probably because their volumes change enough with temperature to be readable on a scale.)

Points to cover:

To set a temperature scale, you need at least two points. It is best to choose temperatures that do not vary to set the scale. For example, the boiling point and freezing point of water are very specific temperatures. In general pure water always freezes at the same temperature and always boils at the same temperature (there are some variations when at different altitudes). Body temperature and room temperature are not good choices because they both can vary. Once these two temperature points are noted on a scale it is possible to figure out where any other temperature would be on that scale.

6. Discuss the history of the thermometer.

Share all or part of the following information with your class.

Points to cover:

In 1724, the German physicist, Daniel G. Fahrenheit, invented the first modern thermometer — the mercury thermometer. He called the temperature of an ice/salt mixture "zero degrees," and called his own body temperature "96 degrees." Fahrenheit then divided the scale into single degrees between 0 and 96. On this scale, the freezing point of pure water happens to occur at 32 (and the boiling point at 212). [Note: After Fahrenheit died in 1736, scientists recalibrated the Fahrenheit scale with 212 as the upper fixed point. With this calibration, normal human body temperature registered at 98.6 rather than 96.]

Anders Celsius, a Swedish astronomer, created a thermometer with a different scale in 1747. Celsius used 0° and 100° for the melting point of snow and the boiling point of water, respectively. The Celsius temperature scale is now part of the "metric system" of measurement (SI). Most of the world and all scientists measure temperature in °C, degrees Celsius.

7. Discuss the relationship between °C and °F.

<u>Discussion goals:</u>
Solicit the students' ideas about the differences between °C, degrees Celsius, and °F, degrees Fahrenheit.

Sample questions:
   Which are bigger units, °C, degrees Celsius, or °F, degrees Fahrenheit? (°C)
   Would you be colder at 0°F or 0°C? (0°F)
   When a thermometer reads 100°C, what is the temperature in °F? (212°F)

Points to cover:
It is important to remember that both Celsius and Fahrenheit are measuring the same thing (temperature) and are therefore interchangeable.

> The relationship between °C and °F is: °F = 9/5 (°C) + 32

Check-in   (5 min)

8. Complete the Check-in exercise.

Write the following question on the board for students to complete individually.

- The temperature is 37°C in Spain in July. How does this compare with body temperature, which is 98.6°F?
- Will 37°C feel warm or cold? Explain your reasoning.

9. Discuss the Check-in exercise.

Get a sense of the level of understanding by asking students to defend their answer.

<u>Discussion goals:</u>
Solicit the students' ideas about how temperature and climate are related.

Sample questions:
   Which is higher, 37°C or 98.6°F?
   Room temperature is around 77°F. How will 37°C feel?

Make sure that students understand that °C are larger than °F so for the same temperature, °C are higher. If the temperature is 37°C, then °F = 9/5 (37) + 32 = 98.6°F. This is the same as body temperature and well above room temperature, so it will feel rather hot.

10. Wrap-up

Assist the students in summarizing what was learned in this class.
- Liquids expand upon heating and contract upon cooling.
- The change in volume of a liquid can be used to measure temperature changes.

Homework

11. Assign the following for homework.

Use the homework provided with the curriculum or assign your own.

Homework – Investigation II – Lesson 1

1. The doctor tells you your body temperature is 40°C. Are you sick? Use the formula to convert this temperature to °F. Show your work.

2. The freezing point of water is 0°C. What is the freezing point in °F? Use the formula to convert to °F.

3. When the temperature in °Celsius is doubled from 10°C to 20°C, is the temperature doubled on the Fahrenheit scale? Why or why not?

4. You will be traveling to Japan where the temperature forecast is for a temperature of 30°C during the day, dropping to 25°C overnight. Your friend recommends that you bring clothing for warm weather. Is this a good recommendation? Why or why not?

5. If the temperature changes by one degree from 20°C to 21°C, is the change in height of the liquid in the thermometer the same as when the temperature changes from 60°C to 61°C? Explain your thinking.

          Weather © UC Regents, LHS Living by Chemistry, 2003.

Hot Enough

Name: _____

Period: _____ Date: _____

Purpose: In this lesson, you will examine how changes in volume of a liquid with temperature can be used to create a thermometer.

Procedure
1. Begin warming water in one of the beakers and keep it at a low boil. If the water level decreases, add more water.
2. Place ice water in a second beaker.
3. Place water at room temperature in a third beaker.
4. Fill the glass vial to the very top with water with food coloring added.
5. Put the straw through the hole in the stopper.
6. Place the stopper with the straw on the vial. Push the stopper down so it seals the vial. You should see some water move up the straw.
7. Place the bottom of the vial into the ice water. Observe what happens.
8. Mark the level the water reaches on the straw.
9. Place the vial into the boiling water. Observe what happens.
10. Mark the level the water reaches on the straw.

Answer the following questions
1. What do you observe when you place the vial in ice water and boiling water?

2. What happens to the density of the liquid in the vial when it is placed in the boiling water? Explain your reasoning.

3. Consider how to determine the temperature in the room.

   a) Is the temperature in the room closer to the temperature of boiling water or ice water? Explain your reasoning.

   b) Create a scale for measuring temperature by assigning numbers to the places you marked on the straw. What numbers did you chose and why?

   c) By marking a scale on your straw you have created a **thermometer.** Based on your newly created temperature scale, what is the temperature in the room? Show your work.

4. Suppose you measure a height of 5.4 cm when a liquid in a tube is in ice water and a height of 7.4 cm when the same liquid is in boiling water. You decide to call the temperature of ice 32°F and the temperature of boiling water 212°F.

   a) Mark these two points on the graph.

   b) The height of the liquid at room temperature is 5.9 cm. Use the graph to determine the temperature in the room.

   c) If your tube of liquid reads 6.2 cm, what is the temperature in the room?

   d) Use your graph to determine what height would you read on your tube for a temperature of 150°F.

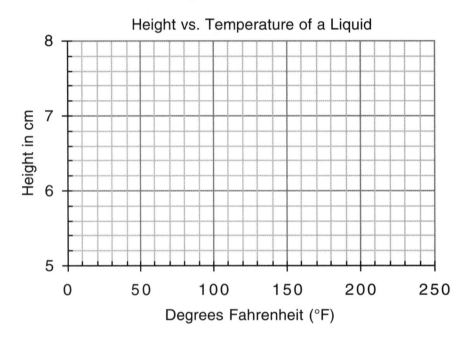

5. Imagine that you call the temperature of ice water 0°C and the temperature of boiling water 100°C. Compare this with the Fahrenheit scale.

   a) Place these two points on the graph below for the temperature of ice water and the temperature of boiling water. Draw a straight line through the two points. (Use this graph to assist you with the following questions.)

   b) When the temperature is 0°C, is it also 0°F?

   c) Which is colder 40°C or 40°F? Explain your reasoning.

   d) Which is larger, °C or °F? Explain your thinking.

Weather © UC Regents, LHS Living by Chemistry, 2003.

e) If a weather forecast says it's 30°C in Tokyo, what temperature would it be in °F?

f) If a weather forecast says it's 50 °F in Washington DC, what is the temperature there in °C?

These two temperature scales: °C and °F, are known as **"degrees Celsius"** and **"degrees Fahrenheit."**

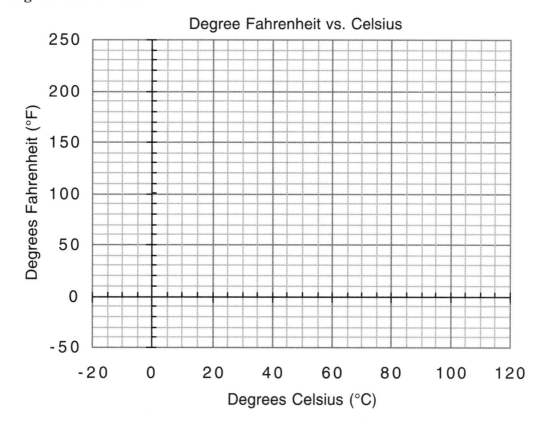

6. The formula for converting between degrees Celsius and degrees Fahrenheit is °F = 9/5 (°C) + 32. Suppose the temperature in Spain is 35°C

   a) Use the formula to convert to °F.

   b) Check your answer on the graph.

Making sense:
What is happening to the water in the vial to make it move up and down the straw at different temperatures?

If you finish early…
Explain why you need to measure the height for two different temperatures to define a temperature scale. Why can't you just measure the height at one temperature?

BEFORE CLASS...

LESSON 2 – Full of Hot Air

Key Ideas:
The last lesson demonstrated volume changes in liquids due to changes in temperature. Gases and solids also change volume (and density) with temperature changes. When gases are heated their volumes increase and their densities decrease. This is why hot air rises.

What Takes Place:
In this lesson students will construct a device that allows them to measure the changes in volume of a trapped column of air as its temperature changes. First they explore qualitatively how heated air takes up more space than cooler air. Then students will heat the air in a capillary tube, trap a small bead of oil in the tube, and measure the volume of the trapped air as the tube cools.

Materials (for each pair of students)
- Student worksheet
- Test tube
- Test tube holder
- Beaker of room temperature water with food coloring added to the water
- Beaker with water to place on hot plate and boil water (can be used by more than one pair of students)
- Thermometer
- 1.5 mm capillary tube closed on one end
- 2 small rubber bands
- Ruler
- Permanent marker
- Oil in a small vial or beaker – about 1/4 to 1/2 inch of liquid (can be used by more than one pair of students)
- Hot plate (can be used by more than one pair of students)
- Beakers of ice
- Small beaker of rock salt

Investigation II – Heating Matter
LESSON 2 – Full of Hot Air

Students continue to explore the effects of temperature changes on matter. In the previous lesson, students observed that liquids expand upon heating. This lesson focuses on what happens to gases upon heating. Students construct a device to measure volume changes of air trapped in a tube. They keep track of the temperature for each volume measured and plot these data on a graph. This graph of volume vs. temperature will be examined further in the next lesson. The lesson concludes with a discussion of why warm air rises.

Exploring the Topic

1. Introduce the ChemCatalyst exercise.

Write the following exercise on the board for stu

Meteorologists recognize that warm air rises. Us
questions below.

- Which has a larger volume, warm air or cold
  Explain your thinking.
- Which is denser, warm air or cold air? Explai
- Which molecules are moving faster, those in
  Explain your thinking.

making a thermometer

2. Discuss the ChemCatalyst exercise.

Use the discussion to get a sense of students' initial ideas.

Discussion goals:
Assist students in sharing their initial ideas on the subject of gas volume and temperature.

Sample questions:
  How do the volume of a liquid and its density change as the temperature changes? (Think about how a thermometer works.)
  How does the density of warm air compare with the density of cold air?
  Why do you think warm air rises?
  What do you think happens to the motions of the gas molecules as the temperature increases?

Listen to students' ideas without judgment. They are likely to surmise that gases expand upon heating, since they know from the previous lesson that liquids expand upon heating. This means that the same mass of warm air occupies a larger volume and has a smaller density. Warm air rises because it has a smaller density than the surrounding air. Get students thinking about motions of molecules. Since warm air expands, the molecules are probably moving faster.

3. Explain the purpose of the activity.

If you wish you can write the main question on the board.

Points to cover:
Tell students they will trap a small amount of gas in a capillary tube using an oil plug. As the gas volume changes, the oil plug will move inside the capillary tube. They will be answering the question: "What is the relationship between the volume and temperature of a fixed amount of gas?"

Activity – Full of Hot Air   (15–20 min)

4. Explain the procedure. (Worksheet)

Tell students that they will be doing two similar activities to determine the relationship between volume and temperature. In the first part, they will use a test tube to examine the relationship qualitatively. In the second part, they will use a capillary tube attached to a thermometer to examine the relationship quantitatively.

Demonstrate how to attach the capillary tube to a thermometer with the open end near the bulb. Use two tiny rubber bands to attach the tube to the thermometer. Emphasize the importance of holding the thermometer as straight as possible when immersing it in the boiling water. [Note: The first readings students obtain will be between 70°C and 80°C.]

Part I: Qualitative observations

Materials (per pair of students):
test tube
test tube holder
beaker of room temperature water with food coloring added to the water
beaker with water to place on hot plate and boil water
hot plate

Procedure:

1. Put 200 mL of water in a 250 mL beaker. Place the beaker on a hot plate and heat the water to about 80°C (just below boiling). Place a beaker of room temperature water nearby with food coloring.
2. **Heat the air**: Using a test tube holder turn the test tube upside down into a beaker of boiling water. Hold the test tube as vertical as possible.
3. **Cool the air and observe:** When you don't see any more bubbles from the test tube,

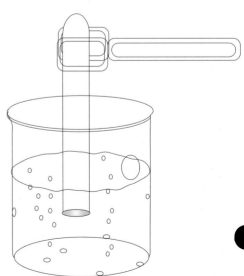

remove the test tube quickly. Put it into a beaker of water at room temperature, again with the open end down.

Answer the following questions:
1. What is in the test tube before you did anything? (air)
2. Why do you observe bubbles going from the test tube to the beaker as it is heated? (air is escaping from the test tube)
3. Why doesn't water move up the test tube when it is placed in boiling water initially? (because there is air in the test tube)
4. Why does water move up the test tube when you place the hot tube in water at room temperature? (the air in the test tube cools and contracts)
5. The next step is to quantify how the volume of a gas changes with the temperature. Look at the next lab activity.
   a) Mark on the diagram where the volume of gas is that you will be measuring.
   b) You will heat the gas in a capillary tube and then cool it. Do you predict the volume of the gas in the capillary tube will increase or decrease as it cools. Explain your thinking.

Part II: Quantitative observations

Materials (per pair of students)
thermometer
1.5 mm capillary tube closed on one end
2 small rubber bands
ruler
permanent marker

Materials (to be shared by four students)
oil in a small vial or beaker - about 1/4 to 1/2 inch of liquid
hot plate
beaker with water to place on hot plate and boil water
beaker of ice
small beaker with rock salt

Procedure:
1. **Attach the tube:** Use two rubber bands to attach a capillary tube to a thermometer with the open end near the bulb as shown.

2. Put 200 mL of water in a 250 mL beaker. Place the beaker on a hot plate and heat the water until it boils.

3. **Heat the air:** Heat the air inside the capillary tube by placing the thermometer and capillary tube directly into the boiling water so that the capillary tube is nearly covered with water. Hold the thermometer as straight as possible.

4. **Trap some oil:** When the temperature reaches 100°C, remove the thermometer and capillary tube from the boiling water. As soon as you remove the tube from the boiling water the air inside the tube will begin to cool. Trap some oil inside the capillary tube by quickly dipping the thermometer and capillary tube in oil so that the open end of the capillary tube is in the oil. As soon as a small amount of oil has been drawn up into the capillary tube, remove the thermometer and capillary tube from the oil.

5. **Mark your starting place:** Use the permanent marker to make a mark on the capillary tube at the side of the oil plug nearest the closed end. At the same time read the temperature off the thermometer and record it in the data table below.

6. **Allow the tube to cool and record the changes:** As the air in the tube continues to cool and contract, the oil plug will move accordingly. Make at least four more marks on the tube and record the temperature each time.

7. **Use ice to cool it more:** Continue cooling the tube of air by immersing it in ice water to which salt has been added.

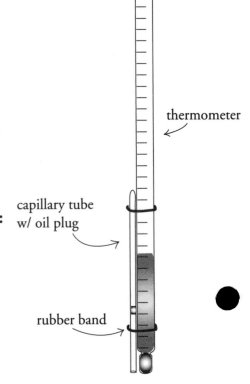

thermometer

capillary tube w/ oil plug

rubber band

8. When you are finished marking the tube use your metric ruler to measure the various lengths of air that you marked at various temperatures. Record your data in the column labeled height.

9. **Calculate the volume of air:** Calculate the volume of the cylinder of air at each temperature. Assume the radius of the capillary tube is 0.75 mm. The volume of a cylinder is given by the formula $V = \pi r^2 h$, where $\underline{r}$ is the radius of the base, and $\underline{h}$ is the height. Enter the data in your table.

Temperature (°C)	Height (mm)	Volume (mm³)
80	71	141
65	67	134
40	63	126
25	60	120
10	55	109
–5	53	106

Answer the following questions:

1. Graph the data with volume on the y-axis and temperature on the x-axis. Label the y-axis. Draw the best straight line that you can through your data points.

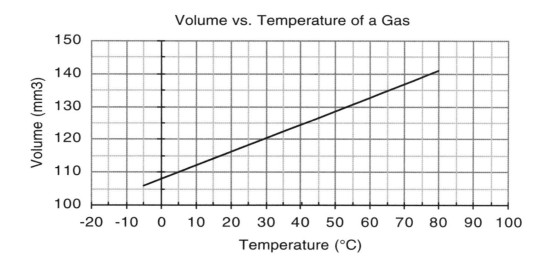

2. What happens to the volume of the gas when the gas is heated? (increases)

3. What happens to the volume of the gas when the gas is cooled? (decreases)

4. What would be the volume of the gas at 50°C?

5. Explain how you could use this tube as a thermometer.

6. Use your capillary tube to measure the temperature in the room.

7. When the temperature is zero, is the volume of gas zero? (no)

Making Sense:
Explain why the oil plug was moving up the capillary tube.

Making Sense Discussion   (10 min)

Major goals: The first goal of this discussion is to make sure the students understand why the oil plug was moving in the capillary tube and what they were measuring. The second goal is to relate the change in volume of a gas with a change in density. Since warm air expands, it is less dense, and therefore rises, while cool air contracts and sinks.

5. Process the activity.

Create a data table on the board such that teams may enter their data for the five different temperatures.

<u>Discussion goals:</u>
Discuss what was happening in the test tube and in the capillary tube. Make sure students understand that air is trapped in the test tube and capillary tube.

Suggested questions:

What did you discover when you heated and cooled the tiny air sample?

When you placed the capillary tube in the hot water, why didn't water move up the tube?

Once you remove the tube from the hot water, what happens to the air?

Why does oil move up the tube?

What happens to the oil as the tube cools?

Students should be able to tell you that the volume of the gas increased when the gas sample was heated, and that the volume of the gas decreased when the gas sample was cooled, just like the volume of liquid changes in a thermometer.

6. Discuss why warm air rises.

<u>Discussion goals:</u>
Solicit students' ideas about the relationship between temperature, volume, and density.

Sample questions:

When the sun warms water vapor, does the density of the vapor increase or decrease? Explain your thinking. (decreases)

What happens to the air molecules themselves as they are heated?

Why does warm air rise? (the molecules move faster and farther apart, the air expands, its volume increases and its density decreases)

Why does cool air sink? (the molecules move slower and closer to one another, the air contracts, its volume decreases and its density increases)

Check-in   (5 min)

7. Complete the Check-in exercise.

Write the following question on the board for students to complete individually.

• What happens to the volume and density of 10 g of air as it is heated? Explain your thinking.

8. Discuss the Check-in exercise.

Get a sense of the level of understanding by asking students to defend their choices.

<u>Discussion goals:</u>
Check to see that students understand the relationship between gas volume and temperature.

Suggested questions:
What happens to the volume of a gas as it is heated?
What happens to the density of the gas upon heating?

Students should realize that the volume increases, and therefore, the density decreases.

9. Wrap-up

Assist the students in summarizing what was learned in this class.

- The volume of a fixed amount of gas increases as the temperature increases.
- When the volume of a gas increases its density decreases.
- Because warm air expands, it is less dense, and it rises. Likewise, cool air contracts, it is denser, and it sinks.

Homework

10. Assign the following for homework.

Use the homework provided with the curriculum or assign your own.

Homework – Investigation II – Lesson 2

1. Explain how you think a hot air balloon works. How could the balloon go up and down using just the air?

2. Where is the air denser – in a room where the temperature is 20°C or in a room where the temperature is 35°C? Explain.

3. Two party balloons are inflated. Both contain exactly the same amount of gas. One is inflated outside in the back yard where the air temperature is 102°F. The other is inflated inside the air-conditioned house where the air temperature is 64°F. What differences will there be between the two balloons? Explain why.

4. Test to see if warm air rises in your home. Use a thermometer and take the temperature of a room at floor level. Take the temperature of the same room about an inch from the ceiling. Record your readings.

Full of Hot Air

Name: _____

Period: _____ Date: _____

Purpose: The purpose of this lesson is to allow you to observe and record volume changes in a gas as a result of temperature changes.

Part I: Qualitative observations

Procedure:

1. Put 200 mL of water in a 250 mL beaker. Place the beaker on a hot plate and heat the water to about 80°C (just below boiling). Place a beaker of room temperature water nearby with food coloring.

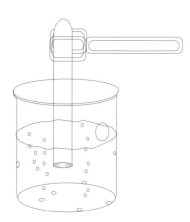

2. **Heat the air**: Using a test tube holder turn the test tube upside down into a beaker of boiling water. Hold the test tube as vertical as possible.

3. **Cool the air and observe:** When you don't see any more bubbles from the test tube, remove the test tube quickly. Put it into a beaker of water at room temperature, again with the open end down.

Answer the following questions:

1. What is in the test tube before you did anything?

2. Why do you observe bubbles going from the test tube to the beaker as it is heated?

3. Why doesn't water move up the test tube when it is placed in boiling water initially?

4. Why does water move up the test tube when you place the hot tube in water at room temperature?

5. The next step is to quantify how the volume of a gas changes with the temperature. Look at the next lab activity.

   a) Mark on the diagram where the volume of gas is that you will be measuring.

   b) You will heat the gas in a capillary tube and then cool it. Do you predict the volume of the gas in the capillary tube will increase or decrease as it cools. Explain your thinking.

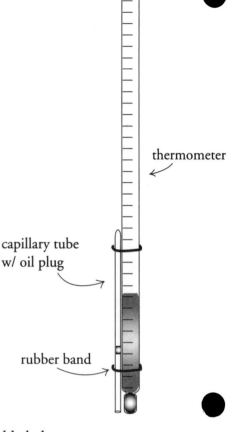

Part II: Quantitative observations

Procedure:

1. **Attach the tube:** Use two rubber bands to attach a capillary tube to a thermometer with the open end near the bulb as shown.

2. Put 200 mL of water in a 250 mL beaker. Place the beaker on a hot plate and heat the water until it boils.

3. **Heat the air:** Heat the air inside the capillary tube by placing the thermometer and capillary tube directly into the boiling water so that the capillary tube is nearly covered with water. Hold the thermometer as straight as possible.

4. **Trap some oil:** When the temperature reaches 100°C, remove the thermometer and capillary tube from the boiling water. As soon as you remove the tube from the boiling water the air inside the tube will begin to cool. Trap some oil inside the capillary tube by quickly dipping the thermometer and capillary tube in oil so that the open end of the capillary tube is in the oil. As soon as a small amount of oil has been drawn up into the capillary tube, remove the thermometer and capillary tube from the oil.

5. **Mark your starting place:** Use the permanent marker to make a mark on the capillary tube at the side of the oil plug nearest the closed end. At the same time read the temperature off the thermometer and record it in the data table below.

6. **Allow the tube to cool and record the changes:** As the air in the tube continues to cool and contract, the oil plug will move accordingly. Make at least four more marks on the tube and record the temperature each time.

7. **Use ice to cool it more:** Continue cooling the tube of air by immersing it in ice water to which salt has been added.

8. When you are finished marking the tube use your metric ruler to measure the various lengths of air that you marked at various temperatures. Record your data in the column labeled height.

9. **Calculate the volume of air:** Calculate the volume of the cylinder of air at each temperature. Assume the radius of the capillary tube is 0.75 mm. The volume of a cylinder is given by the formula $V = \pi r^2 h$, where $\underline{r}$ is the radius of the base, and $\underline{h}$ is the height. Enter the data in your table.

Temperature (°C)	Height (mm)	Volume (mm³)

Answer the following questions:

1. Graph the data with volume on the y-axis and temperature on the x-axis. Label the
    y-axis. Draw the best straight line that you can through your data points.

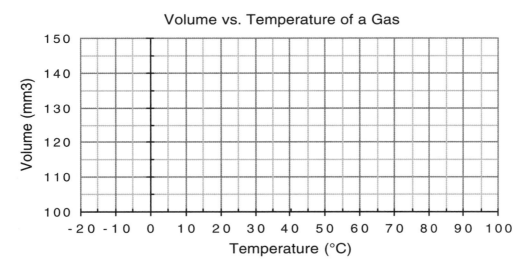

2. What happens to the volume of the gas when the gas is heated?

3. What happens to the volume of the gas when the gas is cooled?

4. What would be the volume of the gas at 50°C?

5. Explain how you could use this tube as a thermometer.

6. Use your capillary tube to measure the temperature in the room.

7. When the temperature is zero, is the volume of gas zero?

Making Sense:
Explain why the oil plug was moving up the capillary tube.

BEFORE CLASS...

LESSON 3 – Absolute Zero

Key Ideas:
Celsius and Fahrenheit are the two most commonly used temperature scales. The Kelvin scale is a third temperature scale. It is used primarily by scientists when they are working with the temperatures of gases. The Kelvin scale simply moves the Celsius scale up 273 units, so that when the temperature of a gas is zero its volume is also zero. Zero degrees Kelvin corresponds to –273 ˚C. When the Kelvin scale is used, the mathematical relationship between volume and temperature of a gas is directly proportional. Charles' Law states that the volume of a given mass of gas is directly proportional to its Kelvin temperature, if pressure is kept constant.

What Takes Place:
Before the activity, the Kelvin scale and absolute zero are introduced to the students. Students then work with data on a worksheet to understand the relationship between temperature and volume of a gas. The Kelvin scale and the Celsius scale are compared and the proportionality of volume to temperature in a gas is evident for the Kelvin scale. Charles' Law is introduced and students complete some simple practice problems.

Materials: (per team of 2 students)
- Student Worksheet
- Transparency – Kelvin scale

Investigation II – Heating Matter
LESSON 3 – Absolute Zero

In this lesson students will do a further analysis of the experiment they did in the previous lesson. First, they consider how to change the temperature scale so that zero volume corresponds to zero temperature. This new temperature scale, called the Kelvin scale, leads students to the proportional relationship between volume and temperature in Kelvin. This proportional relationship is known as Charles' law. Temperature is then related to motions of molecules. At higher temperatures, the molecules move faster; at absolute zero on the Kelvin scale, all motion stops.

Exploring the Topic   (5–10 min)

1. Introduce the ChemCatalyst exercise.

Write the following exercise on the board for students to complete individually.

The lowest recorded temperature in the solar system was on Triton, a moon of Neptune, and was recorded to be –235°C.

- Do you think carbon dioxide would be a solid, liquid, or gas at this temperature? Explain your reasoning.
- As the temperature gets lower and lower, the volume of a gas gets smaller and smaller. What do you think happens to the motions of the molecules?

2. Discuss the ChemCatalyst exercise.

Use the discussion to get a sense of students' initial ideas.

Discussion goals:
Assist students in sharing their initial ideas on the subject of gas volume and temperature.

Sample questions:
What do you think will happen to gaseous carbon dioxide molecules when the temperature gets as low as –235°C? Explain your thinking.
Do you think Triton has a gaseous atmosphere? Explain your thinking.
Do you think the molecules will move closer together or further apart as they are cooled?
If molecules are held in a smaller space, do you think they are moving as fast as when they are in a larger space?
What is the smallest volume you think a gas could occupy? Explain your thinking.
What is the lowest temperature you think a substance can reach? Explain your thinking.

Listen to students' ideas without judgment. They know that carbon dioxide can be made into dry ice, and that dry ice is at a very low temperature, so they should be able to surmise that carbon dioxide is a solid on Triton. Nitrogen and oxygen also condense at the temperature on Triton, so there is no gaseous atmosphere. If molecules occupy a smaller space, they are probably not moving as rapidly as they do when they occupy a larger space. We might expect that the volume can only decrease to zero (matter can only contract to near nothing), and that there is a temperature below which matter cannot cool (when motion stops).

3. Introduce the Kelvin scale. (Transparency)

Display the transparency showing volume vs. temperature in °C as shown below. Show how to change the scale from °C to K as the discussion proceeds.

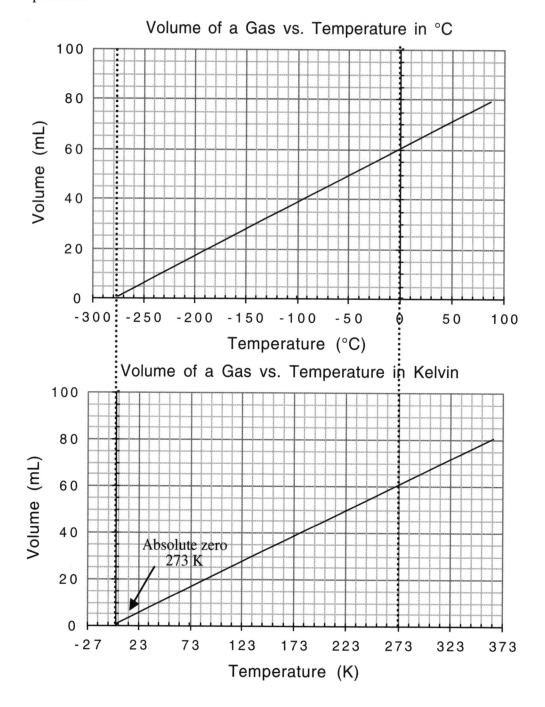

Weather © UC Regents, LHS Living by Chemistry, 2003.

<u>Discussion goals:</u>
Share information about the Kelvin scale.

Sample questions:

Can the volume of a gas be negative? Why or why not? (No, volumes cannot be negative. Matter cannot occupy negative space.)

What is the lowest temperature that you think can be obtained on the Celsius scale? (-273°C because this is where the volume goes to zero.)

Suppose we define this temperature, where the volume is zero, as 0 K. What is 0°C in Kelvin? (273 K)

What might be an advantage of the Kelvin scale? (It makes sense to stop the temperature scale when the volume is zero. The line then goes through the origin (0,0).)

Points to Cover:
The temperature at which the volume is 0 (y = 0) is –273°C. If we shift the temperature scale to the left by 273° (add 273° to each temperature), then the temperature will be zero when the volume is zero. This new temperature scale is called the Kelvin scale.

0 Kelvin is referred to as **absolute zero.** This is considered to be the lowest temperature that could possibly be reached. (Notice that the symbol for degree, "°" , is not used for the Kelvin scale by convention.) At absolute zero all substances are solids, except for He, which remains a liquid to the lowest temperatures measured. Since the volume of a gas is zero at absolute zero, it is believed that at 0 K the motions of atoms and molecules stop.

Absolute zero has never been attained in the laboratory. The lowest temperature reached in a laboratory is about 0.00001 K. The lowest temperature recorded on earth was –89°C, recorded in Antarctica. This is equivalent to 184 K. The lowest recorded temperature in the solar system was on Triton, a moon of Neptune, and was recorded to be –235°C or 38 K. At this temperature the surface of Triton is thought to consist of oceans of nitrogen and glaciers of methane. The Kelvin scale is mostly used whenever we need to make predictions about the volume of gases.

Conversion between degrees Kelvin and degrees Celsius: K = 273 + °C

Absolute zero is the temperature at which the volume of a gas and its temperature are both zero. Absolute zero is only found on the Kelvin scale and is equivalent to –273 °C.

---

4. Explain the purpose of the activity.

If you wish you can write the main question on the board.

Points to cover:

Tell students they will be exploring the relationship between volume and temperature of a gas in more detail. They will be answering the question, "Why is the Kelvin scale useful when working with gases?"

Activity – Absolute Zero   **(15 min)**

5. Pass out the worksheets. (Worksheet)

Ask students to work in pairs on their worksheets.

Part I: A quantity of gas was heated to various temperatures. Each time the temperature changed, the volume of the gas was measured in milliliters. The temperature was sometimes measured in degrees Celsius and sometimes in degrees Kelvin. Note that V represents volume in the table and T represents temperature.

Fill in the remainder of the table:

Trial	Temperature (°C)	Temperature (K)	Volume (mL)	Ratio: V/T (for T in °C)	Ratio: V/T (for T in K)
1	10.0	278	500	50	1.8
2	50.0	323	570	11.4	1.8
3	100.0	367	660	6.6	1.8
4	200.0	467	840	4.2	1.8
5	283	556	1000	3.5	1.8
6	838	1111	2000	2.4	1.8

Use the table to answer the following questions:

1. What do you notice about the ratio of volume to temperature for the different trials? (It is constant if the temperature is expressed in degrees Kelvin.)

2. When the temperature was doubled in degrees Celsius, did the volume also double? (no)

3. When the temperature was doubled in degrees Kelvin, did the volume also double? (yes)

4. Whenever the volume doubled, did the temperature also double? (only in K)

5. What appears to be the difference between using the Kelvin scale and the Celsius scale in this situation? (Kelvin scale – volume and temperature are directly proportional)

Part II: Imagine there are two hot air balloons ready for launch. One hot air balloon (balloon A) is large and the other (balloon B) is small. The air in each balloon is heated and the temperature and volume of the gas is recorded. The following graph shows the data for each balloon.

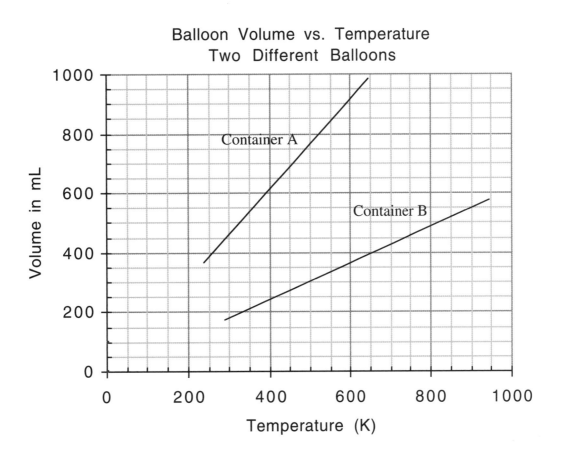

1. What is the ratio of volume to temperature for the gas in Balloon A? Show your work. (1.5)

2. What is the ratio of volume to temperature for the gas in Balloon B? Show your work. (0.6)

3. Compare the ratio of volume to temperature.

   a) Is the ratio V/T always the same for Balloon A? (yes)

   b) Is the ratio V/T always the same for Balloon B? (yes)

   c) Is the ratio V/T the same for both balloons? (The V/T ratio does not change for Balloon A or for Balloon B, but the ratios for the two balloons are different from each other.)

4. Predict the volume of the gas in Balloon A if the temperature is 500 K. (700 L)

5. Predict the volume of the gas in Balloon B if the temperature is 500 K (300 L)

6. At what temperature do the two balloons have the same volume? (They have zero volume at 0 K)

Part III: Imagine that you are getting ready to go up in one of these hot air balloons. Around noon you fill a balloon to a volume of 50,000 L at 100.0°C. Later the day becomes cloudy and chilly, and the temperature inside the balloon drops to 50.0°C.

1. Do you predict that the balloon will get bigger or smaller? Explain your reasoning. (smaller, the volume of gas will drop with the temperature)

2. What is the ratio V/T at the beginning of the day? (Be sure to use Kelvin). (50,000 L / (273+100) K = 134 L/K)

3. What is the ratio V/T when the temperature drops to 50.0°C? (134 L/K)

Making sense:
What is the volume of the balloon described in Part III when the temperature is 50°C? (Be sure to use Kelvin.) (134 L/K x (273+50) K = 43,282 L)

Making Sense Discussion   **(15 min)**

Major goals: The main goal of this lesson is to introduce students to the first gas law: Charles's Law. They should understand the proportional relationship between the volume and temperature of a gas. In addition, they should gain a little practice in solving problems using Charles' Law.

6. Discuss the relationship between V and T.

Create a data table on the board such that teams may enter their ratios for V/T for Part I of the worksheet.

Discussion goals:
Assist students in sharing their conclusions about the relationship between volume and temperature of a gas using the Celsius and Kelvin scales.

Suggested questions:
What did you discover about the ratio V/T?
Does it matter which temperature scale you used? Why or why not?
If the temperature in K doubles, what happens to the volume?
If the temperature in °C doubles, does the volume double?
If the volume doubles, does the temperature always double?

Ratio: V/T (for T in °C)	Ratio: V/T (for T in K)
50	1.8
11.4	1.8
6.6	1.8
4.2	1.8
3.5	1.8
2.4	1.8

If you have a ratio of V/T = 1.5 for one point on a line, what will the ratio of V/T be for a different point on that line? (it will always be the same, in this case 1.5)

Suppose you want to draw a graph of volume vs. temperature in Kelvin. Why is it only necessary to measure one volume and temperature? (one point is always the origin (0, 0) – this is not true on the Celsius scale)

Because one of the points on a line of volume vs. temperature is always (0, 0) if the temperature is measured in Kelvin, you only need to measure one volume and one temperature to draw a graph for a given gas and make predictions at other temperatures and volumes.

7. Introduce Charles's Law.

Points to cover:

If you measure the temperature of any gas in degrees Kelvin, the graph of volume vs. temperature for that gas will result in a straight line going through the origin (0, 0). This means that the volume of a gas is proportional to its temperature. That is, when the volume doubles, the temperature doubles. Likewise, when a volume measurement triples, it means the temperature has tripled, and so on. This mathematical relationship does not hold true for the Celsius scale. If the temperature is measured in degrees Celsius, it is necessary to convert the temperature to Kelvin before doing any predictions and calculations.

This proportional relationship was discovered by a French scientist in 1802 and is known as **Charles' Law.**

> **Charles' law** states that for a given mass, the volume of gas is directly proportional to its Kelvin temperature, if the pressure is kept constant.
>
> In symbols, Charles' law states that if P is constant, V/T stays constant as long as T is measured in Kelvin.

Charles' Law, put more simply, says that if the temperature of a gas is increased, then the volume of the gas will increase proportionally. Also, if the temperature of a gas is decreased, the volume of the gas will decrease proportionally. Although a similar relationship can also be observed in other phases (i.e. the thermal expansion of water in the bulb thermometer), Charles's law only applies to the volume changes that take place when the temperature of a **gas** is changed.

Jacques Charles was a French scientist born in the mid 1700's. Charles was a pioneering balloonist, and invented the hydrogen filled balloon. He learned a great deal about gases while developing this sport. He experimented with gases and determined the relationship between gas temperature and volume.

8. Use Charles's Law in a practice problem.

Complete the Making Sense problem as a class. Solicit student help.

Discussion goals:
Assist students in determining a new gas volume and a new temperature given an initial volume and temperature.

Sample Problem:
Imagine that you go hot air ballooning. First thing in the morning you fill a balloon to a volume of 36,000 L at 80°C. Later, while making an ascent to a higher altitude, the air inside the balloon is heated to 105˚C. What happens to the volume of the balloon? Calculate the exact volume of the balloon at 105 ˚C.

Use V_1 to represent the starting volume and V_2 to represent the volume at the end of the problem. T_1 represents the starting temperature and T_2 the final temperature.

Here are three possible ways to solve the problem:
- Proportional analysis: $V_1/T_1 = V_2/T_2$
- Dimensional analysis: $V_2 = T_2 (V_1/T_1)$
- Use a graph.

Suggested questions:
  What is the ratio of V/T? (Be sure to use Kelvin). (36,000 L / (273+80)K = 102 L/K)
  What is the ratio V/T if the temperature rises to 120°C? (102 L/K)
  What is the volume of the balloon at 105°C? (Be sure to use Kelvin.) (102 L/K x (273+105) K = 38,556 L)

Check-in   (5 min)

9. Complete the Check-in exercise.

Write the following question on the board for students to complete individually.

- What change in volume results if 60.0 mL of gas is cooled from 27.0°C to 2.0°C?

10. Discuss the Check-in exercise.

Get a sense of the level of understanding by asking students to defend their choices.

Discussion goals:
Check to see that students understand the relationship between gas volume and temperature, and how to apply the mathematical formula in Charles's Law.

Suggested questions:

What happens to the volume of the gas?

What are the temperatures in Kelvin? (T_1 is 300 K and T_2 is 275 K)

What is the value of V_2? (55 mL)

How much does the volume change? (it decreases by 5 mL)

The initial temperature is $27+273 = 300$ K and the final temperature is $2 + 273 = 275$ K. The new volume is $(60.0$ mL $/ 300$ K$) (275$ K$) = 55$ mL.

11. Wrap-up

Assist the students in summarizing what was learned in this class.

- Charles's Law can be described by the formula $V_1/T_1 = V_2/T_2$ (provided the temperature is measured in Kelvin)
- Absolute zero is the temperature at which the volume of a gas is 0.

Homework

12. Assign the following for homework.

Use the homework provided with the curriculum, or assign your own.

Homework – Investigation II – Lesson 3

** Remember... all temperatures must be converted to Kelvin!!!

1. Calculate the decrease in temperature when 2.00 L of a gas at 20.0°C is compressed to 1.00 L.

2. A sample of air occupies 600.0 mL at 20.0°C. What is the volume of the air at 60.0°C?

3. A gas occupies 900.0 mL at a temperature of 27.0°C. What is the volume of the gas at 132.0°C?

4. You measure 300.0 mL of a gas at 17.0°C. What is its volume at 10.0°C?

5. At 27.00°C a gas has a volume of 6.00 L. What will the volume be at 150.0°C?

6. At 225.0°C a gas has a volume of 400.0 mL. What is the volume of this gas at 127.0°C?

7. You had a birthday party with helium balloons during the day, when the temperature was 27.0°C. You left your balloons outside overnight and the temperature dropped to 20.0°C. By how much does the volume of the balloons decrease?

8. Calculate the decrease in temperature when 2.0 L at 20°C is compressed to 1 L. Show at least 2 different ways to solve this problem.

Absolute Zero

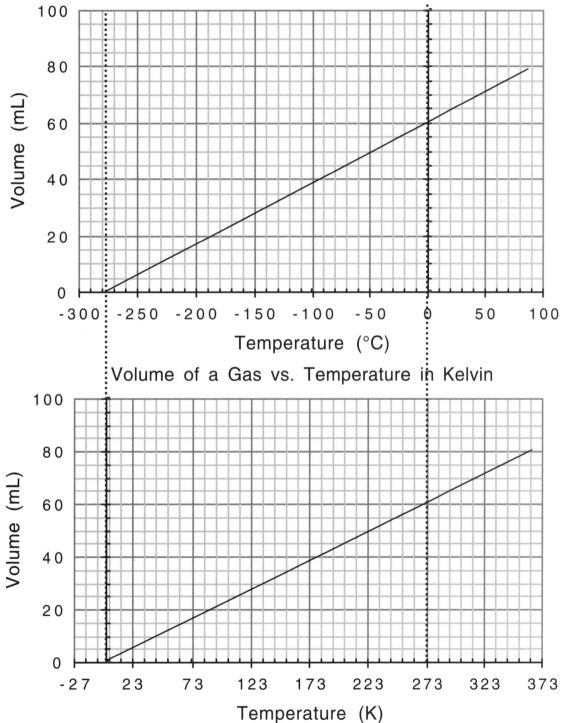

Absolute Zero

Name: _____

Period _____ Date: _____

Purpose: This lesson allows you to examine the relationship between volume and temperature in gases and introduces you to the Kelvin scale.

Part I: A quantity of gas was heated to various temperatures. Each time the temperature changed, the volume of the gas was measured in milliliters. The temperature was sometimes measured in degrees Celsius and sometimes in degrees Kelvin. Note that V represents volume and T represents temperature.

Fill in the remainder of the table:

Trial	Temperature (°C)	Temperature (K)	Volume (ml)	Ratio: V/T (for T in °C)	Ratio: V/T (for T in K)
1	10.0		500		
2	50.0		570		
3	100.0		660		
4	200.0		840		
5		556	1000		
6		1111	2000		

1. What do you notice about the ratio of volume to temperature for the different trials?

2. When the temperature was doubled in degrees Celsius, did the volume also double?

3. When the temperature was doubled in degrees Kelvin, did the volume also double?

4. Whenever the volume doubled, did the temperature also double? What appears to be the difference between using the Kelvin scale and the Celsius scale in this situation?

Part II: Imagine there are two hot air balloons ready for launch. One hot air balloon (balloon A) is large and the other (balloon B) is small. The air in each balloon is heated and the temperature and volume of the gas is recorded. The following graph shows the data for each balloon.

1. What is the ratio of volume to temperature for the gas in Balloon A? Show your work.

2. What is the ratio of volume to temperature for the gas in Balloon B? Show your work.

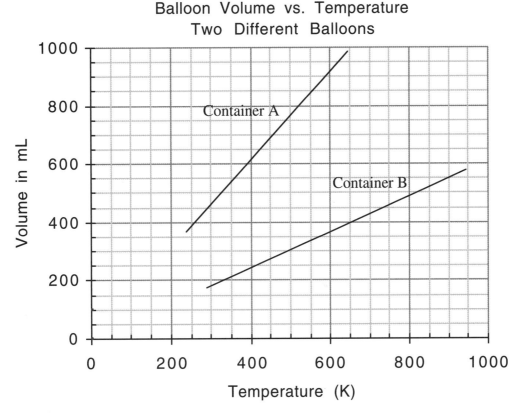

3. Compare the ratio of volume to temperature.

    a) Is the ratio V/T always the same for Balloon A?

    b) Is the ratio V/T always the same for Balloon B?

    c) Is the ratio V/T the same for both balloons?

4. Predict the volume of the gas in Balloon A if the temperature is 500 K. Predict the volume of the gas in Balloon B if the temperature is 500 K.

5. At what temperature do the two balloons have the same volume?

Part III: Imagine that you are getting ready to go up in one of these hot air balloons. Around noon you fill a balloon to a volume of 50,000 L at 100.0°C. Later the day becomes cloudy and chilly, and the temperature inside the balloon drops to 50.0°C.

1. Do you predict that the balloon will get bigger or smaller? Explain your reasoning.

2. What is the ratio V/T at the beginning of the day? (Be sure to use Kelvin).

3. What is the ratio V/T when the temperature drops to 50.0°C?

Making sense question:
What is the volume of the balloon described in Part III when the temperature is 50°C? (Be sure to use Kelvin.)

BEFORE CLASS...

LESSON 4 – It's Only a Phase

Key Ideas:
An ice cube is heated until it passes through all of its phases, and
the temperature of the water is graphed over time. The resultant graph consists of a
sloped line, a plateau, another sloped line, and another plateau. This graph is known
as the heating curve of water. The melting temperature and boiling temperature of
water are accurately reflected on this graph by the two plateaus.

What Takes Place:
Students begin this lesson with a cube of ice. They work in teams of two heating this
solid form of water and recording its temperature until it has almost boiled away.
They graph the data they've collected and begin to speculate on what is happening at
different places on the graph. The vocabulary associated with phase changes is more
thoroughly introduced.

Materials: (per team of 2 students)
* Student worksheet
* 250 mL beakers (one per pair)
* Ice cubes (directly out of the freezer so that they have not begun melting, if
  possible)
* Thermometers
* Oven mitt
* Hot plate
* Ring stand and clamp to hold the thermometer (optional)

Investigation II – Heating Matter
LESSON 4 – It's Only a Phase

This lesson focuses on phase changes of water. Students measure the temperature over time as an ice cube is heated until most of the water has boiled away. They construct a graph of the data that they collected. The graph will have several plateaus on it that reflect the fact that the temperature of water during a phase change does not change. These plateaus will be explored in more depth in the following lesson.

Exploring the Topic   (5–10 min)

1. Introduce the ChemCatalyst exercise.

Write the following exercise on the board for students to complete individually.

Suppose you put a pot of water on the stove on "high" (about 350° F or 170°C). After the water boils for about ten minutes the temperature of the water is 212˚F.

- What is happening to the water?
- Why is the temperature of the water 212˚F and not 350˚F like the stove?

2. Discuss the ChemCatalyst exercise.

Use the discussion to get a sense of students' initial ideas.

Discussion goals:
Assist students in describing what they observe when heat is added to a substance.

Sample questions:
   What is happening to the water?
   How hot do you think the water will get?
   Will the water ever stop heating up? Why or why not?
   What is the boiling temperature of water?
   What does the boiling temperature of a substance tell you?
   Do you think all liquids have the same boiling temperature? Why or why
     not?

Many students think that the water will keep getting hotter on the stove if the heat is on high and it is boiling. They may not know that the water will heat to 212°F (100°C) and then stay at that temperature until it has boiled away entirely. It is not necessary to elicit the "correct" answer, simply solicit the students' ideas and their explanations.

3. Explain the purpose of the activity.

If you wish you can write the main question on the board.

Points to cover:
Tell students they will be exploring the effect of heat on a substance. They will be answering the question, "What happens to the temperature of water as it is heated?"

Activity – It's Only a Phase   (15 min)

4. Explain the procedure and pass out the worksheets. (Worksheet)

Have students work in teams of 2 or 4. Briefly explain the procedure, then pass out worksheets. Tell students to focus their observations on the phases (solid, liquid, gas, or combination) present in the beaker.

Materials
250 mL beakers (one per pair)
ice cubes (directly out of the freezer so that they have not begun melting, if
    possible)
thermometers
oven mitts
hot plate
ring stand and clamp to hold the thermometer (optional)

Procedure
1. Work in teams of 2 to 4.
2. Place an ice cube in your beaker.
3. Use your thermometer to record the initial temperature of your ice cube.

Remember: During this experiment do not let the thermometer touch the glass while you are measuring the temperature of the water, otherwise you will be measuring the temperature of the glass and not the water. You may use a clamp to hold the thermometer if this is helpful. Use the mitts to avoid getting burned once the water starts to boil.

Temperature	Time	Phase
data will vary	0 min	solid
	1 min	

4. Start to heat your ice cube by placing the beaker with the ice cube on a hot plate. Keep careful track of the time.

5. Approximately once every minute, measure the temperature.

6. Record the time and temperature in the data table.

7. Pay attention to what phase or phases are present and note these in the last column of the table.

8. Continue heating until the water is boiling and almost gone. Remove the beaker from the hot plate before all the water has boiled away.

9. Graph the data according to the instructions on the next page.

Process the data:

1. Make a graph with temperature on the y-axis and time on the x-axis.

2. On the graph, label the areas where the following phase or phases are present: solid, both solid and liquid, liquid, both liquid and gas.

3. Label the temperature at which ice melts and the temperature at which water boils (melting point and boiling point of water).

Answer the following questions:

1. Describe your graph.

2. How warm can an ice cube get? Explain.

3. The boiling point of water is 100°C. What do you think the boiling point of a substance tells you?

Making Sense:

Why do you think the graph is not a straight line?

Making Sense Discussion   **(15 min)**

Major goals: The goal of this discussion is to introduce students to the heating curve of water. Students should also be introduced to some standard vocabulary associated with phase changes, both words used by chemists and by meteorologists. The heating curve will be debriefed in more detail in the following lesson.

5. Briefly process the graph. (Transparency)

Display the transparency. Tell students they have created what is called the **heating curve** of water – tracking temperature and phase over time.

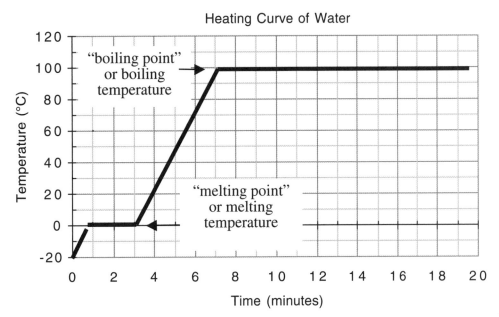

Discussion goals:
Assist students in sharing their data and observations.

Suggested questions:
  What did you discover when you heated the ice?
  What did your graph look like?
  What did you determine was the melting point of water?
  What is the boiling point of water?
  What happens when the temperature reaches 100°C

6. Give formal definitions of melting point and boiling point.

Write the words solid, liquid, and gas next to each other on the board as shown in the sketch below. Add words related to phase changes as they come up in the discussion.

Discussion goals:
Assist students in refining their understanding of the words associated with substances going from one phase to another.

Sample questions:
  What does it mean when we say that a substance is boiling?
  What does it mean when we say that a substance is melting?
  What do you know about the temperature of ice if there is no liquid water in
    contact with the ice? (It will be below 0°C)
  How are melting and freezing related? (they happen at the same
    temperature)
  Is boiling related to any other phase change? (condensation is the reverse
    phase change)

Points to Cover:
When a substance melts, it passes from the solid phase to the liquid phase. When it freezes, the reverse process takes place and the substance goes from liquid to solid. The temperature at which a solid changes into a liquid is called the **melting point** of that substance. The temperature at which a liquid changes into a solid is called the **freezing point** of the substance. The melting point and the freezing point are the same temperature. The **boiling point** is the temperature at which a substance passes from the liquid phase to the gas phase.

If you examine the heating curve of water both the melting point and the boiling point are lines because the temperature stays constant over time. Thus, the melting point of water is a single specific temperature, 0°C, and the boiling point of water is a single specific temperature, 100 °C. Because melting and boiling each occur at a single temperature, they are called "points" (although on the graph of temperature vs. time, they are lines).

When we track the change in temperature over time as a substance is changing phase we create what is called a **heating curve** for that substance. As you can see, the heating curve for water doesn't really involve any curves – it's a series of straight lines.

When water becomes a gas even though it is not boiling it is called evaporation. When a substance changes from a gas to a liquid it is called condensation. As we learned before, sublimation is a change from solid directly to gas. No liquid is observed. If a gas goes directly to a solid, we call that **solidification**. Whenever water falls in any form from a cloud as solid or liquid, it is called **precipitation** by meteorologists. Precipitation can be snow, or sleet, or rain.

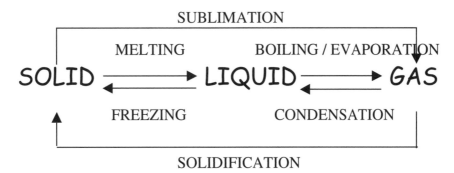

SUBLIMATION

MELTING   BOILING / EVAPORATION

SOLID ⟶ LIQUID ⟶ GAS

FREEZING   CONDENSATION

SOLIDIFICATION

Fixed temperatures for a given substance

MELTING/ FREEZING POINT is a fixed temperature where solid and liquid coexist

BOILING POINT is a fixed temperature where liquid and gas coexist

SUBLIMATION / SOLIDIFICATION POINT is a fixed temperature where solid and gas coexist

Processes that occur at various temperatures

EVAPORATION / CONDENSATION is a change from liquid to gas or gas to liquid at temperatures below the boiling point.

PRECIPITATION is the term meteorologists use to describe the condensation of water vapor to form snow, sleet, or rain.

Check-in   **(5 min)**

7. Complete the Check-in exercise.

Write the following question on the board for students to complete individually.

- How long was the water in your beaker at 100°C?
- Describe what was happening to the water during this time.

8. Discuss the Check-in exercise.

Get a sense of the level of understanding by asking students to defend their choices.

Discussion goals:

Check to see that students understand that the temperature of boiling water is constant at 100°C.

Suggested questions:

What temperature is water when it is boiling?

How long did your water stay at 100°C?

What was happening while the water stayed at a constant temperature?

The temperature of the water rises until it is 100°C, then it stays at 100°C while the water boils and turns to water vapor.

9. Wrap-up

Assist the students in summarizing what was learned in this class.

- The heating curve of water beginning with ice and ending with boiling water shows a sloped line, a plateau, another sloped line, and another plateau.
- The two plateaus show that the temperature remains constant when ice melts and water boils.

Homework

10. Assign the following for homework.

Use the homework provided with the curriculum or assign your own.

Homework – Investigation II – Lesson 4

1. Describe what you think would happen to the water if you placed a pan of water in the oven at 400°F.

2. Evaporation is defined as the process by which a substance is converted from a liquid state to a gaseous state. When a substance evaporates it does not need to be boiling. What evidence do you have in your daily life that evaporation occurs without boiling?

3. Describe evidence in your daily life that condensation occurs (substances going from a gaseous state to a liquid state).

Transparency

It's Only a Phase

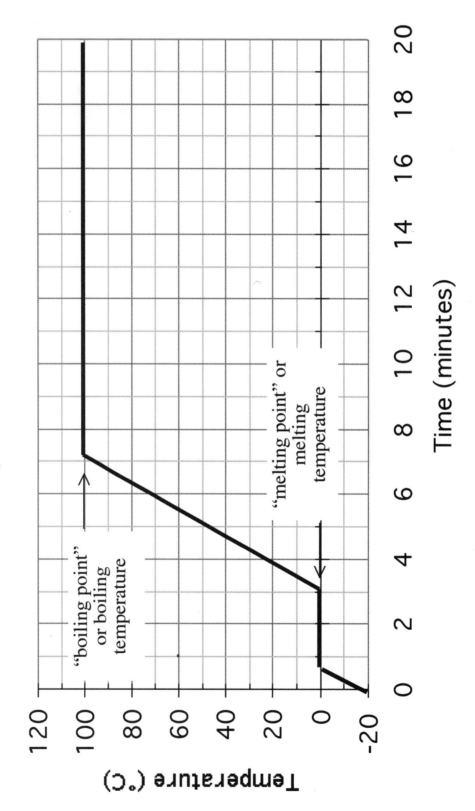

Heating Curve of Water

Weather © UC Regents, LHS Living by Chemistry, 2003.

It's Only a Phase

Name: _____

Period:_____Date:_____

Purpose: This lesson allows you to track the temperature of water over time as heat is going into the system.

Materials:

250 mL beaker	Ring stand and clamp to hold the thermometer (optional)
Ice cubes	Oven mitts or hot pads
Thermometers	Hot plate

Procedure:

1. Work in teams of 2 to 4.

2. Place an ice cube in your beaker.

3. Use your thermometer to record the initial temperature of your ice cube.

Remember: During this experiment do not let the thermometer touch the glass while you are measuring the temperature of the water, otherwise you will be measuring the temperature of the glass and not the water. You may use a clamp to hold the thermometer in place if this is helpful. Use the mitts to avoid getting burned once the water starts to boil.

4. Start to heat your ice cube by placing the beaker with the ice cube on a hot plate. Keep careful track of the time.

5. Approximately once every minute, measure the temperature.

6. Record the time and temperature in the data table.

7. Pay attention to what phase or phases are present and note these in the last column of the table.

8. Continue heating until the water is boiling and almost gone. Remove the beaker from the hot plate before all the water has boiled away.

9. Graph the data according to the instructions on the next page.

Temperature	Time	Phase

121

Processing the data:
1. Make a graph with temperature on the y axis and time on the x axis.
2. On the graph, label the areas where the following phase or phases are present: solid, both solid and liquid, liquid, both liquid and gas.
3. Label the temperature at which ice melts and the temperature at which water boils (melting point and boiling point of water).

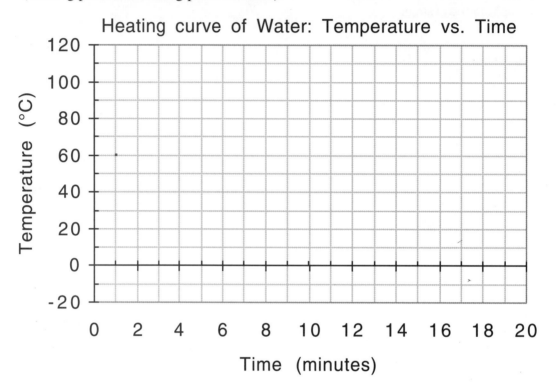

Answer the following questions:
1. Describe your graph.

2. How warm can an ice cube get? Explain.

3. The boiling point of water is 100°C. What do you think the boiling point of a substance tells you?

Making Sense:
Why do you think the graph is not a straight line?

BEFORE CLASS…

LESSON 5 – The Heat is On

Key Ideas:

The heating curve of water provides a great deal of information about what is going on during phase changes. Two plateaus on the line reflect the fact that when two phases of water are present at the same time the temperature of the water does not change. Thus, temperature and heat can be seen to be different concepts.

What Takes Place:

Students work in pairs to complete a worksheet examining the heating curve of water in greater detail. They come to understand that heat and temperature are different, but related concepts. They are introduced to the concept of heat capacity and given definitions for heat and temperature.

Materials:

• Student worksheet

Investigation II – Heating Matter
LESSON 5 – The Heat is On

This lesson focuses on debriefing the heating curve experiment in the previous lesson. The graph of the heating curve for water has two plateaus on it, reflecting the fact that when two phases of water are present, the temperature does not change. The temperature only changes when the water has changed phase completely. These observations lead to a discussion of the differences between temperature and heat.

Exploring the Topic   (5–10 min)

1. Introduce the ChemCatalyst exercise.

Write the following exercise on the board for students to complete individually. Draw a simplified graph of the heating curve of water.

Below is a graph showing the heating curve of water.

- Describe what is happening during the flat portions of the graph.
- How can heat be going into the system and the temperature still stay the same?

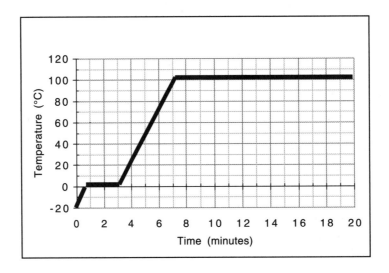

2. Discuss the ChemCatalyst exercise.

Use the discussion to get a sense of students' initial ideas.

Discussion goals:
Assist students in beginning to explore the difference between heat and temperature.

Sample questions:
What is happening during the flat portions of the graph?

What does it mean that something is boiling?

What is happening to the heat that is going into the system?

What is going on with the water molecules during a phase change?

What do you think the temperature is measuring?

Listen to students' ideas about what is happening when the temperature is staying the same on the heating curve.

3. Explain the purpose of the activity.

If you wish you can write the main question on the board.

Points to cover:

Tell students they will be examining heating curves and phase changes in more detail. They will be answering the question, "Why does the temperature stay the same when you add heat to melting ice or boiling water? "

Activity – The Heat is On   (15 min)

4. Pass out the worksheets. (Worksheet)

Heating curve of water

A graph of the heating curve for water is shown below. The graph is not to scale but it is drawn to emphasize differences in the amount of time required for each of the 5 steps.

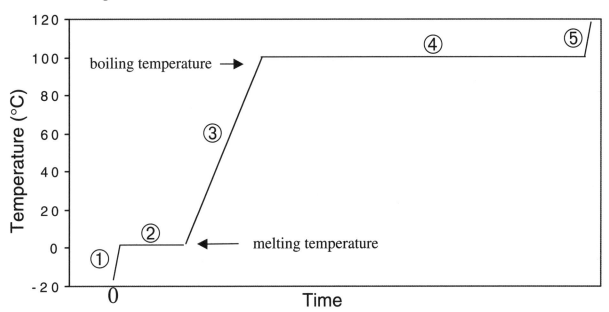

Refer to the drawing to answer the following questions.

1. For each of the five stages shown on the graph, list what phase or phases are present:

    Stage One: (solid)   Stage Four: (liquid/gas)

    Stage Two: (solid/liquid)   Stage Five: (gas)

Stage Three: (liquid)

2. Label where each of the following is happening on the graph: melting, boiling, warming.

3. Describe what is happening at Steps 2 and 4 on the graph where the temperature does not change for a period of time. (At each of those stages in the heating curve, water is still undergoing a phase change and more than one phase is present in the beaker.)

4. What is happening when the line is slanted? (water is being warmed and the temperature is increasing)

5. At what point on the graph is all of the ice gone? (when the temperature begins to rise above 0°C)

6. At what point on the graph is all of the liquid gone? (when the temperature begins to rise above 100°C.)

7. If there is more than one phase of water present, what does it tell you about the temperature of the water? (the temperature is not changing with time)

8. If there is only one phase of water present, what do you know about the temperature of the water? (the temperature is changing with time)

9. What patterns do you see in the heating curve? (three slanted lines connected by flat lines, flat lines for two phases, slanted lines for one phase present)

10. Do you think heating other substances and plotting temperature vs. time would result in a similar pattern or heating curve? Why or why not? (answers will vary but other substances do have similar heating curves)

11. Look at the graph from the previous class. For the same amount of water, does it take more heat to melt ice, or to boil water completely? Explain your thinking. (It takes more heat to boil water – line is much longer on the graph.)

Making sense:
Explain in your own words what you think the difference is between heat and temperature.

If you finish early:
Look at the graph from the previous class. Does it takes more *time* to increase the temperature of 10 grams of ice or 10 grams of liquid water by 10°. Explain your answer. (The graph shows that it would take less time to increase the temperature of 10 grams of ice than 10 grams of water. The line is steeper.)

Making Sense Discussion   (15–20 min)

Major goals: The goal of this discussion is to begin to articulate the difference between heat and temperature. Students should focus on what is happening macroscopically at each stage on the heating curve. This should then be translated into what is happening on a particulate level during these same stages. Students should be briefly introduced to the concept of heat capacity.

5. Explore the heating curve of water.

Sketch the heating curve on the board and add labels as ideas are discussed.

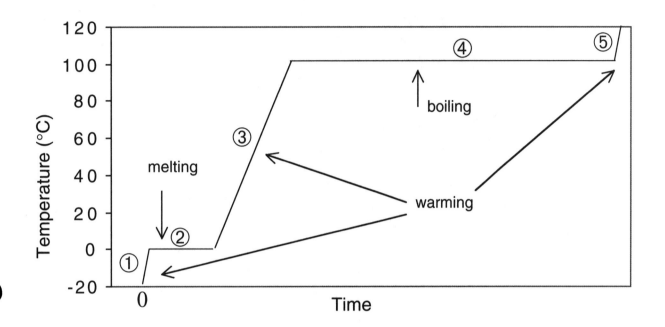

Discussion goals:
Assist students in refining their understanding of the heating curve.

Sample questions:
How does heat affect ice at the melting point? (causes ice to change phase and become liquid)

How does heat affect liquid water at the boiling point. (causes water to change phase)

Adding heat raises the temperature of liquid water. What do you think happens to the water molecules as heat is added?

Points to Cover:
Heat is a form of energy. When the beaker containing water is heated, energy is being transferred into the system. When a system contains only one phase (solid, liquid or gas), the temperature will increase when it receives energy. Thus, if the substance is not undergoing a phase change, the result of added heat is an increase in temperature. When the system begins to undergo a phase change it appears that the heat is used to melt the ice or boil the water rather than raise the temperature.

In summary, we observe two main outcomes as a result of the heat going into the system: (1) the water is changing phase, and (2) the water is changing temperature. According to our heating curve these two things are happening at different stages. During steep parts of the curve the water is changing in temperature. During flat parts of the curve, the water is changing phase.

6. Focus on phase change alone.

You may wish to display the transparency from the previous class.

Points to cover:
Let's focus on the first thing that is happening as a result of the heat energy going into the system – the phase change. This is represented by the flat places on the heating curve. If you look at the length of time it takes for the water to boil completely and the length of time it takes for the ice to melt completely, it appears that it takes more energy to boil water than to melt the same amount of ice. This is true. It takes 6.8 times as much heat to boil water than to melt ice. These differences are shown in the graph with a longer horizontal line for Step 4 compared with Step 2.

It makes sense that more heat is required for boiling compared with melting. When ice melts, the heat is transferred into increased motion of the water molecules. In ice, the molecules are held fixed in place. In liquid water, the water molecules are still attracted strongly to one another, but they can move relative to one another. In contrast, when water boils, the attractive interactions between the water molecules must be overcome in order to set the molecules free in the gas phase. It take more heat to overcome the attractive interactions between molecules (to boil a substance) compared with overcoming the interactions that hold molecules fixed in place (to melt a substance).

7. Focus on temperature change alone.

You may wish to display the transparency from the previous class.

Points to cover:
Now focus on the second thing that is happening as a result of heating the water – the change in temperature. If our graph were drawn really accurately we would easily see that the lines at Steps 1 and 5 are much steeper than the line at Step 3. Thus it takes more energy to change the temperature of liquid water than that of ice or water vapor. Scientists would say that liquid water has a higher **heat capacity** than solid water or gaseous water. We can put more heat *into it* before it changes temperature than we can put into the ice. We will explore heat capacity in greater detail in the next lesson and relate it to the weather on our planet.

It takes twice as much heat per gram per degree to raise the temperature of water compared with ice and water vapor. The graph reflects this by showing a steeper line for Steps 1 and 5 than for Step 3.

8. Discuss the difference between heat and temperature.

Provide students with basic definitions for heat and temperature.

Discussion goals:

Assist students in sharing their ideas about the differences between heat and temperature.

Sample questions:

What do you think is the difference between heat and temperature?

When you transfer heat energy, it always goes from the hot to the to cold object. Give an example.

Points to Cover:

Heat is the transfer of energy between two objects due to temperature differences. Imagine that it is a very cold winter day. You have very warm hands while another person has icy cold hands. A temperature difference exists. If you hold hands with this person, energy is transferred from your hand (the warmer hand) to the other person's hand. (Heat flow always occurs from hot to cold.) If we were to measure the temperature of the other person's skin before and after holding hands, we would find that it had increased. The temperature of an object therefore determines the direction of heat flow between it and another object.

> **Heat** is the transfer of energy between two objects due to temperature differences.

Temperature, on the other hand, is directly related to the movement of the molecules of the substance you are measuring (also known as the kinetic energy of the substance). Temperature is simply a scale used to measure the kinetic energy of the atoms and molecules in substances. Thus, when the temperature of a substance increases, we can also assume that the particles of that substance are moving more rapidly than before.

> **Temperature** is a scale that measures the average kinetic energy (or speed) of particles in a substance due to their random motion.

Check-in   (5 min)

9. Complete the Check-in exercise.

Write the following question on the board for students to complete individually.

- If you heat a glass of ice water will its temperature automatically go up? When will its temperature increase? Explain.

10. Discuss the Check-in exercise.

Get a sense of the level of understanding by asking students to defend their choices.

Discussion goals:
Check to see that students understand the relationship between heat and temperature.

Suggested questions:
    What will happen to the temperature of the ice water if you heat it?
    When will the ice water increase in temperature?

The ice water will remain at the same temperature as long as two phases are present in the glass. When all of the ice has melted the water will begin to increase in temperature.

11. Wrap-up
Assist the students in summarizing what was learned in this class.
- When ice is in the process of melting (changing phase) the temperature remains at 0°C. When water is in the process of boiling (changing phase), the temperature remains constant at 100°C.
- If only one phase of a substance is present in a system that is being heated, the temperature of that substance increases.
- Temperature is a measure of the kinetic energy of the molecules of a substance.
- Heat is a process of energy transfer, the direction of which is determined by temperature.

Homework

12. Assign the following for homework.
Use the homework provided with the curriculum or assign your own.

Homework – Investigation II – Lesson 5

Here is a heating curve for a substance other than water.

1. How is this curve different from the heating curve for water?

2. How do you think this substance will be different from water?

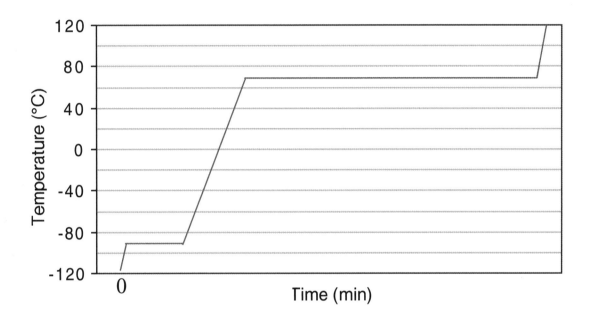

The Heat is On

Name: _____

Period: _____ Date: _____

Purpose: This lesson processes the heating curve of water in greater detail, examining what is happening at each stage.

Heating curve of water

A graph of the heating curve for water is shown below. The graph is not to scale but it is drawn to emphasize differences in the amount of time required for each of the 5 steps.

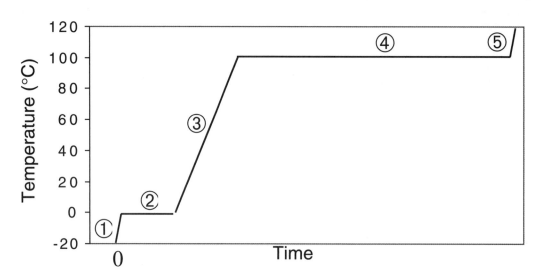

Refer to the drawing to answer the following questions.

1. For each of the five stages shown on the graph, list what phase or phases are present:

    Stage One: Stage Four:

    Stage Two: Stage Five:

    Stage Three:

2. Label where each of the following is happening on the graph: melting, boiling, heating.

3. Describe what is happening at Steps 2 and 4 on the graph where the temperature does not change for a period of time.

4. What is happening when the line is slanted?

5. At what point on the graph is all of the ice gone?

6. At what point on the graph is all of the liquid gone?

7. If you have more than one phase of water present what does it tell you about the temperature of the water?

8. If you have only one phase of water present what do you know about the temperature of the water?

9. What patterns do you see in the heating curve?

10. Do you think other heating other substances and plotting temperature vs. time would result in a similar pattern or heating curve? Why or why not?

11. Look at the graph from the previous class. For the same amount of water, does it take more heat to melt ice, or to boil water completely. Explain your thinking.

Making sense question
Explain in your own words what you think the difference is between heat and temperature.

If you finish early:
Look at the graph from the previous class. Does it takes more *time* to increase the temperature of 10 grams of ice or 10 grams of liquid water by 10°. Explain your answer.

BEFORE CLASS...

LESSON 6 – Hot Cement

Key Ideas:

Liquid water has a very high heat capacity. A lot of heat can go into the substance with very little change in temperature. The large specific heat capacity of liquid water has a great effect on the weather of the planet. Areas of land near the oceans experience a much more temperate climate than inland regions.

What Takes Place:

The discussion of heat capacity continues in this lesson. The teacher introduces specific heat capacity at the beginning of class and sets up an experiment to compare the specific heat capacities of soil and water. Students work in pairs to complete a worksheet providing them with data about the specific heat capacities of several substances. The final temperatures of the soil and water samples are compared with the temperatures at the beginning of the experiment. The effect of specific heat capacity on climate is discussed.

Materials:
- Student worksheet
- 50 g potting soil
- 50 mL tap water
- 2 plastic cups
- 1 desk lamp with high intensity bulb
- 2 thermometers

Weather © UC Regents, LHS Living by Chemistry, 2003.

Investigation II – Heating Matter
LESSON 6 – Hot Cement

The focus of this investigation has been on how changes in temperature affect matter. Now students will look more generally at how heat from the sun affects weather and climate. Students begin by examining differences in average temperatures in two cities – one on the ocean and one inland. Specific heat capacity is introduced. The teacher sets up an experiment to compare the effect of heat from the sun on soil and water. On their worksheets students compare data for sand, water, air, and metal. They then apply their knowledge of specific heat capacity to understanding why certain regions of the globe have large changes in climate while others do not.

Exploring the Topic   (5–10 min)

1. Introduce the ChemCatalyst exercise.

Write the ChemCatalyst exercise on the board for students to complete individually.

Below are the average daily temperatures for two cities in the United States:

San Francisco, California:	Wichita, Kansas:
Winter: 50 ˚F.	Winter: 38 ˚F
Spring: 56 ˚F	Spring: 55 ˚F
Summer: 59 ˚F	Summer: 93 ˚F
Fall: 61 ˚F	Fall: 63 ˚F
Average annual rainfall: 19 inches	30 inches
Average annual snowfall: 0 inches	15.5 inches

- What differences do you notice about the data for the two cities?
- What could account for the differences in average temperature?

2. Discuss the ChemCatalyst exercise.
Use the discussion to get a sense of students' initial ideas.

Discussion goals:
Solicit students' ideas about regional differences in climate.

Sample questions:
What differences did you notice in the average temperatures of the two cities?
What do you think is responsible for these differences?
What is meant by the term "climate"?

Why doesn't San Francisco have snow?

What kinds of things might be responsible for differences in climate from place to place?

Listen to students' ideas without judgment. Students may speculate that altitude or latitude play a part in these differences, and these would be good directions to go in. However, these cities are at approximately the same latitude and while there is a thousand feet difference in elevation, it shouldn't be the sole cause of the differences. Students may mention the proximity of the ocean to San Francisco and its possible effect on the weather of the San Francisco Bay Area.

3. Introduce specific heat capacity.

Points to cover:

In the last lesson we learned that it takes more heat to change the temperature of liquid water compared with ice and water vapor. The amount of heat needed to raise the temperature of 1 gram of a substance by 1°Celsius is called the **specific heat capacity**.

Heat is measured in calories. It takes one calorie to raise the temperature of one gram of water 1°C. Thus, the specific heat capacity of water is 1.00 cal / gram °C.

4. Set up experiment/ demonstration of heat capacity.

Materials

50 g potting soil

50 mL tap water

2 plastic cups

1 desk lamp with high intensity bulb

2 thermometers

Suggested demonstration:

Tell students that you are going to do a specific heat capacity experiment with two of the most common substances on the planet: water and soil. Tell them that after doing their worksheet they will predict which will have a higher temperature after fifteen or twenty minutes under a hot lamp. They will also predict how much hotter the warmer substance will be. The rate of heating of any substance depends both on the chemical composition of the substance and on its mass. Thus it is necessary to use equal masses of each substance we are comparing.

Use about 50 g grams of each substance – 50 mL water and 50 g soil. Place each substance in a plastic cup and measure the starting temperature of each. Place a desk lamp very close to the surface of each substance. Tell students you will return to the experiment in about fifteen minutes to find out which substance has gotten hotter and by how much.

5. Explain the purpose of the activity.

If you wish you can write the main question on the board.

Points to cover:
Tell students they will explore how heat from the sun affects sand, water, air, and metal. They will then relate this exploration to differences in average temperatures in different regions of the world. The main question is: "How do the specific heat capacities of water and soil affect the climate of the earth?"

Activity – Hot Cement   (15 min)

6. Explain the procedure and pass out the worksheets.

Tell students that they will examine data showing the change in temperature of 10.0 g of sand, water, air, and metal after they have been in direct sunlight for several time intervals up to 1 hour.

Heating substances in the sun
The following table shows the temperature after 10.0 g of four different substances have been in direct sunlight for up to 60 minutes.

Time (min)	Air (°C)	Water (°C)	Sand (°C)	Metal (°C)
0 (initial)	25°C	25°C	25°C	25°C
15.0	28.9°C	26.2°C	30°C	35°C
30.0	32.5°C	27.5°C	35°C	45°C
45.0	36.2°C	28.8°C	40°C	55°C
60.0	40°C	30°C	45°C	65°C

Graph the data.

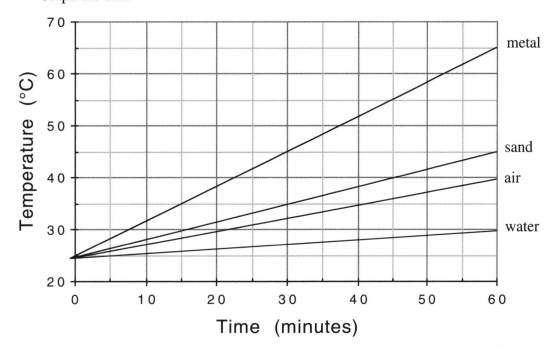

Answer the following questions:

1. Put the substances in order of the time required to heat them from slowest to fastest. (water, air, sand, metal)

2. Which do you think will cool the fastest? Explain your reasoning. (metal will cool the fastest because the line is steepest – steepest rate of change)

3. When you boil water in a pot on the stove, which heats faster, the metal or the water? (the metal pot heats faster)

4. If you place 10 g of hot metal at 100°C into water at 25°C, what will happen to the temperature of each? Will the metal cool by a little or a lot? Will the water warm by a little or a lot? (water will go up in temp, metal will go down, metal will change temperature more than the water)

Specific heat capacity is the amount of heat required to raise the temperature of 1 g of a substance by 1 degree.

5. Which substance has the highest specific heat capacity? (water)

6. Here are the heat capacities of the four substances: 0.10 cal/ g °C, 0.25 cal/ g °C, 1.0 cal/ g °C , and 0.2 cal/ g °C. Match each substance with its specific heat capacity. (water: 1.0, sand: 0.2, air :0.25, metal : 0.1)

7. Which substance has the lowest heat capacity? (metal)

8. If something has a high specific heat capacity will it take a lot of heat or a little heat to change its temperature? (small range of temperature, like water)

9. Which will heat faster, a swimming pool or the ocean? Explain your thinking. (swimming pool – less mass)

10. If you have more grams of a substance, will it take more time or less time to heat the substance? (more time to heat more mass)

11. Use the data in the table to determine how hot 20.0 g of water will be after 60 minutes. (It will take twice as long as 10.0 grams of water so should be 27.5 °C if it started at 25.0 °C)

12. How do you think specific heat capacity affects the weather? (weather is more moderate because large bodies of water do not change temperature as much – air above oceans is therefore more moderate)

13. In the late afternoon after the sun has been shining, what do you think happens to the temperature of the air as it moves from the ocean to the land? Explain your reasoning. (temperature of air is heated as it moves over land because earth is hotter than water)

14. Why is the range of temperature small over the ocean? (because ocean has a small range of temperature)

15. Why is the range in temperature so large in the center of the United States? (heat capacity of soil is smaller, thus the temperature of the soil and the air over the soil fluctuates more)

16. What difference in temperature do you predict for the soil and water samples? Explain your reasoning.

Making sense question:
Use specific heat capacity to explain why some regions have very mild climates and other regions have severe climates with a wide range of temperatures.

If you finish early…
The winds blow from west to east across the United States. Use this fact to explain why the west coast city of San Francisco is warmer in the winter and cooler in the summer than the East Coast city of Washington D.C. Both are at the same latitude.

Making Sense Discussion   **(15 min)**

Major goals: This is the final lesson in the investigation focusing on the effects of temperature on matter. Students should have a solid understanding of specific heat capacity and should be able to relate heat capacity to regional differences in climate.

7. Discuss specific heat capacity.

Also, process the results of the soil and water experiment at the beginning of class.

Discussion goals:
Solicit the students' understanding of specific heat capacity.

Sample questions:
What did you conclude about how long it takes to heat sand, water, air, and metal?
Why do you think we use metal pots for cooking?
When you boil water in a pot on the stove, which heats faster, the metal or the water?
What is specific heat capacity?
Which has a higher specific heat capacity, the ocean or the land?
If you have 10 g of water and 100 g of water, which will heat faster?
What did you predict for the soil and water experiment? What were the results?
Predict the heat capacity of soil from the outcome.

Points to cover:

Different substances require different amounts of heat in order to raise their temperature. Substances with a high specific heat capacity require more heat to raise the temperature. For example, 1 gram of water takes five times as long to heat by 1 degree compared with 1 gram of sand.

If it takes a long time to heat a substance, it will also take a long time to cool that substance. For example, if you place a hot metal in cold water, the metal will cool a lot, whereas the temperature of the water will not increase much.

The heat capacity of soil is somewhere around 0.25 cal / g °C. This means that it takes four times as long to change the temperature of the water than it does to change the temperature of the soil. Thus, the soil should have a temperature change four times that of the water. If the water changed two degrees in temperature, the soil should have changed eight degrees in temperature.

Optional information:

Raising the temperature of a substance raises the average motion of the atoms or molecules in that substance. The extent to which it is possible to change the temperature of a substance is directly related to the extent to which it is possible to change the average motion of the atoms. Whether or not one can change the average motion of the atoms of a substance depends on the type of bonding in the substance.

Metals heat rapidly because of their metallic bonds. Remember, the nuclei are located in a sea of electrons. Those electrons are easy to move. Water has a particularly high specific heat because water molecules are attracted strongly to one another. They have very strong intermolecular bonds (polar bonds are covered in the Smells Unit). The hydrogen atom on one water molecule is attracted to the oxygen atom on a second water molecule. This restricts the motions of the molecules, and thus, a lot of heat is required to move the water molecules. Air heats up in a moderate amount of time (not particularly fast, not slow). While it is easy to move molecules in the gas phase, heat energy is transferred through collisions between atoms and molecules. Since air molecules are small and there is a lot of space between them, collisions do not happen very frequently.

8. Discuss climate. (Transparency)

<u>Discussion goals:</u>
Solicit the students' ideas about how proximity to the ocean affects the temperature and climate of a region.

Sample questions:
Where is the range of temperature the greatest on the map?
What areas have little change in climate throughout the year?

Why do some places in North America have more distinct seasons with a
   wide range of temperatures, and some do not?
Why does proximity to the ocean affect the temperature?

Points to cover:
The high specific heat of the ocean helps keep the temperature in coastal areas
much more moderate than that in areas further inland. The ocean keeps air
temperatures cooler in the summer, but also serves to keep temperatures from
getting very low in the winter. Further inland the effects of heating by the sun
and cooling by the absence of the sun are felt much more as air temperatures
have a much greater range.

Check-in   (5 min)

9. Complete the Check-in exercise.

Write the following question on the board for students to complete
individually.

- Consider the climate on the Hawaiian Islands. The temperature is 37°C in
  July. Do you expect the temperature to be different in January? Why or
  why not?

10. Discuss the Check-in exercise.

Get a sense of the level of understanding by asking students to defend their
answer.

Discussion goals:
Confirm that students have a sense of how heat capacity affects climate.

Sample questions:
   What type of climate do you expect for the Hawaiian Islands?
   Since the Islands are surrounded by water, do you expect much seasonal
      change?

The climate does not change much on the Hawaiian Islands because they are surrounded by
water.

11. Wrap-up

Assist the students in summarizing what was learned in this class.
- The specific heat capacity of a substance is the heat required to raise the
  temperature of one gram of that substance by one degree Celsius.
- The high specific heat capacity of water has an effect on the climate of the
  planet. Places close to oceans will experience more moderate ranges in
  temperature. Places far from bodies of water will experience more extreme
  fluctuations in temperature.

Homework

12. Assign the following for homework.

Use the homework provided with the curriculum or assign your own.

Homework – Investigation II – Lesson 6

1. You are at the ocean. The water, the beach and the air are all heated by the same amount of sunlight. Which will get hotter? Explain why you think so.

2. Below is a table of specific heat capacities.

Substance	Specific Heat Capacity – cal / g°C
water (liquid)	1.00
iron	
aluminum	
water vapor	
gold	
alcohol	
ice	
wood	
copper	
soil	

   a) Which substance will take the least a____ of heat to change its temperature?

   b) Which substance will take the most amount of heat to change its temperature?

   c) Put the substances in order from the slowest heating substance to the fastest.

   d) Would it be better to make a hot water bottle or a hot alcohol bottle to warm your feet in bed? Explain you thinking.

3. If ten calories of heat go into one gram of water its temperature will go up ten degrees Celsius.

   a) If you put ten calories of heat into one gram of ice how much temperature change would you expect?

   b) If you put ten calories of heat into one gram of iron, how much temperature change would you expect?

4. If you are barefoot on a really hot day, would you rather step into a hot puddle of water or keep your feet on the hot concrete? Explain why.

Average Temperatures in January

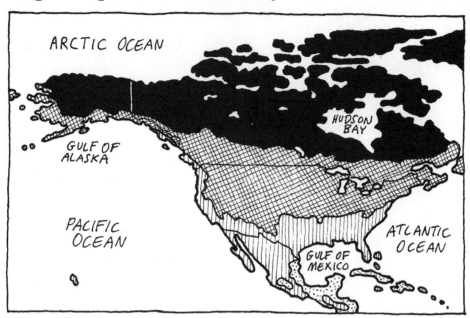

Average Temperatures in July

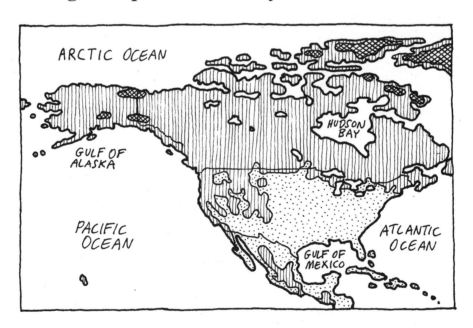

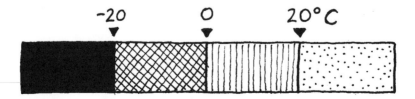

Weather © UC Regents, LHS Living by Chemistry, 2003.

Hot Cement

Name: _____

Date: _____ Period: _____

Purpose: This activity allows you to compare the specific heat capacities of various substances.

Heating substances in the sun
The following table shows the temperature after 10.0 g of four different substances have been in direct sunlight for up to 60 minutes.

Time (min)	Air (°C)	Water (°C)	Sand (°C)	Metal (°C)
0 (initial)	25°C	25°C	25°C	25°C
15.0	28.9°C	26.2°C	30°C	35°C
30.0	32.5°C	27.5°C	35°C	45°C
45.0	36.2°C	28.8°C	40°C	55°C
60.0	40°C	30°C	45°C	65°C

Graph the data.

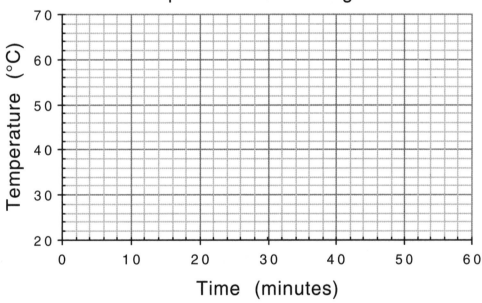

Answer the following questions:
1. Put the substances in order of the time required to heat them from slowest to fastest.

2. Which do you think will cool the fastest? Explain your reasoning.

3. When you boil water in a pot on the stove, which heats faster, the metal or the water?

4. If you place 10 g of hot metal at 100°C into water at 25°C, what will happen to the temperature of each? Will the metal cool by a little or a lot? Will the water warm by a little or a lot?

Specific heat capacity is the amount of heat required to raise the temperature of 1 g of a substance by 1 degree.

5. Which substance has the highest specific heat capacity?

6. Here are the heat capacities of the four substances: 0.10 cal/ g °C, 0.25 cal/ g °C, 1.0 cal/ g °C , and 0.2 cal/ g °C. Match each substance with its specific heat capacity.

7. Which substance has the lowest heat capacity?

8. If something has a high specific heat capacity will it take a lot of heat or a little heat to change its temperature?

9. Which will heat faster, a swimming pool or the ocean? Explain your thinking.

10. If you have more grams of a substance, will it take more time or less time to heat the substance?

11. Use the data in the table to determine how hot 20.0 g of water will be after 60 minutes.

12. How do you think specific heat capacity affects the weather?

13. In the late afternoon after the sun has been shining, what do you think happens to the temperature of the air as it moves from the ocean to the land? Explain your reasoning.

14. Why is the range of temperature small over the ocean? Why is the range in temperature so large in the center of the United States?

15. What difference in temperature do you predict for the soil and water samples? Explain your reasoning.

Making sense question:
Use specific heat capacity to explain why some regions have very mild climates and other regions have severe climates with a wide range of temperatures.

If you finish early…
The winds blow from west to east across the United States. Use this fact to explain why the West Coast city of San Francisco is warmer in the winter and cooler in the summer than the East Coast city of Washington, D.C. Both are at the same latitude.

Unit 3: Weather

Investigation III:
Moving Matter

Contents of Investigation III   *Page*

Investigation III Summary:

Moving Matter

Investigation III consists of six lessons that focus air pressure. The investigation begins with a series of demonstration that show how the pressure of air inside a flexible container equalizes with the pressure of the air on the outside. Students increase the pressure on a sample of air contained in a syringe and observed the volume of the air in the second lesson. Boyle's law and Gay Lussacs law are introduced in the next two lessons. Students consider how temperature and volume affect air pressure. The combined gas law in used in the fifth lesson to monitor volume changes in a weather balloon as it ascends. In the final lesson, changes in volume, temperature, and pressure of air are used to understand the direction of air movement and wind.

In Investigations I and II students explored volume, density, phase, temperature, and heat. This led to discussions of average amounts of rainfall and average temperatures in the United States. In Investigation III, students learn the meaning of high and low pressure. They can explain how differences in air pressure cause winds.

Lesson 1 – Balancing Act. In this lesson, students consider the forces exerted by gases. The lesson begins with a consideration of what air pressure is. Next a series of demonstrations are performed. These demonstrations focus on how forces exerted by gases inside a container of variable volume are balanced by forces due to the gases on the outside of the container.

Lesson 2 – Feeling Under Pressure. The purpose of today's class is to explore the relationship between pressure and volume of gases. Gas pressure and volume exist in inverse relationship to one another (given constant temperature). Students are first introduced to the definition of pressure as force per unit of area. Students then experiment with squeezing air in a closed container (a syringe) measuring the force required by using a bathroom scale. They graph and begin to interpret the results.

Lesson 3 – Getting Squeezed. So far in this investigation, students have been introduced to the concept of air pressure and learned that the pressure of a gas is inversely related to its volume (for a constant amount and temperature). In this lesson students take the data from the previous experiment a bit further. They learn that a graph of P vs. $1/V$ is a straight line with a zero intercept. This leads to the proportional relationship between pressure and reciprocal volume, known as Boyles' law.

Lesson 4 – Egg in a Bottle. Thus far, we have considered how pressure changes when the volume changes (Boyle's law). In this lesson the students will be introduced to the relationship between pressure and temperature (Gay-Lussac's law). Then they will practice applying these two gas laws to determine what happens to the pressure inside an unopened glass bottle of soda (fixed volume) and unopened bag of chips (variable volume) after hiking up a mountain. Finally, all three gas laws are reviewed, including Charles' law.

Lesson 5 – What Goes Up... In this lesson students learn the combined gas law. They follow the progress of a weather balloon as it moves into the atmosphere. The balloon will have competing forces working on it. The decreasing air temperature will cause the volume of the balloon to decrease. The decreasing air pressure will cause the volume of the balloon to increase. By analyzing the volume, temperature, and pressure of the weather balloon at different points it is possible to discover which variable will affect the volume of the gas more, the temperature or the pressure.

Lesson 6 – Air On the Move. In this lesson, the knowledge of the gas laws is used to think about the direction of air movement. Students predict the direction of lateral winds and consider how air is transported up and down in the atmosphere.

BEFORE CLASS...

LESSON 1 – Balancing Act

Key Ideas:
Air pressure can be defined as the force per area that results
from air molecules striking the walls of whatever container or object they come in
contact with. When the volume of an air sample is decreased the molecules will
collide with the walls of the container more frequently, and the result is greater
pressure. When a disparity in pressure exists between two regions of air, the system
will stabilize itself by equalizing the two pressures. Meteorologists monitor high and
low air pressure systems on the planet in their quest to predict the weather.

What Takes Place:
Students view a series of demonstrations about air pressure. In each demonstration air
is trapped inside a container. The pressure of the air in the container or on the outside
of the container is changed. Students write down their observations, make drawings to
show the various pressures, and discuss with a partner what they think happened.
Then each demonstration is discussed as a class. Finally, air pressure is defined on a
molecular level.

Materials:
- Student worksheet
- 12 balloons
- 2 liter plastic bottle
- 2–3 empty aluminum soda cans
- Hot plate
- Tap water
- 1 pair of tongs
- Tall clear plastic cup
- 1 large beaker of water
- 3 feet of clear tubing
- 2 50-mL plastic syringes
- 1 plastic cup (9-oz wide-mouth Solo cups work well)
- 1 laminated card to fit over mouth of cup
- 1 large shallow plastic tub to catch spills
- Vacuum pump (1 flask, two-holed stopper, and 2 pieces of glass tubing if a
  vacuum pump is unavailable)
- Vacuum desiccator or a side-arm flask with a stopper (for use with the vacuum
  pump)
- Fresh large marshmallows if you have a vacuum pump (use mini marshmallows if
  you use a syringe instead of a vacuum pump)

Investigation III – Moving Matter

LESSON 1 – Balancing Act

In this lesson, students consider the forces exerted by gases. The lesson begins with a consideration of what air pressure is. Next a series of demonstrations are performed. These demonstrations focus on how forces exerted by gases inside a container of variable volume are balanced by forces due to the gases on the outside of the container.

Exploring the Topic   (5–10 min)

1. Introduce ChemCatalyst exercise. (Transparency)

Write the following exercise on the board for students to complete individually.

Below is a weather map for the United States for September of 2003.

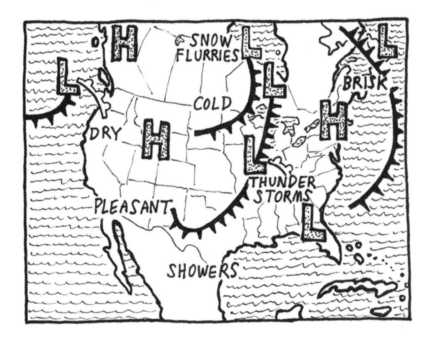

- What do the large H and L symbols stand for on the map?
- What do you think these areas have to do with weather?

2. Discuss the ChemCatalyst exercise.

Use the discussion to get a sense of students' initial ideas.

Discussion goals:
Assist students in sharing their initial ideas about how high and low pressure relate to weather.

Sample questions:

What do you think the H and L symbols on the weather map mean?

What do you think high pressure on a weather map means?

How is high pressure air different from low pressure air?

What do you think air pressure is?

Listen to students' ideas without judgment. Students may know that air pressure has something to do with the push exerted by the air. Some may know that high pressure is associated with blue skies and fair weather. Students may also notice that it is windy between high and low pressure regions.

3. Explain the purpose of the activity.

If you wish you can write the main question on the board.

Points to cover:

Tell students that they will assist you in doing a series of demonstrations to investigate air pressure further. These demonstrations will assist in answering the question: "What happens when there are changes in air pressure?"

Activity – Balancing Act   **(20–25 min)**

4. Conduct the demonstrations. (Worksheet)

Tell students that you will be conducting a series of demonstrations with some assistance from the class. After each one, students will have time to discuss the demonstration with a partner, and to answer the questions on the worksheet.

[Note: Seven different demonstrations are described below. You can do all of them, or only some of them depending on the availability of materials.]

Materials (per class)

12 balloons

2-liter plastic bottle

2–3 empty aluminum soda cans

hot plate

tap water

1 pair of tongs

tall clear plastic cup

1 large beaker of water

3 feet of clear tubing

2 syringes

1 plastic cup (9-oz wide-mouth Solo cups work well)

1 laminated card to fit over the mouth of the plastic cup

1 large shallow plastic tub to catch spills

vacuum pump (1 flask, two-holed stopper, and two pieces of glass tubing if a
   vacuum pump is unavailable)
vacuum desiccator or a side-arm flask with a stopper (for use with the vacuum
   pump)
fresh large marshmallows if you have a vacuum pump (use mini
   marshmallows if you use a syringe instead of a vacuum pump)

BALLOON IN A BOTTLE

Predict: Which balloon will inflate faster?

Put an un-inflated balloon inside a bottle. Fold the opening of the balloon
back over the mouth of the bottle so that it stays in place. Apply your lips
to the bottle and try to inflate the balloon. Do this as a race with one
balloon inside the bottle and another outside the bottle.

Explain: Why was the balloon in the bottle harder to inflate?

[Note: For health reasons you will need one balloon for each student who tries to do the
demonstration.]

COLLAPSING CAN

Predict: What will happen when the heated can is cooled suddenly?

Place 5 mL of water in the bottom of an empty aluminum soft drink can.
Heat the can on a hot plate until you see steam coming out of the opening.
Use tongs to quickly invert the can into a dishpan filled halfway with cold
water. The can will collapse suddenly and dramatically.

Explain: What causes the can to collapse?

SUBMERGED CUP

Predict: Will the paper get wet?

Fill a large beaker about 2/3 full with water. Crumple a dry piece of paper
and squeeze it to the bottom of the plastic cup. Invert the cup making sure
that the paper stays up in the cup and immerse it completely under water
holding it as vertically as possible. Take the cup back out of the water and
put it on a paper towel to let the water drip off. Take the crumpled paper
out of the cup to show that it remained dry.

Explain: Why didn't the paper in the cup get wet?

HOSE WITH WATER

Predict: How is it possible to change the water levels?

Hold a three-foot piece of clear plastic tubing in a U-shape with the open
ends pointing up. Fill the tube about half full of water. Place a syringe
with the barrel pushed down halfway on one side of the tube. Make sure
the seal to the syringe is airtight. Push the barrel of the syringe in. Observe

what happens to the water levels on both sides of the tube. Pull the barrel of the syringe out. Observe what happens to the water levels.

Explain: Why do the water levels change on either side of the tube as the barrel of the syringe is pushed in and pulled out?

CUP AND CARD

Predict: What will happen when the cup, water, and card are turned upside down?

Fill a clear plastic cup partially with water. Place a card over the top of the cup. Cardboard will work, but waterproof poster board or laminated cardstock is preferable. Hold the card to the mouth of the cup and invert. You can now let go of the card: it remains suspended and the water does not spill out.

Explain: Why doesn't the card fall?

EXPANDING BALLOON (Version 1 – with a vacuum pump)

Predict: What will happen to the balloon?

Inflate a balloon to about 2 or 3 inches in diameter. Place the balloon inside a flask that can be evacuated such as a side arm flask or a dessicator. Seal the container (e.g., put a stopper on the flask) and connect it to a vacuum pump. Turn on the vacuum pump to increase the size of the balloon. Then allow the air back in to decrease the size of the balloon.

Explain: Why does the balloon increase in size in the vacuum chamber?

EXPANDING BALLOON (Version 2 – without a vacuum pump)

Predict: What will happen to the balloon?

Obtain a flask with a two-holed rubber stopper that fits into the mouth of the flask. Put a piece of glass tubing through the two holes in the stopper. Attach a balloon or plastic bag to the bottom of one of the pieces of glass tubing so that there is an airtight seal. Put the stopper on the flask so that the balloon is on the inside. If you "suck" on the glass tubing that does not have the balloon attached to it, the balloon will inflate slightly inside the flask. You can also use an aspirator to remove air from the flask.

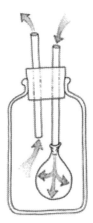

Explain: Why does the balloon increase in size in the vacuum chamber?

MARSHMALLOWS (Version 1 – with a vacuum pump)

Predict: What will happen to the marshmallows?

Place several marshmallows inside a flask that can be evacuated such as a side arm flask or a desiccator. Seal the container (e.g., put a stopper on the flask or the dome lid on the desiccator) and connect it to a vacuum pump. Turn on the vacuum pump to increase the size of the marshmallows. Then allow the air back in to decrease their size. They will be smaller than they were when you started.

Explain: Why does the marshmallow increase in size inside the vacuum chamber? Why is the final size of the marshmallow (after the air is returned to the vacuum chamber) smaller than the original size?

MARSHMALLOWS (Version 2 – without a vacuum pump)

Predict: What will happen to the marshmallows?

Put a marshmallow inside a plastic syringe. Move the plunger down close to the marshmallow with the opposite end open to allow air to escape. Do not crush the marshmallow. Seal the tip of the syringe and pull back on the plunger. The marshmallow grows bigger. Then, push the plunger back in. The marshmallow grows smaller.

Explain: Why does the marshmallow increase in size when you pull back on the plunger of the syringe?

Answer the following questions:
For each demonstration, describe what happened. Make a diagram with arrows to show what is happening with the air in each experiment. Arrows should show the direction in which the air is *pushing*.

Demo	Observations	Diagram of what happened
Balloon in a bottle	Difficult to blow up balloon in bottle.	
Collapsing can	Can heated with water inside collapses when cooled.	
Submerged cup	Paper inside of cup stays dry. Air stays inside cup as it is submerged.	
Hose with Water	Water levels on the two sides of the U-shaped tubing are changed with a syringe.	

Cup and card	Card hangs below the inverted cup with water.	
Expanding balloon	Balloon expands in size as air is removed from chamber, then shrinks when air is put back in the chamber.	
Marsh-mallows	Marshmallow expands when air is removed, then shrinks when air is put back in.	

Making sense questions:

What evidence do you have that air pressure changes?

How are air pressures equalized in each demonstration?

What can cause changes in air pressure?

Making Sense Discussion   (15 min)

Major Goals: Most of this discussion may actually take place as each demonstration is conducted. Students should be allowed to share what they observed and what they think happened in each case. It is important to focus on how air pressure changed in each demo and, then, how each system ultimately stabilized the air pressure. Air pressure should be defined and air pressure as it relates to weather should be briefly touched on.

5. Discuss what happened in each demonstration.

Ask groups of students to put their drawings on the board with arrows showing air pressures. Some sample drawings are included below. Ask students to consider air pressure inside and outside of each container.

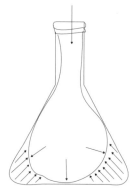

Balloon in a flask demo

 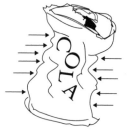

Crushed can demo

Weather© UC Regents, LHS Living by Chemistry, 2003.

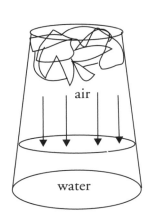

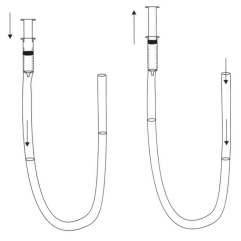

Paper in cup demo   Hose with water demo

Discussion goals:
Assist the class in sharing explanations of what happened for each demonstration.

Sample questions:
   Why is it so difficult to inflate the balloon inside the flask?
   What causes the can to collapse?
   Why does the paper stay dry?
   Why do the water levels change on either side of the U-tube as the barrel of
      the syringe is pushed in and pulled out?
   Why doesn't the card fall?
   Why does the balloon increase in size in the vacuum chamber?
   Why does the marshmallow increase in size inside the vacuum chamber?
   Why is the final size of the marshmallow (after the air is returned to the
      vacuum chamber) smaller than the original size?

Points to cover:
In each demonstration air is trapped somewhere. In each demonstration the pressure of the trapped air is changed or the pressure of the air on the outside of the container with the trapped air is changed.

Balloon in a Bottle: In the first demo we tried to inflate a balloon inside a flask. The flask already has air in it from the surrounding atmosphere. When we try to put air into the balloon we meet with the pressure from the air already in the container on the outside of the balloon. The air pressure inside the balloon and outside the balloon push against each other. Ultimately the air pressure inside and outside of the balloon will be equal.

Collapsing Can: In the second demonstration, water inside a soda can is heated to boiling and fills the can with water vapor. Some of this water vapor can be seen escaping from the can in the form of steam. When the can is placed upside down in cold water the water vapor is turned quickly into liquid water. The result is a dramatic decrease in air pressure inside the can. The can collapses quickly as the air pressure inside and outside the can stabilize and become equal.

Submerged Cup: In this demo some paper is squished into the bottom of a cup. Now there is air and paper in the cup. When the cup is inverted in some water, the air trapped inside the cup is squeezed into a smaller space and exerts a pressure on the water. As a result the water only goes part of the way up the inside of the cup. The paper stays dry.

Hose with Water: In this demonstration one end of a hose is sealed off with a syringe. The space available for that trapped air can be made smaller or larger by moving the plunger on the syringe. The water in the hose can be seen to move as a result of the increase or decrease in air pressure at one end. The air pressure of the trapped air is always in balance with the air pressure outside the hose because the water inside the hose is able to move. The unequal water levels are a direct measure of difference in air pressure trapped in the syringe and in the atmosphere.

Cup and Card: A cup with water and air inside is inverted with a card covering the mouth of the cup. This causes the card to be suspended, and the water does not spill out of the cup. The air pressure pushing up on the card from the atmosphere is larger than the weight of the water and the card. [Note: If you observe carefully, you will notice that a small amount of water spills out when you invert the cup. This decreases the volume of water inside the cup and increases the volume occupied by the air on the inside. The result is that the air pressure on the inside is less than the air pressure on the outside.]

Expanding Balloon: A slightly inflated balloon is placed inside a vacuum chamber and the air outside the balloon is pumped out. The balloon increases in size. The pressure from the air outside the balloon is decreasing as the air is pumped out of the chamber. Thus the balloon increases in size until the air pressure outside the balloon and the air pressure inside the balloon are equal.

Chubby Marshmallows: Marshmallows have tiny pockets of trapped air within them. When the air outside the marshmallows is removed, the air inside the marshmallows expands and the marshmallows puff up. The air pressure in the pockets inside the marshmallows is equalizing with the air pressure outside the marshmallows. Some of the air pockets within the marshmallows will burst, so when air is put back in the chamber the marshmallows may actually be smaller than they were before.

In all the demonstrations, air was trapped in a container in which the volume could vary. These "stretchy" containers included balloons, water, and sugar pockets inside the marshmallow. In each demonstration, the air pressure is changed by changing some part of the system (air is added to a balloon, air is heated and then cooled quickly, air is squeezed in a syringe, etc.) Because of the stretchiness of the containers, each system was able to stabilize until the air pressure outside and inside the containers was equal.

6. Define air pressure.

Points to cover:
As you may have already deduced from the demonstrations, air pressure is a result of molecules and atoms colliding with and pushing on the walls of whatever container they are in.

> **Air pressure** can be defined as the force caused by the molecules of the gases striking the walls of the container they are in.

Imagine you have a container of air molecules. When those air molecules are forced into a smaller space they will hit the walls of their container more often. This will be observed as greater air pressure. When those air molecules are given a larger space to occupy they won't hit the walls of the container as often. This will be observed as less air pressure.

It is also important to remember that there are air molecules around us all the time. These molecules collide with each other and with the surface of objects on the planet. As a result, there is air *pressure* all around us, all the time. This is called **atmospheric pressure.** We are so used to the atmospheric pressure that we usually forget that it's there. However, if you are standing at sea level and it is about 25°C out, you are experiencing one atmosphere of pressure – called 1 **atm**.

Air pressure is affected by the volume of the container it is in. Other factors, such as the temperature of the air or the number of molecules of air, also affect air pressure. These factors will be studied in greater detail later in the investigation. Our next lesson will focus on the relationship between air pressure and volume. All of the things we learn about air pressure also apply to other gases as well, such as helium, oxygen, or fluorine.

7. Discuss high and low air pressure and weather.

Discussion goals:
Assist the class in understanding how high and low air pressure may affect the weather.

Sample questions:
What do you think causes a low pressure region?
Why are winds associated with areas where there are pressure differences?

Points to cover:

Weather forecasters measure air pressure in order to help them to predict the weather. The H on a weather map is associated with a region of high pressure. The L on a weather map is associated with a region of low pressure. High pressure areas are associated with stable weather and clear skies. Low pressure areas are associated with unstable conditions, meaning that the conditions are changing rapidly. This is because air moving towards the low pressure areas often brings clouds and precipitation. If a meteorologist mentions that the pressure is falling, he or she may also predict a storm is coming. (Recall from the ChemCatalyst in Lesson I-1 that the center of a hurricane is at a low pressure.)

Air moves from areas of high pressure to areas of low pressure. This movement of air accounts for some of the winds we experience in the weather. However, air does not move in a straight line from high pressure to low pressure. As the earth rotates slowly, the air is dragged along from left to right. Since the rotation is faster at the poles compared with the equator, there is a tendency for air to spiral clockwise in the northern hemisphere and counterclockwise in the southern hemisphere. However, the rotation of the earth is not the only force acting on the air. Air in areas of high pressure is pushed outward towards areas of low pressure where it is drawn inward.

The result of forces due to differences in pressure and the rotation of the earth is that air moves clockwise around high pressure system in the northern hemisphere. Air moves counterclockwise around a low pressure system in the northern hemisphere. The illustration shows air spiraling from a high pressure region towards a low pressure region.

Check-in   (5 min)

8. Complete the Check-in exercise.

Write the following question on the board for the class to complete.

- When we fly in a commercial airplane we often feel the change in air pressure in our ear canals. It feels painful. Using what you learned today, explain what you think is going on.

9. Discuss the Check-in exercise.

Get a sense of the level of understanding by asking students to share their ideas.

Discussion goals:

Check to see that students understand that the pressures due to air in your head become unbalanced with respect to the pressures due to the air on the outside.

Suggested questions:

Describe the pressures acting on your eardrum.

What happens to the pressures due to air as you go to high altitudes?

Why do your ears pop?

10. Wrap-up

Assist the students in summarizing what was learned in this class.

- Gas pressure is defined as the force per area caused by the molecules of a gas colliding with and pushing on the walls of its container.
- When pressure due to gases in a container balance pressure due to air on the outside, the container stops expanding or contracting.

Homework

11. Assign the following for homework.

Use the homework provided with the curriculum or assign your own.

Homework – Investigation III – Lesson 1

1. There are spaces in the human body that contain trapped air, like the joints in your wrists, knees, and ankles. In your life you may have heard an older person complaining that, "I could feel an ache in my bones and I knew that a rainstorm was coming". Explain why they could feel this ache, if rainstorms are often preceded by a decrease in atmospheric pressure.

2. For a very dramatic real life example of a "collapsing can" accident go to the website listed here: http://www.delta.edu/slime/cancrush.html. Now, explain in your own words what happened to the railroad tanker.

3. Outside the atmosphere, there are extremely few molecules to collide with the outside walls of a balloon. Therefore the air pressure inside the balloon is much greater than the air pressure outside of the balloon. Describe what would happen to an inflated balloon if it were suddenly put in space outside the atmosphere.

ChemCatalyst: Weather map for the United States for September of 2003

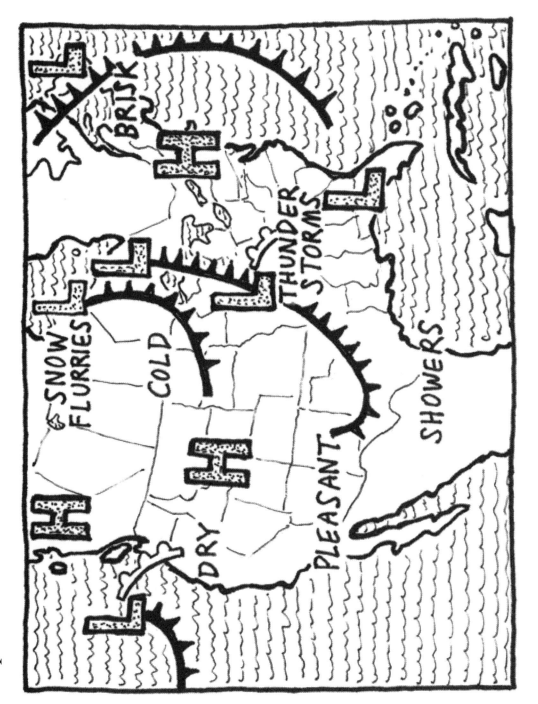

- What do the large H and L symbols stand for on the map?
- What do you think these areas have to do with weather?

Balancing Act

Name _____

Period _____   Date_____

Instructions: For each demonstration, describe what happened. Make a diagram with arrows to show what is happening with the air in each experiment. Be sure to include what happens to the air in the atmosphere in addition to the air contained inside the balloon, can, cup, hose, and marshmallows.

Station	Observations	Diagram of what happened
Balloon in a bottle		
Collapsing can		
Submerged cup		
Water in hose		

Weather© UC Regents, LHS Living by Chemistry, 2003.

Cup and card		
Expanding balloon		
Marsh-mallows		

Making sense questions:

What evidence do you have that air pressure changes?

How are air pressures equalized in each demonstration?

What can cause changes in air pressure?

BEFORE CLASS...

LESSON 2 – Feeling Under Pressure

Key Ideas:

Pressure is measured as the force per unit of area. The pressure of a gas is inversely proportional to the volume the gas occupies. In other words, when one variable gets larger, the other variable gets smaller, and vice versa.

What Takes Place:

This is a two-part activity. Students first explore pressure by covering the end of a syringe with their fingertip and pushing the plunger. They work in pairs for this portion of the activity and answer a few worksheet questions. Part II of the activity involves using a syringe that has been capped off with air trapped inside the chamber. Several student volunteers work to push the plunger down on a syringe that is placed on top of a bathroom scale. The weight is read off the scale and reflects the force required to push the syringe to a certain volume. Both the volume and the weight data are collected by the class and graphed.

Materials:

- Student worksheet
- Two medium-sized party balloons
- Approximately two cups of sand
- 16 50-mL plastic syringes (without caps on the tips)
- 1 50-mL plastic syringes per bathroom scale (with caps securely glued onto the tips)
- bathroom scale – one mandatory, more if available

Investigation III – Moving Matter

LESSON 2 – Feeling Under Pressure

The purpose of today's class is to explore the relationship between pressure and volume of gases. Gas pressure and volume exist in inverse relationship to one another (given constant temperature). Students are first introduced to the definition of pressure as force per unit of area. Students then experiment with squeezing air in a closed container (a syringe) measuring the force required by using a bathroom scale. They graph and begin to interpret the results.

Exploring the Topic   (5–10 min)

1. Introduce the ChemCatalyst exercise.

Prepare two medium-sized party balloons before class. Blow one up to a fairly large volume with air. Use a funnel to fill the other one with as much sand as you can get into it. (It will still be smaller than the first balloon.) Show students the balloons and write the following questions on the board for them to complete individually.

- Which balloon contains the greatest volume of material? Explain why you think so.
- Which balloon weighs more?
- Which material is exerting more pressure on the walls of the balloon? How can you tell?

2. Discuss the ChemCatalyst exercise.

Use the discussion to get a sense of students' initial ideas.

Discussion goals:
Assist the students in sharing their initial ideas about air pressure and the pressure due to the weight of an object.

Sample questions:
Which balloon has the greater volume of material?
Which balloon weighs more?
Why is the sand balloon flat on the bottom?
How is pressure measured?

The balloon full of air occupies a greater volume. The sand weighs more. However, the pressure from the air molecules on the inside walls of the balloon is quite high and causes the balloon to stretch considerably. The sand balloon is flat on the bottom because the weight of the sand is pushing down on the balloon. The air balloon has equal pressure on all parts of the walls, thus the balloon is rounded.

3. Introduce measurement of pressure.

Points to cover:

If you were to hold each balloon in your hand you could feel the different pressures being exerted by these two different substances. The force from the sand would push straight down against your hand. The force from the air can be felt in the extreme tightness of the balloon.

Pressure is defined as a force per unit area. The downward pressure exerted by the sand balloon is greater than the downward pressure exerted by the air balloon. This is because the sand balloon has a greater mass and weighs more. However, gas pressure is due to the collisions of molecules against a surface. The air inside the air balloon exerts a greater pressure on the inside surface of the balloon compared with the sand. This is because the air molecules are moving fast and colliding with the inside walls of the container. Thus, the pressure inside the air balloon is greater than the pressure inside the sand balloon and the balloon is stretched tight.

Pressure is measured differently in these two cases. The sand balloon exerts a downward pressure. The force in this case is the weight of the balloon and its contents due to gravity (F = mass x gravity). The weight of the sand is distributed over the bottom of the balloon.

The air molecules exert a pressure on the walls of the air balloon. The force is due to the rapidly moving air molecules colliding with the walls of the balloon (F = mass x acceleration). The forces due to the moving air molecules are distributed over the inside surface of the balloon.

Because pressure is defined as force per unit of area, air pressure can also be measured in pounds/inch^2. The air pressure in tires is measured in psi, or pounds per square inch. Remember, the pressure exerted by the atmosphere all around us is measured in atm, or atmospheres. We will learn more about measuring pressure at a later time.

> **Pressure** is defined as the force per unit area.

4. Explain the purpose of the activity.

If you wish you can write the main question on the board.

Points to cover:

We have already discovered that a mathematical relationship exists between the temperature and volume of a gas (Charles's Law). In today's class we will be using downward pressure (weight) per area to measure the pressure of some trapped air. Tell students they will be answering the question: "What is the relationship between pressure and volume for gases (if we keep the temperature and amount of gas constant)?"

Activity – Feeling Under Pressure   (15 min)

5. Explain the procedure for Part I. (Worksheet)

Tell students that they will be using a syringe as a container with a volume that can change. To begin, they will make pressure observations while using their fingertip to cover the bottom of the syringe. After passing out materials allow students about 5 to 10 minutes to experiment with the syringe and answer the questions in Part I of the worksheet before proceeding to Part II as an entire class.

Materials (for each pair of students)
16 50-mL plastic syringes (uncapped)

Part I: Qualitative observations

1. Work in pairs.
2. Cover the tip of the syringe with your fingertip. Be sure to make a good seal.
3. Record the volume of gas in the syringe, using the scale on the syringe.
4. Apply pressure to the syringe, causing the plunger to read 40 mL.
5. Apply more pressure to the syringe, so that the inside volume is 30 mL, 20 mL, and so on.
6. Record your observations and answer the questions below.

Answer the following questions:

1. What did you feel when you pushed the plunger down from 40 mL to 30 mL to 20 mL. (It is harder to go from 30 mL to 20 mL compared with 40 mL to 30 mL.)

2. Are you able to push the plunger all the way to the bottom? Explain why or why not. (No, because there is still air inside the syringe and it pushes back.)

3. Does the amount of air inside the syringe change? Explain your thinking. (No, because the air cannot escape from the inside with your finger sealing the tip.)

6. Collect weight vs. volume data.

Ask a couple of volunteers to perform similar explorations with the syringe, except that the tip of the syringe will be placed on a bathroom scale. For this part of the experiment, the cap provided with the syringe needs to be sealed to the tip of the syringe with epoxy so that air cannot escape.

Materials:

1 50-mL plastic syringe (or more if available, with the caps sealed to the tip with epoxy)

1 bathroom scale (or more if available)

Caution: The cap on the tip of the syringe should always be pointed down, away from eyes.

Part II: Do the following as a demonstration:

1. Work as a class, with several volunteers performing the experiment. (Three volunteers works well for this demonstration. If you have more materials you may have more than one group completing these measurements at once.)

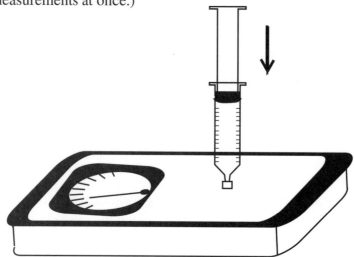

2. Hold the syringe with the tip on top of a bathroom scale.
3. One student should depress the plunger slightly.
4. A second student should read the volume.
5. A third student should read the number of pounds that is exerted on the bathroom scale.
6. All students should record the data in the table provided.
7. Repeat for at least 5 volumes.

Sample Data:

Trial	Volume (mL)	Weight (lbs)	Pressure (lbs per in^2)
1	50 mL	0	0
2	40 mL	10	3.2
3	30 mL	15	4.8
4	20 mL	25	8.0
5	15 mL	35	11.1
6	10 mL	55	17.5

Answer the following questions:

1. Fill in the table with the results of the demonstration.

2. Convert the weight to pressure by dividing by the area to get pounds per square inch. The area is π times the radius of the syringe squared (Area = πr^2) (For a 2 cm diameter syringe, the area = $\pi(1)^2 = 3.14$ cm^2)

3. Make a graph of pressure versus volume. Put pressure on the y axis and volume on the x-axis.

4. Describe what happens to the pressure as the volume decreases. (As the volume decreases, the pressure increases)

5. Use you graph to estimate the following:

    a) If the volume is reduced to 32 mL what will the pressure be?

    b) If the volume is reduced to 16 mL what will the pressure be?

6. Explain why the number of molecules in the syringe didn't change, but the volume did. (No molecules could escape. The volume changed because of pressure applied to the plunger of the syringe.)

7. Describe the relationship between pressure and volume. (Pressure is inversely proportional to volume. When pressure increases, volume decreases.)

Making sense:
Why is it so difficult to push the plunger in as the volume gets smaller?

Making Sense Discussion   (15 min)

Major goals: This lesson will be debriefed in more detail in the following lesson. For now it is important that students get an opportunity to share their experiences with the syringe. They take a look at the graph and interpret its outcome, noting the inverse relationship between pressure and volume. If you wish you can have students correct for the additional pressure on the syringe due to the atmosphere, however this is not mandatory.

7. Briefly discuss Part I of the activity.

Discussion goals:
Discuss what happens to the air inside the syringe as the plunger is pushed in.

Sample questions:
  What happens to the air on the inside of the syringe as the plunger is pushed in? (Does the amount of air change?)

Explain why the volume of air can change even if the number of air molecules does not change.

Can you decrease the volume to zero? Why or why not?

Why does it get harder and harder to depress the plunger as the volume gets smaller and smaller?

Students should observe that it becomes harder and harder to depress the plunger as the volume gets smaller. The air inside the syringe is being compressed into a smaller and smaller space. Since no air is escaping, the number of air molecules does not change, only the volume the molecules occupy. In other words, the molecules in the air are getting closer to one another. All matter occupies some space, so the volume inside cannot go to zero. Indeed, you cannot even get close to zero because the air molecules are "pushing back" with high pressure on the walls of the container due to their motions.

8. Briefly discuss the weight changes.

Draw a graph on the board and ask student volunteers to graph the data that was collected today.

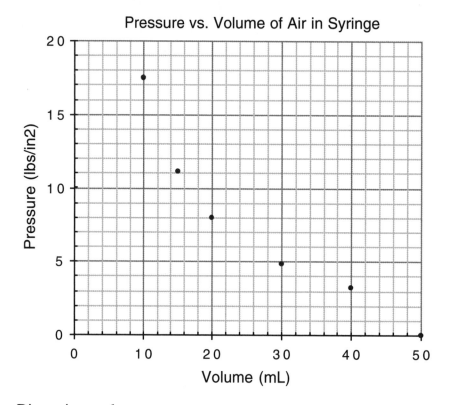

Discussion goals:

Discuss how the weight on the scale changes as the volume of air in the syringe is decreased.

Sample questions:

What does the graph of your data look like? (a curve, does not begin at the origin)

Why do you think the graph is not a straight line? (it takes more and more force the smaller the volume)

Explain what happens to the weight on the scale as you depress the plunger. (the weight increases)

How did you calculate the pressure from the weight?

Use your graph to estimate the pressure for 32 mL and 16 mL.

Describe how the pressure varies as the volume gets smaller. (the pressure increases more dramatically as the volume gets smaller)

Why is it so difficult to push the plunger in as the volume gets smaller? (because the air molecules are colliding more frequently with the walls of the container, and hence the pressure is increasing)

Note: The points on the graph are not exactly those expected for the equation P = constant (1/V). This is because the pressures need to be corrected for the fact that when the weight on the bathroom scale measures zero, there is 1 atm pushing down on the balance. In other words, when the balance reads zero, it is still "weighing" the atmosphere. The correction for atmospheric pressure is given below should you choose to use it. For now, focus on the inverse relationship between pressure and volume.

Points to cover:

The graph reflects the fact that as the volume of the syringe decreases it takes more and more force to push the molecules of air into that space. The graph also reflects the fact that the relationship between pressure and volume is an *inverse* one. In other words, as the value of one gets bigger the value of the other gets smaller.

Gas pressure and volume have an **inverse** relationship. When the volume of a given amount of gas is decreased, its pressure increases. When the volume of a given amount of gas is increased, its pressure decreases.

Inform students that you will examine the data from this activity in more detail in the next lesson.

Students should observe that as the volume is decreased, the weight increases. However, it is easier to push the plunger in a little bit. The more the plunger is pushed in, the smaller the volume is for the same amount of gas to occupy and the harder it is to push in.

9. Briefly discuss the correction due to atmospheric pressure.

This portion of the discussion is optional.

Points to cover:

When the scale reads zero pounds there is one atmosphere pressure on the scale and on the syringe. This is because the atmosphere around us always exerts a force of one atmosphere (at sea level). So, any measurement taken using the bathroom scale will have to have one atmosphere added at the end. By the way, 1 atm = 14.7 lbs/in^2.

The weight is the force applied over the area of the plunger. Thus, it is necessary to divide the weight that was measured by the cross-sectional area of the plunger in order to get lbs/in^2. You can accomplish this by measuring the diameter of the syringe in inches and using Area $= \pi\, r^2$.

$$\text{Pressure} = \frac{\text{weight in pounds}}{\text{area of cross section of syringe}} + 14.7 \text{ lbs/in}^2$$

Check-in   (5 min)

10. Complete the Check-in exercise.
Write the following question on the board for students to complete individually.

Imagine you have a plastic bottle that is capped. It contains nothing but air.

- What happens to the volume the bottle if you squeeze the bottle tightly?
- What happens to the pressure inside the bottle when it is squeezed?

11. Discuss the Check-in exercise.
Get a sense of the level of understanding by asking students to defend their choices.

Discussion goals:
Check to see that students understand the relationship between pressure and volume of air inside a container.

12. Wrap-up
Assist the students in summarizing what was learned in this class.
- Pressure and volume have an inverse relationship, that is, when one gets larger, the other gets smaller.

Homework

13. Assign the following for homework.
Use the homework provided with the curriculum or assign your own.

Homework – Investigation III – Lesson 2

1. You blow up a balloon before going SCUBA diving. You put on your gear and descend to 30 ft with the balloon. The total pressure from the ocean at that depth is measured at 2 atmospheres (2 atm). Assume temperature is constant.

   a) What happens to the volume of the balloon?

   b) What happens to the pressure of the air on the inside of the balloon?

2. You are filling a bicycle tire with air using a bicycle pump. It gets harder and harder to push the plunger on the pump the more air is in the tire. Explain what is going on.

Feeling Under Pressure

Name: _____

Period:_____ Date: _____

Purpose: This activity allows you to compare the pressure and volume of a sample of air.

Part I: Experimenting with pressure.
1. Work in pairs.
2. Cover the tip of the syringe with your fingertip. Be sure to make a good seal.
3. Record the volume of the syringe, using the scale on the side of the syringe.
4. Apply pressure to the syringe, causing the plunger to read 40 mL.
5. Apply more pressure to the syringe so that the inside volume is 30 mL, 20 mL, and so on.
6. Record your observations and answer the questions below.

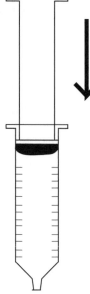

Answer the following questions:
1. What did you feel when you pushed the plunger down from 40 mL to 30 mL to 20 mL?

2. Are you able to push the plunger all the way to the bottom? Explain why or why not.

3. Does the amount of air inside the syringe change? Explain your thinking.

Part II : Quantitative data.
You will collect quantitative data as a class.

1. Fill in the table with the results of the demonstration.

2. Convert the weight to pressure by dividing by the area to get pounds per square inch. The area is the radius of the syringe squared times π (Area = πr^2)

Trial	Volume (mL)	Weight (lbs)	Pressure (lbs per in^2)
1			
2			
3			
4			
5			
6			

3. Make a graph of pressure versus volume. Put pressure on the y axis and volume on the x axis.

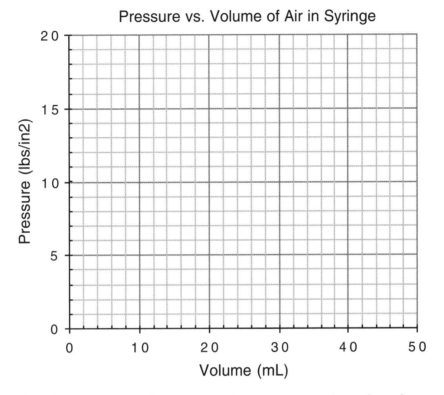

4. Describe what happens to the pressure shown on the scale as the volume of the air decreases.

5. Use your graph to estimate the following:

    a) If the volume is reduced to 32 mL what will the pressure be?

    b) If the volume is reduced to 16 mL what will the pressure be?

6. Explain why the number of molecules in the syringe didn't change, but the volume did.

7. Describe the relationship between pressure and volume.

Making sense:
Why is it so difficult to push the plunger in as the volume gets smaller?

BEFORE CLASS...

LESSON 3 – Getting Squeezed

Key Ideas:
Boyle's Law describes the mathematical relationship between gas
pressure and volume (if the temperature and amount of gas are kept constant).
Boyle's Law can be written as $P_1V_1 = P_2V_2$ or as $P_1V_1 = k$, where k is a constant.
The first equation may be easier for students to grasp, although the second equation
clearly implies that the product of the pressure and volume of a gas is always the
same number for a quantity of gas at fixed temperature. If the quantity or temperature
changes, the value of k changes.

What Takes Place:
Students will consider some data relating the pressure of a gas to its volume. They
will use a worksheet to assist them in figuring out several ways to compute the value
of a new volume or pressure. During the discussion they graph pressure against
inverse volume and note the proportional relationship. Boyle's Law is introduced and
several methods for solving pressure and volume problems are discussed.

Materials:
• Student worksheet

Investigation III – Moving Matter

LESSON 3 – Getting Squeezed

So far in this investigation, students have been introduced to the concept of air pressure and learned that the pressure of a gas is inversely related to its volume (for a constant amount and temperature). In this lesson students take the data from the previous experiment a bit further. They learn that a graph of P vs. 1/V is a straight line with a zero intercept. This leads to the proportional relationship between pressure and reciprocal volume, known as Boyles' law.

Exploring the Topic   (5–10 min)

1. Introduce the ChemCatalyst exercise.

Write the following exercise on the board for students to complete individually.

Imagine you have a 5.0 L tank full of helium at a pressure of 50 atm, and a large weather balloon to fill up.

- How does the volume of the helium gas change as it fills up the balloon?
- How does the pressure of the gas change now that it is in the balloon?

2. Discuss the ChemCatalyst exercise.

Use the discussion to get a sense of students' initial ideas.

Discussion goals:
Assist the students in sharing their initial ideas about how to write a relationship showing how pressure and volume of gases are related.

Sample questions:
What happens to the volume occupied by the helium as you fill up the weather balloon? Explain.
How does the pressure change as a result of emptying the tank into the balloon?
How can you figure out the ending pressure and volume?

Help students think about how pressure and volume are related. As the volume of the gas increases (by virtue of the fact that its going into a very large container), the pressure on it decreases.

3. Explain the purpose of the activity.

If you wish you can write the main question on the board.

Points to cover:

Tell students they will be answering the question: "How can the relationship between pressure and volume be expressed as a mathematical equation?"

Activity – Getting Squeezed   (15 min)

4. Pass out worksheets. (Worksheet)

Ask students to work in pairs to complete the worksheet.

A gas sample occupying a volume of 5.00 liters and at a pressure of 1.00 atm is contained in a cylinder with a movable piston. As the volume inside the piston is decreased, the pressure is measured. The pressures for several volumes of gas are given in the table below.

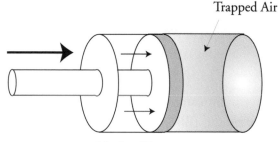

Trapped Air

Moving Piston

Complete the table:

Trial	Pressure (atm)	Volume (L)	P/V (atm per L)	(PV) L atm
1	1.00	5.00	0.20	5.00
2	1.25	4.00	0.31	5.00
3	2.00	2.50	0.80	5.00
4	3.00	1.67	1.80	5.00
5	4.00	1.25	3.20	5.00
6	6.00	0.83	7.23	5.00

Remember: 1 atm is equal to one atmosphere of pressure.

Answer the following questions:

1. What do you notice about the product of PV (pressure times volume)? (stays the same – always equal to 5.00)

2. What do you notice about the ratio P/V (pressure/volume)? (it changes)

3. When the pressure doubles, what happens to the volume? (decreases – in half)

4. When the volume doubles, what happens to the pressure? (decreases – in half)

5. Plot the data on the graph and connect the points with a curve.

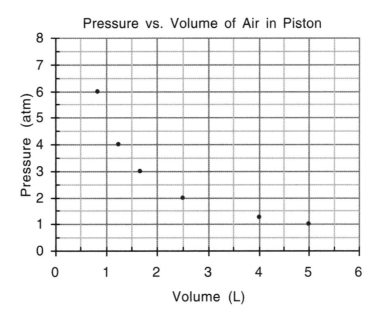

6. Use the graph to estimate the volume of the gas when the pressure is 1.50 atm. (around 3.3 L)

7. It is clear from the data table that PV (pressure times volume) is always the same number. Use this information to help you calculate the volume of the gas in the piston if the pressure is 1.50 atm. Show your work.

(If PV = 5.00 then 1.5 V = 5.00. Thus, the new $V = \dfrac{5.00}{1.50} = 3.33$ L)

8. What will the pressure be of the gas inside the piston if the volume was 2.00 L? (Use the same method you used for Problem #7.) (2.5 atm)

9. Imagine that you fill a balloon to 1.0 atm and a volume of 1.0 L. Suppose you take the balloon to the top of a mountain where the pressure is only 0.5 atm.

   a) Do you predict that the balloon will become bigger or smaller? Explain your reasoning. (balloon will get bigger, less pressure on it)

   b) What will the volume of the balloon be at 0.5 atm? (Assume the temperature remains constant.) (2.0 L)

Making sense:
Explain the best way to figure out the new volume of a gas if you know the following:

P_1 - beginning pressure V_1 - beginning volume P_2 - new pressure

If you finish early...
A 2.0 L plastic bottle full of air is sealed on top of a mountain where the pressure is 0.75 atm. Describe 3 different ways you can determine the volume of the bottle when you return to sea level where the air pressure is 1.0 atm.

Making Sense Discussion (15 min)

Major goals: The main goals of this discussion are to introduce Boyle's Law and to clarify the math behind Boyle's Law so that students may complete pressure and volume computations successfully. A particulate explanation for the relationship between the volume and pressure of a gas can be offered as well.

5. Discuss the relationship between P and V.

Have students draw two graphs on the board during this discussion.

<u>Discussion goals:</u>
Assist students in sharing their conclusions about the mathematical relationship between P and V.

Suggested questions:
What did you discover about the ratio P/V? (varies)
What did you discover about the product PV? (a constant)
Show what your graph looked like on the worksheet. (curve)
What does it mean that P and V are inversely proportional to one another?

Points to cover:
If P and V are inversely proportional to one another it makes sense to graph pressure against the *inverse* of the volume. By calculating 1/V for the data in the table, we can come up with a graph of P vs. 1/V. (Ask students to complete this task.)

P	1/V
1.0	0.2
2.0	0.4
3.0	0.6
4.0	0.8
5.0	1.0
6.0	1.2

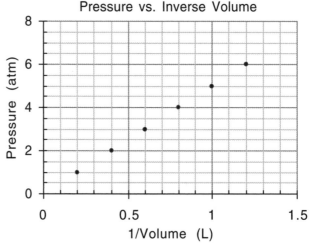

In the situation with the piston, we discovered that P_1V_1 is always the same. It was always equal to 5.00. Whenever we wanted to determine a new volume or a new pressure we could use this information to calculate a new value.

It turns out that for any situation where the temperature of the gas and the amount are kept constant, pressure times volume is always a constant number. In other words, PV = k, where k is a constant.

It is important to emphasize that k is a different number for a different amount of gas or a gas at a different temperature. For each new situation, it is necessary to determine the value of k from the initial values of P_1 and V_1.

6. Introduce Boyle's Law.

Discussion goals:
Assist students in determining a new gas volume given an initial pressure and volume and a new pressure.

Suggested questions:
   If the pressure of a gas is suddenly decreased, what happens to the volume?
   What are all the ways you can find V_2, given P_1, V_1, and P_2?
   Does every gas have the same value for P_1V_1? Explain. (no, P_1V_1 varies depending on the situation – temperature and amount of gas)

Possible ways to solve the problem:
1.   Proportional analysis: $P_1V_1 = P_2V_2$ or $P_1V_1 = k$, a constant.
2.   Dimensional analysis: $V_2 = V_1 (P_1/P_2)$
3.   Use a graph – it is only necessary to graph one point P and 1/V and draw a line through the origin (0,0).

Points to Cover:
The scientist who is credited with discovering the mathematical relationship between the volume and pressure of a gas was a British scientists named Robert Boyle. In 1662, he showed an inverse relationship between pressure and volume: when one increases, the other decreases. **Boyle's law,** put more simply, says that if the pressure of a gas is increased, then the volume of the gas will decrease. Also, if the pressure of a gas is decreased, the volume of the gas will increase.

It must also hold true that, if the volume of a container of gas is decreased the pressure of the gas increases. And… if the volume of a container of gas is increased, the pressure of the gas decreases.

Boyle's Law states that the pressure of a given amount of gas is indirectly proportional to volume, if the temperature is kept constant.

Although this relationship can also be observed in other phases (i.e. the compression of a solid in a press), Boyle's law only applies to the drastic volume changes that take place when the pressure of a gas is changed.

Boyle's law $P_1V_1 = P_2V_2$ where the temperature and amount of
                                                     gas are constant

This can also be written: $P_1/P_2 = V_1/V_2$

Boyle was one of the first scientists to show that air is "elastic", that is, it resists compression (when you push down on the plunger of the syringe you can feel the increased pressure). Boyle called this quality "springiness". He also noted how gases expand to fill the available space (gases will expand to fill whatever container they are in). Boyle came up with two different particulate explanations to explain gas pressure: (1) He postulated that air is composed of particles that repel each other – like coiled up springs and (2) He suggested that air is composed of whirling particles that push each other away by impacts.

7. Use the kinetic view of gases to explain the observations.

A very useful way to present information of a kinetic view of gases is to set up one or more computer animations. Here are two websites:

1. A Study Aids site by Granada Hills High School. Select Properties of Gases on the home page and you will be led to a variety of animations and simulations of the gas laws.
http://www.jozie.net/JF/chemclass/Chemistry/StudyAids/studyaids.htm

2. The following site features some chemistry study aids put out by Prentice-Hall, Inc. Scroll down and click on Gases.
http://cwx.prenhall.com/petrucci/medialib/media_portfolio/index.html

Discussion goals:
Discuss how the gas molecules collide with the walls of the container more frequently as the volume decreases.

Sample questions:
   Why do the gas molecules exert pressure on the walls of the container? (they are moving and collide with the container walls)
   Do the molecules collide more often with the walls of a smaller container or a larger container? (smaller container)
   Since the temperature does not change, the average speeds do not change. Why does the pressure increase when the volume decreases?

Points to cover:
In the previous investigation, a **kinetic molecular view of gases** was introduced. The word "kinetic" refers to the fact that the gas molecules are in constant motion. The average speeds of the molecules depend on the temperature: The molecules move faster as the temperature increases.

Now consider how the kinetic molecular view can help us understand Boyle's law. When the volume that a gas occupies decreases, the area of the container walls decreases. The pressure increases because the gas molecules collide more frequently with the walls of the container. Since the temperature stays constant, the average speeds of the gas molecules do not change. This means that the forces exerted by the molecules on the container walls do not change.

However, since the area is smaller, the force per unit area (pressure) exerted by the moving gas molecules on the walls of the container is larger. Hence the pressure of a gas increases when the volume occupied by that gas decreases.

Check-in   (5 min)

8. Complete the Check-in exercise.

Write the following question on the board for students to complete individually.

A balloon full of gas occupies 7.5 L and is at a pressure of 1.0 atm. Calculate the new pressure of the gas if the balloon is taken underwater to a depth where its new volume is 2.5 L.

- Did the volume of the balloon decrease or increase when it was taken underwater?
- What do you predict will happen to the pressure, will it increase or decrease? Explain your thinking.
- What is the new pressure? Show your work.

9. Discuss the Check-in exercise.

Get a sense of the level of understanding by asking students to defend their choices.

Discussion goals:
Check to see that students understand the relationship between pressure and volume.

Sample questions:
How will the pressure change as the balloon is taken underwater?
What are the values for P_1 and V_1?
What is the value of V_2?
What is the new pressure, P_2?

The relationship between P and V is:
$$P_1V_1 = P_2V_2$$
This can be rearranged to give
$$P_2 = P_1V_1/ V_2$$
Substituting gives
$$P_2 = (1.0 \text{ atm})(7.5 \text{ L}) / 2.5 \text{ L} = 3.0 \text{ atm}$$

10. Wrap-up

Assist the students in summarizing what was learned in this class.
- Boyle's Law can be described by the formula $P_1V_1 = P_2V_2$ provided the temperature and amount of gas are held constant.

Homework

11. Assign the following for homework.

Use the homework provided with the curriculum or assign your own.

Homework – Investigation III – Lesson 3

1. A balloon can be filled with helium to 5.0 L without bursting. Suppose the balloon is filled to a volume of 0.50 L initially, and the gas pressure is 1.00 atm. Then you release the balloon. As the balloon rises in the atmosphere, the pressure gets lower. (Assume that the temperature is constant.) At what pressure will the balloon burst?

2. A gas occupies 22.8 liters at a pressure of 4 atm. What is the volume when the pressure is increased to 6 atm?

3. If the pressure on a gas is decreased by one-quarter, how large will the volume change be?

4. A 1.5 liter flask is filled with nitrogen gas at a pressure of 12.0 atmospheres. What size flask would be required to hold this gas at a pressure of 2.0 atmospheres?

Getting Squeezed

Name: _____
Period:_____ Date: _____

Purpose: This activity allows you to gain practice with calculations of gas pressure and volume.

A gas sample occupying a volume of 5.00 liters and at a pressure of 1 atm is contained in a cylinder with a movable piston. As the volume inside the piston is decreased, the pressure is measured. The pressures for several volumes of gas are given in the table below.

Complete the table:

Trial	Pressure (atm)	Volume (L)	P/V (atm per L)	PV L atm
1	1.00	5.00		
2	1.25	4.00		
3	2.00	2.50		
4	3.00	1.67		
5	4.00	1.25		
6	6.00	0.83		

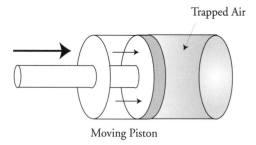

Trapped Air

Moving Piston

Remember: 1 atm is equal to one atmosphere of pressure.

Answer the following questions:
1. What do you notice about the product of PV (pressure times volume)?

2. What do you notice about the ratio P/V (pressure / volume)?

3. When the pressure doubles, what happens to the volume?

4. When the volume doubles, what happens to the pressure?

5. Plot the data on the graph and connect the points with a curve.

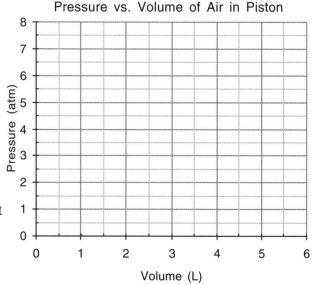

Pressure vs. Volume of Air in Piston

Weather © UC Regents, LHS Living by Chemistry, 2003.

6. Use the graph to estimate the volume of the gas when the pressure is 1.50 atm.

7. It is clear from the data table that PV (pressure times volume) is always the same number. Use this information to help you calculate the volume of the gas in the piston if the pressure is 1.50 atm. Show your work.

8. What will the pressure be of the gas inside the piston if the volume was 2.00 L? (Use the same method you used for Problem #7.)

9. Imagine that you fill a balloon to 1.0 atm and a volume of 1.0 L. Suppose you take the balloon to the top of a mountain where the pressure is only 0.5 atm.

   a) Do you predict that the balloon will become bigger or smaller? Explain your reasoning.

   b) What will the volume of the balloon be at 0.5 atm? (Assume the temperature remains constant.)

Making sense:
Explain the best way to figure out the new volume of a gas if you know the following:

P_1 - beginning pressure V_1 - beginning volume P_2 - new pressure

If you finish early...
A 2.0 L plastic bottle full of air is sealed on top of a mountain where the pressure is 0.75 atm. Describe 3 different ways you can determine the volume of the bottle when you return to sea level where the air pressure is 1.0 atm.

BEFORE CLASS...

LESSON 4 – Egg in a Bottle

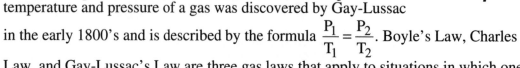

Key Ideas:
Changing the temperature of a gas can change its pressure if the volume is kept constant. The mathematical relationship between temperature and pressure of a gas was discovered by Gay-Lussac in the early 1800's and is described by the formula $\dfrac{P_1}{T_1} = \dfrac{P_2}{T_2}$. Boyle's Law, Charles Law, and Gay-Lussac's Law are three gas laws that apply to situations in which one variable (P, V, or T) stays constant and the other two change.

What Takes Place:
Students are introduced to Gay-Lussac's Law at the beginning of class. A demonstration using a hard-boiled egg and a flask gets students thinking about the relationship between gas pressure and temperature. Students complete a worksheet that allows them to gain some proficiency completing gas law problems. They compare pressure changes for a gas in a container of variable volume with a gas in a container of fixed volume.

Materials:
- Student worksheet
- Several hard boiled eggs (shelled)
- 1000 mL Erlenmeyer Flask
- Bunsen burner
- Oven mitt

Investigation III – Moving Matter
LESSON 4 – Egg in a Bottle

Thus far, we have considered how pressure changes when the volume changes (Boyle's law). In this lesson the students will be introduced to the relationship between pressure and temperature (Gay-Lussac's law). Then they will practice applying these two gas laws to determine what happens to the pressure inside an unopened glass bottle of soda (fixed volume) and unopened bag of chips (variable volume) after hiking up a mountain. Finally, all three gas laws are reviewed, including Charles' law.

Exploring the Topic   (5–10 min)

1. Introduce the ChemCatalyst exercise.

Write the following exercise on the board for students to complete individually.

You start at sea level where the pressure is 1.0 atm. Suppose you climb high up a mountain where the pressure is 0.75 atm. Assume the temperature does not change.

- Does the pressure inside your unopened bag of potato chips change? Explain.
- Does the pressure inside your unopened glass bottle of soda change? Explain.

2. Discuss the ChemCatalyst exercise.

Use the discussion to get a sense of students' initial ideas.

<u>Discussion goals:</u>
Assist students in sharing their initial ideas on how the pressure changes in containers with variable volume vs. containers with fixed volume.

Sample questions:
What happens to the outside pressure as you go up the mountain? (decreases)
If the pressure on the outside of the bag of chips decreases, what will happen to the pressure on the inside? (it will equalize with the outside pressure)
The bag can change size to equalize the pressures on the inside and the outside. Will the volume of the bag be larger or smaller when the pressures equalize? (larger)

If the pressure on the outside of the glass bottle of soda decreases, what will happen to the pressure on the inside? (the pressure cannot equalize by changing volume)

When you open the glass bottle of soda, the pressure inside equalizes with the pressure outside. What happens when you open the bottle of soda when the outside atmospheric pressure has decreased? (the soda sprays out)

Thinking about air pressure on the inside and outside of a gas sample is not easy. Help students realize that there are two types of situations we want to consider: gas samples in containers with variable size and gas samples in containers with fixed size. Listen to their ideas about what happens when the pressure on the outside is decreased in each case. You may need to go over the meaning of the word fixed with students. The more common meaning of the word is "repaired" and this may be what comes to mind for some of the students.

3. Introduce Gay-Lussac's Law.

Remind students of the demonstrations they helped you do in Lesson III-1. In several of these demonstrations, the pressure of a gas sample in a container was equalized with the pressure of the air on the outside by changing the size of the container. Recall the expanding marshmallows when surrounding air was evacuated. Now we want to consider what happens when the volume of the container is fixed.

Suggested demonstration:
This demonstration requires a hard boiled egg (shelled) and a 1000 mL Erlenmeyer flask. Heat the flask on a pre-heated hot plate for about several minutes. Remove the flask from the hot plate with an oven mitt. Place the egg on the opening of the flask so that it makes a seal. Observe what happens as the air inside the flask cools (the egg gets pushed into the flask). (You can speed up the process by placing the flask in cool water.) Turn the flask upside down so that the egg falls into the opening of the flask. Holding the flask sideways with an oven mitt, reheat the flask on the bottom until the egg is pushed back out.

Discussion goals:
Assist students in sharing their ideas about why the egg was pushed into the flask and then back out again.

Sample questions:
What happens to the air inside the flask when it is heated?
When the egg is used as a "stopper" the air inside the flask is at constant volume. Explain why.
What happens to the speed of the molecules inside the flask as the air in the flask cools?
What happens to the pressure inside the flask? Explain your thinking.
The egg was *pushed* not sucked into the flask. Explain what this means.

Points to cover:

Gay-Lussac was a French scientist who experimented with the pressure and temperature of gases. In the early 1800's, he showed that if the temperature of a gas is increased, then the pressure of that gas also increases if the volume remains the same.

> **Gay-Lussac's law** states that the pressure of a given amount of gas is directly proportional to temperature, if the volume is kept constant.

This relationship is expressed as: $\dfrac{P_1}{T_1} = \dfrac{P_2}{T_2}$

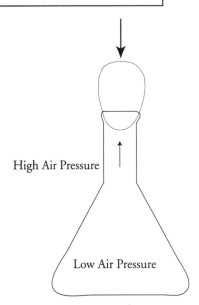

High Air Pressure

Low Air Pressure

In the demonstration, the volume of air inside the flask did not change (as long as the egg served as a stopper). As the air inside the flask cooled, the pressure of the air inside the flask decreased. Since the air pressure decreased inside the flask, the force exerted by the air inside the flask on the egg pushing it out became less than the force exerted by the air on the outside pushing the egg in. When the difference became too great, the egg was pushed inside the flask.

Notice that the egg was not "sucked" into the flask. It is important that students understand that gases never suck. Rather, the force that they exert is a result of air pushing from areas of high pressure to areas of low pressure.

The observations can be explained using the **kinetic molecular theory of gases.** Since the temperature decreases, the average speeds of the gas molecules also decrease. Since they are moving more slowly, they exert less pressure upon the walls of the container.

4. Explain the purpose of the activity.

If you wish you can write the main question on the board.

Points to cover:

Tell students they will be practicing applying Gay-Lussac's law and Boyle's law to understand changes in pressure. The main question is: "What causes changes in the pressure of a gas inside a container?"

Activity – Egg in a Bottle   **(15 min)**

5. Pass out worksheets.

Tell students that they will be solving gas law problems using Charles' Law, Boyle's Law, and Gay-Lussac's Law. In using these laws, it is important to keep in mind that two variables are changing at a time, and the third does not change. The amount of gas also stays the same.

1. **Gas in a container with a volume that can change.** You fill a balloon with air to a volume of 240.0 mL. The air temperature is 25.0°C and the air pressure is 1.0 atm. You carry the balloon with you up a mountain where the air pressure is 0.75 atm and the temperature is 25.0°C.

    a) When the balloon is carried up the mountain, what changes? (the volume and pressure of the air change) What stays the same? (the temperature)

    b) The air pressure on the outside of the balloon has decreased. Can the air pressure on the inside decrease so that the pressures are equal? Why or why not? (yes, because the volume of the container can change)

    c) What happens to the volume occupied by the air inside the balloon? Explain your thinking. (it increases to equalize the pressures)

    d) Solve for the new volume of the balloon using Boyle's law.

    $$P_1V_1 = P_2V_2 \quad (1.0 \text{ atm})(240.0 \text{ mL}) = (0.75 \text{ atm})V_2 \quad V_2 = 320.0 \text{ mL}$$

    e) P vs. 1/V is a straight line that passes through the origin (0, 0). Make a graph of P vs. 1/V. Determine the new volume of the balloon from the graph. How does the volume compare with your calculation in Part d?

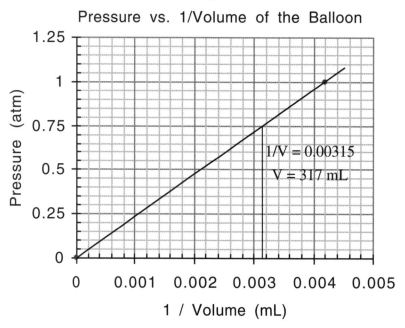

Pressure vs. 1/Volume of the Balloon

1/V = 0.00315
V = 317 mL

1 / Volume (mL)

Weather © UC Regents, LHS Living by Chemistry, 2003.

2. **Gas in a container with a volume that cannot change.** The air inside a 240 mL glass bottle is at 1.0 atm and 25.0°C when you close it. You carry the glass bottle with you up a mountain where the air pressure is 0.75 atm and the temperature is 5.0°C.

   a) The air pressure on the outside of the glass bottle has decreased. Can the volume change so that the air pressure on the inside can decrease? Why or why not? (no, because the volume of the container cannot change)

   b) Do you expect the temperature of the air on the inside of the bottle at the top of the mountain to cool to 5°C? Explain your thinking. (yes, it equalizes with the temperature on the outside)

   c) What happens to the pressure inside the glass bottle? Explain your thinking. (It decreases because the temperature decreases.)

   d) Solve for the new pressure of the gas inside the glass bottle using Gay Lussac's law.

$$\frac{P_1}{T_1} = \frac{P_2}{T_2} \qquad \frac{1.0 \text{ atm}}{298 \text{ K}} = \frac{P_2}{278 \text{ K}} \qquad P_2 = 0.93 \text{ atm}$$

   e) P vs. T is a straight line that passes through the origin (0, 0). Make a graph of P vs. T. Determine the new pressure inside the glass bottle from the graph. How does the pressure compare with your calculation in Part d?

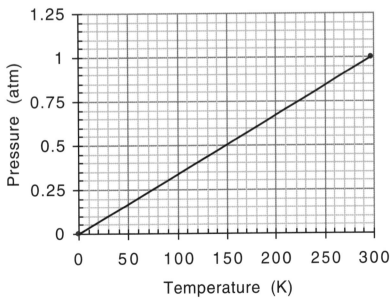

Pressure vs. Temperature of the Balloon

3. **Fill in the table.** The first line of the table gives the volume, pressure, and temperature for a container of gas. The gas starts in a container with a volume of 22.4 L. The pressure is 1.0 atm and the temperature is 300 K. Each subsequent row represents a new set of conditions for this gas. Fill in the blank spaces.

Volume	Pressure	Temperature	Gas law
$V_1 = 22.4$ L	$P_1 = 1.0$ atm	$T_1 = 300$ K	(initial conditions)
11.2 L	1.0 atm	150 K	Charles' law
44.8 L	1.0 atm	600 K	Charles' law
89.6 L	1.0 atm	1200 K	Charles' law
11.2 L	2.0 atm	300 K	Boyle's law
44.8 L	0.5 atm	300 K	Boyle's law
89.6 L	0.25 atm	300 K	Boyle's law
22.4 L	0.5 atm	150 K	Gay-Lussac's law
22.4 L	2.0 atm	600 K	Gay-Lussac's law
22.4 L	4.0 atm	1,200 K	Gay-Lussac's law

a) When the temperature is constant and the volume increases, what happens to the pressure? Provide an example of when this might occur.

b) When the pressure is constant and the temperature decreases, what happens to the volume? Provide an example of when this might occur.

c) When the volume is constant and the pressure increases, what happens to the temperature? Provide an example of when this might occur.

Making sense question:
Describe how the type of container affects how the pressure of the gas inside the container can vary.

If you finish early…
Use the information from the table to write a word problem. Show your answers (Hints: What is constant? What is changing?)

Making Sense Discussion   (15 min)

Key ideas: The main goal of this discussion is to make sure students have some degree of proficiency in solving gas law problems. They should be provided with some simple strategies for approaching gas law problems. Students should be allowed an opportunity to clear up any confusion that may remain regarding the gas laws.

6. Discuss the gas laws.

Review the gas laws.

Discussion goals:
Assist students in refining their understanding of Charles' law, Boyle's law, and Gay-Lussac's law. Make sure they understand when to apply each law and what is being held constant in each case.

Sample questions:
   What can you do to the volume or the temperature of a gas to increase its
      pressure? (either decrease the volume the gas occupies or increase the
      temperature of the gas)
   How does having a container that does not change size affect the gas inside?
   What variable is held constant for each gas law? (Boyle's Law – T constant,
      Charles's Law – P constant, Gay Lussac's Law – V constant)
   Does the amount of gas change when we consider these gas laws? (no)

Points to cover:
The three gas laws help us predict gas temperature, pressure, and volume when two of these variables changes and the third remains fixed. There are two types of containers for the gas: one that can vary in size such as a balloon or a syringe, and one with a fixed size such as a sealed glass bottle.

Gas container with varying size. When the gas is in a container that can vary in size, changing the temperature or the pressure causes the volume to change. Thus, volume and temperature can vary at fixed pressure (Charles' law) and volume and pressure can vary at fixed temperature (Boyle's law).

Gas container with fixed size. A container that is of a *fixed* size is one that does not change size. When a gas is in a container of fixed size, increasing the temperature causes the pressure to increase. Thus, the pressure and temperature can vary at fixed volume (Gay-Lussac's law).

It is important to notice that in all of these cases, gas cannot enter or escape the containers. The amount of gas is fixed. We will explore the effects of changing the numbers of gas molecules in the next investigation.

7. Go over how to solve gas law problems.

Provide students with some simple strategies for approaching gas law problems. Additionally, students may have come up with their own strategies.

Points to cover:
Word problems can seem overwhelming and complex at first glance. There are many strategies that work well in approaching gas law problems. One of

the first things you will want to figure out is which gas law formula to use to solve the problem. In order to determine that, you should first ask yourself which two variables are changing and which variable is staying the same. Often the variable that is being held constant is the easiest to identify. However, in some problems this variable isn't even mentioned at all, and you must therefore assume that it is being held constant (see Problem #2 on the homework).

Another approach that works well is to simply figure out what values you have already been given in the problem, and which value is missing.

Keys to Solving Gas Law Problems:
1. Identify which variable is NOT changing: P, V, or T.
2. Identify the two variables that ARE changing: P, V, and/or T.
3. Identify the gas law formula that should be used to solve the problem.
4. Insert values for P_1, V_1, T_1, P_2, V_2, or T_2 and solve.

For a given amount of gas, the volume V, the temperature T in Kelvin, and the pressure P are related.

Boyle's Law	$P_1V_1 = P_2V_2$	T and amount of gas are constant
Charles' Law	$\dfrac{V_1}{T_1} = \dfrac{V_2}{T_2}$	P and amount of gas are constant
Gay-Lussac's Law	$\dfrac{P_1}{T_1} = \dfrac{P_2}{T_2}$	V and amount of gas are constant

8. Relate today's findings to the weather context.

Points to cover:
We have discussed two ways of changing the air pressure: changing the volume occupied by the air or changing the temperature of the air. Even though air in the atmosphere is not in a container, we can still use these findings to think about changes in air pressure.

High pressure: When there is a high pressure system designated on a weather map, it is usually created because air is moving downward from high altitudes. As air moves down, it is being compressed (the volume occupied by the air is decreasing) and the temperature of the air is increasing. High pressure systems usually bring fair weather because the air is being compressed and warming.

Low pressure: When there is a low pressure system designated on a weather map, it is usually created because air is moving upward to higher altitudes. As the air moves up, it is expanding (the volume occupied by the air is increasing) and the temperature of the air is decreasing. Low pressure systems tend to bring rain because the air is expanding and cooling.

Check-in   (5 min)

9. Complete the Check-in exercise.
Write the following question on the board for the students to complete individually.

- The Gladstone family went for a drive in the desert. In the morning, the air pressure in the tires was around 28 pounds per square inch (psi). Around 3 PM in the afternoon, the tire pressures were around 32 psi. Explain what might be going on.

10. Discuss the Check-in exercise.
Get a sense of the level of understanding by asking students to defend their answer.

Discussion goals:
Confirm that students know which gas law to apply.

Sample questions:
Why is the pressure in the tires higher in the afternoon and lower in the morning?
Is there the same amount of air in the tires both times? Explain your thinking.
Has the tire changed size?
Which gas law would you use?

The increase in pressure is due to a temperature difference, both due to the air temperature and heating of the tires due to friction on the road. If the tires were about 40°F in the morning (277.6 Kelvin) and 110°F in the afternoon (316.5 K), this would account for the pressure change.

11. Wrap-up
Assist the students in summarizing what was learned in this class.
- Pressure and temperature of a gas are proportional if the volume is fixed. That is, when one gets larger, the other gets larger
- When applying the gas law equations, it is important to understand which variable is held fixed.

Homework

12. Assign the following for homework.
Use the homework provided with the curriculum or assign your own.

Homework – Investigation III – Lesson 4

1. A gas is collected in a container at a temperature of 22.0°C and 1.0 atm of pressure. Then the temperature is changed to 25.0°C. What is the new pressure?

2. A gas has a pressure of 0.370 atmospheres at 50.0°C. What is the pressure of the gas at 0°C?

3. A sample of gas at 110 atm of pressure inside a steel tank is cooled from 500.0°C to 0.00°C. What is the final pressure of the gas in the steel tank?

4. A scuba tank is at an initial pressure of 120.0 atm. Calculate the final pressure inside the tank after it cools from 1,000 °C to 25.0°C.

5. If a gas in a closed container is pressurized from 15.0 atm to 18.0 atm and its original temperature was 25.0°C, what would the final temperature of the gas be?

6. A gas is contained in a tank so that its volume does not change. If the temperature of the gas is doubled, what would happen to the pressure? Pretend the gas started out at 273 K.

Weather © UC Regents, LHS Living by Chemistry, 2003.

Egg in a Bottle

Name: _____

Period: _____ Date: _____

Purpose: This activity provides practice with the gas laws. You will explore what happens to the volume, temperature, and pressure of a quantity of air in a container with variable volume and in one with fixed volume.

Answer the following questions:

1. **Gas in a container with a volume that can change.** You fill a balloon with air to a volume of 240.0 mL. The air temperature is 25.0°C and the air pressure is 1.0 atm. You carry the balloon with you up a mountain where the air pressure is 0.75 atm and the temperature is 25.0°C.

    a) When the balloon is carried up the mountain, what changes? What stays the same?

    b) The air pressure on the outside of the balloon has decreased. Can the air pressure on the inside decrease so that the pressures are equal? Why or why not?

    c) What happens to the volume occupied by the air inside the balloon? Explain your thinking.

    d) Solve for the new volume of the balloon using Boyle's law.

    e) P vs. 1/V is a straight line that passes through the origin (0, 0). Make a graph of P vs. 1/V. Determine the new volume of the balloon from the graph. How does the volume compare with your calculation in Part d?

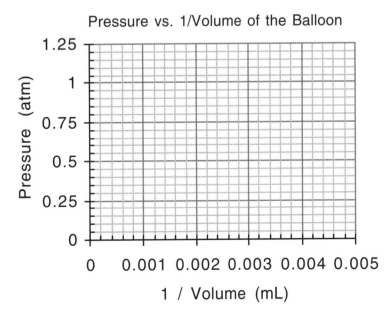

Pressure vs. 1/Volume of the Balloon

2. **Gas in a container with a volume that cannot change.** The air inside a 240 mL glass bottle is at 1.0 atm and 25.0°C when you close it. You carry the glass bottle with you up a mountain where the air pressure is 0.75 atm and the temperature is 5.0°C.

   a) The air pressure on the outside of the glass bottle has decreased. Can the volume change so that the air pressure on the inside can decrease? Why or why not?

   b) Do you expect the temperature of the air on the inside of the bottle at the top of the mountain to cool to 5°C? Explain your thinking.

   c) What happens to the pressure inside the glass bottle? Explain your thinking.

   d) Solve for the new pressure of the gas inside the glass bottle using Gay Lussac's law.

   e) P vs. T is a straight line that passes through the origin (0, 0). Make a graph of P vs. T. Determine the new pressure inside the glass bottle from the graph. How does the pressure compare with your calculation in Part d?

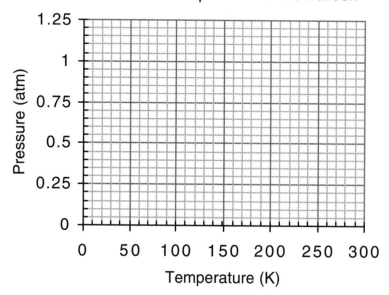

Pressure vs. Temperature of the Balloon

3. **Fill in the table.** The first line of the table gives the volume, pressure, and temperature for a container of gas. The gas starts in a container with a volume of 22.4 L. The pressure is 1.0 atm and the temperature is 300 K. Each subsequent row represents a new set of conditions for this gas. Fill in the blank spaces.

Volume	Pressure	Temperature	Gas law
$V_1 = 22.4$ L	$P_1 = 1.0$ atm	$T_1 = 300$ K	(initial conditions)
11.2 L	1.0 atm	150 K	Charles' law
44.8 L	1.0 atm		Charles' law
	1.0 atm	1200 K	
	2.0 atm	300 K	
	0.5 atm	300 K	
89.6 L		300 K	
22.4 L		150 K	
22.4 L		600 K	
	4.0 atm	1,200 K	

a) When the temperature is constant and the volume increases, what happens to the pressure? Provide an example of when this might occur.

b) When the pressure is constant and the temperature decreases, what happens to the volume? Provide an example of when this might occur.

c) When the volume is constant and the pressure increases, what happens to the temperature? Provide an example of when this might occur.

Making sense question:
Describe how the type of container affects how the pressure of the gas inside the container can vary.

If you finish early...
Use the information from the table to write a word problem. Show your answers (Hints: What is constant? What is changing?)

BEFORE CLASS...

LESSON 5 – What Goes Up...

Key Ideas:

Air pressure in the atmosphere lowers as you go up in altitude. At the same time air temperature decreases as you go up in altitude. The effect of lower air pressure is to increase the volume of an amount of gas. The effect of lower temperature is to decrease the volume of an amount of gas. Both these forces are acting upon a weather balloon as it rises in the atmosphere.

What Takes Place:

Students are introduced to weather balloons and the combined gas law. They complete a worksheet focusing on the ascent of the weather balloon. They wrestle with the question of whether the decreasing air temperature or the decreasing air pressure have a greater effect on the volume of the balloon.

Materials:

*   Student worksheet

Investigation III – Moving Matter
LESSON 5 – What Goes Up...

In this lesson students learn the combined gas law. They follow the progress of a weather balloon as it moves into the atmosphere. The balloon will have competing forces working on it. The decreasing air temperature will cause the volume of the balloon to decrease. The decreasing air pressure will cause the volume of the balloon to increase. By analyzing the volume, temperature, and pressure of the weather balloon at different points it is possible to discover which variable will affect the volume of the gas more, the temperature or the pressure.

Exploring the Topic   (10–15 min)

1. Introduce the ChemCatalyst exercise.

Write the following exercise on the board for students to complete individually.

A weather balloon is inflated to a volume of 12,500 L with helium. When it is released from the ground the air pressure is 1 atmosphere and the air temperature is 17°C.

- At a specific altitude the weather balloon pops and returns to the ground. Use your understanding of the gas laws to explain why this happens.

2. Discuss the ChemCatalyst exercise.

Use the discussion to get a sense of students' initial ideas.

Discussion goals:
Assist students in sharing their ideas on the interplay of temperature, pressure, and volume.

Sample questions:
What conditions will change as the balloon rises into the atmosphere?
How will temperature, pressure, and/or volume affect the weather balloon?
Do any of the gas laws deal with all three variables changing at once?
Which factor will affect the volume of the balloon more, temperature or pressure?

Listen to the students' ideas. They should see that all three of the gas law variables will be changing in this situation. They should begin to integrate the manner in which temperature, pressure, and volume are interrelated and affect each other. In general, as the balloon rises the air temperature and pressure should go down. The decrease in temperature causes the gas in the balloon to contract. The decrease in air pressure causes the gas in the balloon to expand. These two factors will change the volume of the balloon.

3. Introduce students to weather balloons.

Discussion goals:

Assist students in thinking about how the volume of a weather balloon will change as it rises or falls.

Sample questions:

What evidence do you have that the air temperature decreases as altitude increases? (some mountaintops have snow all year round on them)

What evidence do you have that the air pressure decreases as altitude increases? (thin air at high elevations, harder to breathe)

Are any variables staying constant in a weather balloon as it ascends? (just the amount of gas inside the balloon, all other variables are changing: V, T and P)

How do you predict the volume of a weather balloon will change as it ascends? (the balloon should get larger as the air pressure outside the balloon decreases, but the balloon should get smaller as the temperature decreases)

Which variable do you think will affect the balloon more, the temperature change or the air pressure change? In other words, will the volume of the balloon increase or decrease?

Points to cover:

Weather balloons are large balloons filled with helium or hydrogen gas that carry instruments to study the atmosphere at high altitudes. The weather balloon has three parts: the elastic balloon, the instrument package, called a radiosonde, and the parachute. Weather balloons are released twice a day from sites all around the world. There are about 900 release sites around the world; 95 of these sites are in the United States. As the balloon rises, the radiosonde measures the temperature, relative humidity, and pressure of the atmosphere. This information is relayed back to a station via a transmitter. Wind speed and wind direction are calculated from the tracking information. Data from weather balloons is fed into National Weather Service super computers across the country. This information is used to help predict weather around the country.

The pressure of the atmosphere decreases with altitude. The temperature in this region also generally decreases. We've learned that if the pressure outside the balloon decreases, we expect the balloon to expand (at constant temperature). If the temperature of the gas inside the balloon decreases, we expect the balloon to contract (at constant pressure). But temperature, pressure, and volume all change with a weather balloon. We need to combine the gas laws so that we can analyze problems in which volume, temperature, and pressure all vary.

4. Introduce the Combined Gas Law.

Discussion goals:

Assist students in thinking about how the combined gas law relates to Charles', Boyle's, and Gay Lussac's law.

Sample questions:
   What relationship do you have if $P_1 = P_2$? (Charles' law)
   What relationship do you have if $T_1 = T_2$? (Boyle's law)
   What relationship do you have if $V_1 = V_2$? (Gay Lussac's law)

Suggested points to cover:
The **Combined Gas Law** is simply a mathematical compilation of Charles' Law, Boyle's Law, and Gay-Lussac's Law. It allows us to calculate volume, temperature, or pressure when all three variables change. For the weather balloon, we can figure out V_2 if both P_1 and T_1 change. The formula for the combined gas law is:

$$\frac{P_1V_1}{T_1} = \frac{P_2V_2}{T_2}$$

In the combined gas law, the amount of gas is constant. In other words, the number of molecules of gas does not change.

5. Explain the purpose of the activity.

If you wish you can write the main question on the board.

Points to cover:
Students will be using the combined gas law to understand how gas temperature, pressure, and volume interact. The main question is: "How does changing both pressure and temperature of a gas affect the volume?"

Activity – What Goes Up...   **(15 min)**

6. Pass out worksheets. (Worksheet)

Students use the combined gas law to monitor the volume of a weather balloon as it ascends.

Answer the following questions:
A weather balloon is filled to a volume of 12,500 L at **sea level.** The air pressure is 1.0 atm and the temperature is 290 K.

1. **Example.** The weather balloon is released and travels to an altitude of **5,000 ft.** The temperature at that altitude is 278 K. The air pressure is 0.80 atm.

   a) What is the volume of the weather balloon at this altitude?
      Use the Combined Gas Law to solve for the new volume.

Combined Gas Law: $\dfrac{P_1V_1}{T_1} = \dfrac{P_2V_2}{T_2}$, $\dfrac{(1.0 \text{ atm})(12{,}500 \text{ L})}{290 \text{ K}} = \dfrac{(0.8 \text{ atm})(x)}{278 \text{ K}}$ $x = 14{,}978$ L

b) Did the volume of the balloon increase or decrease? Explain why. (The volume of the balloon increased. The air pressure decreased outside the balloon, thus the balloon expanded.)

Solve the next three problems, then fill in the table:

2. **Solve.** The balloon continues to travel upward to an altitude of **10,000 feet** where the air pressure is 0.7 atm and the temperature is 268 K. What is the volume of the weather balloon at this altitude?

3. **Solve.** The balloon continues to travel upward to an altitude of **25,000 feet** where the air pressure is 0.4 atm and the temperature is 238 K. What is the volume of the weather balloon at this altitude?

4. **Solve.** The weather balloon continues to travel upward to an altitude of **40,000 feet** where the air pressure is 0.2 atm and the temperature is 216 K. What is the volume of the weather balloon at this altitude?

Altitude (feet)	Pressure (atm)	Temperature (°F and °C)		Temperature (K)	Volume (L)
0 (sea level)	1.0 atm	63°F	17°C	290 K	12,500 L
5,000 ft	0.8 atm	41°F	5°C	278 K	14,987 L
10,000 ft	0.7 atm	23°F	–5°C	268 K	16,502 L
25,000 ft	0.4 atm	–30°F	–35°C	238 K	25,647 L
40,000 ft	0.2 atm	–70°F	–57°C	216 K	46,552 L

5. Interpret the Chart.

   a) How many degrees does the temperature change in Kelvin from sea level to 40,000 feet?

   b) How much does the pressure change in atmospheres from sea level to 40,000 feet?

   c) Which has a greater effect on the volume of the weather balloon, the temperature of the air, or the air pressure? Explain your thinking.

Making sense question
Explain why the volume of the balloon continued to increase as it rose.

Making Sense Discussion   **(15 min)**

Major goals: Assist students in examining why a weather balloon eventually bursts at high altitude and falls back to the ground. Discuss the role of air pressure and temperature in causing this to happen. Make sure students understand how to use the combined gas law.

7. Explore the vertical progress of the weather balloon.

<u>Discussion goals:</u>
Assist students in sharing their analysis of how the volume of a weather balloon changes as it ascends.

Sample questions:
What happens to the air pressure of the atmosphere with increasing altitude? (Air pressure decreases with altitude.)
What happens to the air temperature of the atmosphere with increasing altitude? (Air temperature decreases with altitude.)
Explain why the volume of the balloon increases with altitude.
Does a decrease in air temperature have any effect on the balloon? Explain. (Yes, the lower temperature does cause some contraction, but it is offset by the expansion caused by the decrease in air pressure.)
The weather balloon continues to rise no matter what conditions we imposed on it. Why? (It's full of helium.)

Points to cover:
The weather balloon rises no matter what the outside conditions. This is because the balloon is full of helium and helium is less dense than air ("lighter than air"). However, if we monitor the volume of the balloon it's possible to discover whether the air pressure or the air temperature of the atmosphere had a greater impact on the balloon.

The weather balloon expands as it rises because the relative change in air pressure is much greater than the relative change in air temperature. In other words, the decrease in air pressure in the atmosphere causes the balloon to expand. This is counteracted slightly by the decrease in temperature in the atmosphere that results in some contraction of the balloon. The net result of a large amount of expansion and small amount of contraction is that the balloon expands overall. It appears that the changing air pressure has a greater effect on the volume of the balloon than the changing air temperature.

Check-in   (5 min)

8. Complete the Check-in exercise.

Write the following question on the board for the students to complete.

A sample of neon gas occupies a volume of 1.0 L at 300 K at 1.0 atm. Suppose you increase the temperature to 600 K and the pressure increases to 4.0 atm.

- Does the volume of the gas increase or decrease? Explain your answer.
- Calculate the volume of the gas at 50°C and 4.0 atm.

9. Discuss the Check-in exercise.

Get a sense of the level of understanding by asking students to defend their choices.

Discussion goals:

Check to see that students can use the combined gas law.

Sample questions:

Which has a greater affect on volume, the increase in pressure or the increase in temperature?

Do you predict that the volume will increase or decrease?

The increase in pressure causes a decrease in volume of a factor of 4. The increase in temperature causes the volume to increase by a factor of 2. The net result is that the volume will decrease by a factor of 2. The final volume is 0.5 L.

10. Wrap-up

Assist the students in summarizing what was learned in this class.

- If volume, temperature, and pressure are all varying, then you can use the combined gas law to determine the effects of changing two variables on the third. $P_1V_1/T_1 = P_2V_2/T_2$ (Amount of gas is constant)

Homework

11. Assign homework.

Use the homework provided with the curriculum or assign your own.

Homework – Investigation III – Lesson 5

1. A gas collected at a pressure of 0.97 atm has a volume of 0.500 L. The pressure is changed to 1.0 atm. The amount of gas and the temperature of the gas are held constant.

    a) Will the volume of the gas increase or decrease? Explain.

    b) Which equation should you use to calculate the new volume of the gas?

    c) Calculate the volume of the gas at a pressure of 1.0 atm.

2. The pressure in an automobile tire was 1.0 atm at 21°C. After driving for an hour, the tire heated up to 55°C. Assume that the tire remained at constant volume and no gas escaped from the tire.

    a) Will the pressure inside the tire increase or decrease? Explain.

    b) Which equation should you use to calculate the new pressure of the tire?

    c) Calculate the pressure of the tire at 55°C.

3. The helium inside a balloon has a volume of 1.5 liters when confined under a pressure of 1.0 atm and a temperature of 25°C. The balloon floats up into the sky where the pressure is 0.95 atm and the temperature is 20°C.

    a) Will the volume of the balloon increase or decrease? Explain.

    b) Which equation should you use to calculate the new volume of the balloon?

    c) Calculate the volume of the balloon at 20°C and 0.95 atm.

5. A gas sample occupies 200 mL at 760 mmHg. What volume does the gas occupy at 400 mmHg?

6. Someone leaves a steel tank of nitrogen gas in the sun. The tank was under a pressure of 150 atm at 27°C to begin with. After several hours the internal temperature rises to 55°C. What is the pressure in the tank now?

What Goes Up...

Name: _____

Period:_____ Date: _____

Purpose: This activity will allow you to track how volume, pressure, and temperature of a gas are interrelated. You will be using the combined gas law to calculate the changes in a weather balloon.

Answer the following questions:

A weather balloon is filled to a volume of 12,500 L at **sea level**. The air pressure is 1.0 atm and the temperature is 290 K. These starting values are listed in the first row of the table below.

1. **Example.** The weather balloon is released and travels to an altitude of **5,000 feet**. The temperature at that altitude is 278 K. The air pressure is 0.8 atm.

   a) What is the volume of the weather balloon at this altitude?

   Use the Combined Gas Law to solve for the new volume.

   Combined Gas Law: $\dfrac{P_1V_1}{T_1} = \dfrac{P_2V_2}{T_2}$, $\dfrac{(1.0\ \text{atm})(12{,}500\ \text{L})}{290\ \text{K}} = \dfrac{(0.8\ \text{atm})(x)}{278\ \text{K}}$ $x = 14{,}978\ \text{L}$

   b) Did the volume of the balloon increase or decrease? Explain why. (The volume of the balloon increased. The air pressure decreased outside the balloon, thus the balloon expanded.)

Solve the next three problems, then fill in the table:

2. **Solve:** The balloon continues to travel upward to an altitude of **10,000 feet** where the air pressure is 0.7 atm and the temperature is 268 K. What is the volume of the weather balloon at this altitude?

3. **Solve:** The balloon continues to travel upward to an altitude of **25,000 feet** where the air pressure is 0.4 atm and the temperature is 238 K. What is the volume of the weather balloon at this altitude?

4. **Solve:** The weather balloon continues to travel upward to an altitude of **40,000 feet** where the air pressure is 0.2 atm and the temperature is 216.5 K. What is the volume of the weather balloon at this altitude?

Altitude (feet)	Pressure (atm)	Temperature (°F and °C)		Temperature (K)	Volume (L)
0 (sea level)	1.0 atm	63°F	17°C	290 K	12,500 L
5,000 ft	0.8 atm	41°F	5°C	278 K	
10,000 ft		23°F	–5°C		
25,000 ft		–30°F	–35°C		
40,000 ft		–70°F	–57°C		

5. Interpret the Chart.

   a) How many degrees does the temperature change in Kelvin from sea level to 40,000 feet?

   b) How much does the pressure change in atmospheres from sea level to 40,000 feet?

   c) Which has a greater effect on the volume of the weather balloon, the temperature of the air or the air pressure? Explain your thinking.

Making sense question

Explain why the volume of the balloon continued to increase as it rose.

BEFORE CLASS...

LESSON 6 – Air On the Move

Key Ideas:

Meterologists look at weather conditions in one area and then use
the motion of the air to predict the weather conditions in a target area. The key idea is
that weather in one area moves to somewhere else. Air temperature and air pressure
affect the movement of air on the planet, both laterally, and vertically. Differentials in air
pressure cause winds on the earth's surface.

What Takes Place:

Students consider how air moves both laterally and vertically. The gas laws are used to
understand air movements. They are introduced to winds.

Materials:

•   Student worksheet

Investigation III – Moving Matter
LESSON 6 – Air On the Move

In this lesson, the knowledge of the gas laws is used to think about the direction of air movement. Students predict the direction of lateral winds and consider how air is transported up and down in the atmosphere.

Exploring the Topic   (10–15 min)

1. Introduce the ChemCatalyst exercise.

Write the following exercise on the board for students to complete individually.

The morning is wind still. The sun is shining. By afternoon, breezes blow off the ocean onto the land.

- If the winds blow from the ocean to the land, where is the pressure higher? Explain your thinking.
- How does the air pressure change when air over the land warms and expands?

2. Discuss the ChemCatalyst exercise.

Use the discussion to get a sense of students' initial ideas.

Discussion goals:
Assist students in sharing their ideas on the direction of air movement.

Sample questions:
How does air pressure determine the direction wind blows?
Which warms faster, the ocean or the land? Explain your thinking. (land)
As the air warms, the volume increases. What happens to the pressure? (decreases)
Explain how to think about the change in pressure when the air temperature increases.

Listen to the students' ideas. They should say that air moves from regions of high pressure to regions of low pressure. Since the wind blows from the ocean to the land, the air over the land is at a lower pressure. The land warms faster because the specific heat capacity of water is higher. More heat is required to warm the air over the ocean. The air over the land expands as it warms, thereby decreasing the pressure.

3. Explain the purpose of the activity.

If you wish you can write the main question on the board.

Points to cover:
Students will be integrating their understanding of the gas laws and applying this understanding to the movement of air. The main question is: "What causes the motion of air in the atmosphere?"

Activity – Air On the Move   **(15 min)**

4. Pass out worksheets. (Worksheet)

Students integrate their ideas about gas laws and the movement of air.

Although air is not in a container, we can imagine an air mass with a fixed amount of air. Use the drawing to help you consider changes in the volume, temperature, and pressure of the air mass to explain air movement.

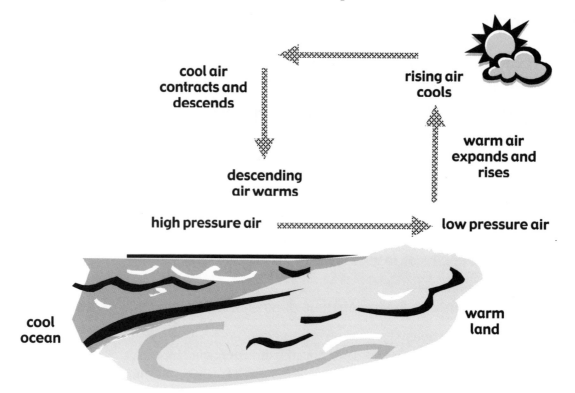

1. **Pressure and lateral air movement**

   a) The weather balloon is between a region of high pressure air and a region of low pressure air. With an arrow show the direction the balloon will travel and explain why. (see Making Sense Discussion)

b) The second picture shows the natural flow of air around the high and low pressure systems. Now predict the balloon's travel. Use an arrow to show the direction in which it will travel and explain why.

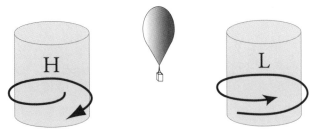

c) The temperature of the air over the land increases on a sunny day. What happens to the volume of the air? (volume increases because warm air expands)

d) Why is the pressure lower over the land compared with the ocean? (as the volume increases, the pressure decreases)

e) Why do afternoon sea breezes normally blow from the ocean across the land? (the air pressure is lower over the land)

f) Why do you think the air moves *out* from the middle of a high pressure system and *in* towards the middle of a low pressure system? (see arrows in above diagram) (the warm air in a high pressure system is expanding and the cool air in a low pressure system is contracting)

2. **Temperature and vertical air movement**

a) What happens to the density of the air as it warms? (decreases)

b) Why does warm air rise? (lower density)

c) What happens to the temperature of the rising air when it reaches higher altitudes? Explain your thinking. (it cools both because the temperature is lower at higher altitudes and also because the pressure is decreasing)

d) Air descending down a mountain slope contracts and warms. Do you predict a high or low pressure system when air is descending? Explain your thinking. (high pressure because air is contracting)

Making sense:
How do temperature and pressure affect air movement on the planet?

Making Sense Discussion   (15 min)

Major goals: Assist students in explaining how air moves laterally and vertically. Clear up any confusion that might exist.

5. Discuss air movement on the planet.

Discussion goals:
Assist students in summarizing their understanding as to what causes movement of air.

Sample questions:
  Why does warm air rise? (as air expands, the density decreases)
  Why do sea breezes blow from the ocean to the land on a sunny afternoon?
  Why is it that warm air rises and cools?
  Why is it that cool air descends and warms?

Points to cover:
Warm air tends to rise and cold air tends to fall. This is because warm air is expanding and the density is decreasing (Charles' law). Cold air is contracting and the density is increasing.

As warm air rises, the volume increases and the pressure decreases (Boyle's law). The warm air subsequently cools. This is both because the temperature is lower at high altitudes, and also because the pressure of the air is decreasing (Gay Lussac's law). Admittedly, it does seem a bit confusing that warm air rises, but then cool because the pressure decreases. We might expect the increase in volume will cause an increase in temperature, but the observations show that the pressure change is more important (combined gas law).

Likewise, as cool air descends, the volume decreases and the pressure increases (Boyle's law). The cool air subsequently warms. This is both because the temperature is higher at lower altitudes, and also because the pressure of the air is increasing (Gay Lussac's law). Admittedly, it does seem a bit confusing that cool air descends, but then warms because the pressure increases. We might expect the decrease in volume will cause a decrease in temperature, but the observations show that the pressure change is more important (combined gas law).

Notice that temperature changes drive the movement of air. Warm air rises, expands, and cools. Then cool air contracts, descends, and warms.

6. Introduce winds.

Draw the following diagrams on the board as you discuss winds.

Discussion goals:
Assist students in summarizing their understanding as to what causes winds.

Sample questions:
  What causes winds?
  Which way do you think air will move if a high pressure region is next to a low
     pressure region?

What direction(s) did you predict the balloon would travel, on your worksheet? Explain your reasoning.

What accounts for the spiraling of air out of a high pressure area and into a low pressure area?

Points to cover:

We will first concern ourselves with air movement in the lower atmosphere.

Areas of high and low pressure on the planet are the major cause of what we call **winds.** Air pressure differences start the wind blowing. The greater the difference in pressures, the stronger the force of the wind.

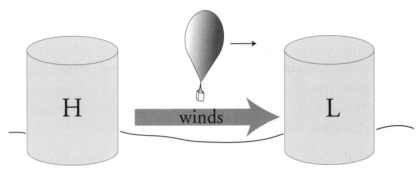

However, winds do not simply blow from an area of high pressure air straight towards an area of low pressure air. As you may recall, the air associated with a high pressure area moves in a clockwise direction around the high. The air associated with a low pressure area moves in a counter-clockwise direction around the low.

The clockwise moving air in a high pressure region is expanding and therefore is also moving *out* from the center of the high. The spiraling air in a low pressure region is contracting and thus moving *into* the center of the low.

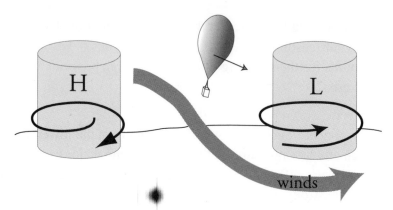

Obviously air temperature and air pressure work together to create movement of air on the planet. Movement of air up and down (vertically) is usually fairly slow. The collection of a lot of mass moving into a low pressure area causes the air to be pushed upward in the low pressure area. Thus the air moves in and up in a low pressure area. The air moves down and out in a high pressure area. Movement of air laterally (sideways across the planet) is much more vigorous and produces what we refer to as winds.

When we talk about winds it's necessary to specify the kinds of winds we are referring to. Some winds occur in the lower atmosphere and others in the upper atmosphere. So far we've focused on winds in the lower atmosphere.

7. Introduce the jet stream.

Points to cover:
When meteorologists talk about the **jet stream** they are referring to winds that are in the upper atmosphere, above 20,000 feet. These winds travel at least 57 mph and are largely responsible for pushing storms around on the planet. You may have seen weather maps with a line drawn to indicate the jet stream.

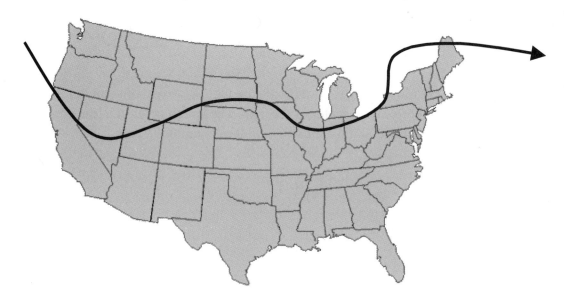

Check-in   **(5 min)**

8. Complete the Check-in exercise.

Write the following question on the board for the students to complete.

Winds tend to blow down the eastern sides of mountains. What type of weather do you expect on the eastern side?

9. Discuss the Check-in exercise.

Get a sense of the level of understanding by asking students to defend their choices.

Discussion goals:
Check to see that students can think about vertical movement of air.

Sample questions:
What happens to the pressure as air descends?
What happens to the volume?
What happens to the temperature?

Deserts are often found on the eastern sides of mountains. The desce3nding air contracts and temperature increases. The result is a high pressure system.

10. Wrap-up

Assist the students in summarizing what was learned in this class.
- Winds are caused by air moving from regions of high pressure to regions of low pressure.
- Air warmed at the earth's surface, expands, rises, and subsequently cools. This creates a low pressure system.
- Cool air descending from high altitudes, contracts, descends, and subsequently warms. This creates a high pressure system.

Homework

11. Assign homework.

Use the homework provided with the curriculum or assign your own.

Homework – Investigation III – Lesson 6

1. Look at a weather map for where you live. Use the weather map to predict the weather for tomorrow in two different locations. Check you answer tomorrow by looking at a weather map.

On the Move

Name: _____
Period:_____ Date: _____

Purpose: To integrate ideas about the gas laws and apply them to air movement.

Answer the following questions:

Although air is not in a container, we can imagine an air mass with a fixed amount of air. Use the drawing to help you consider changes in the volume, temperature, and pressure of the air mass to explain air movement.

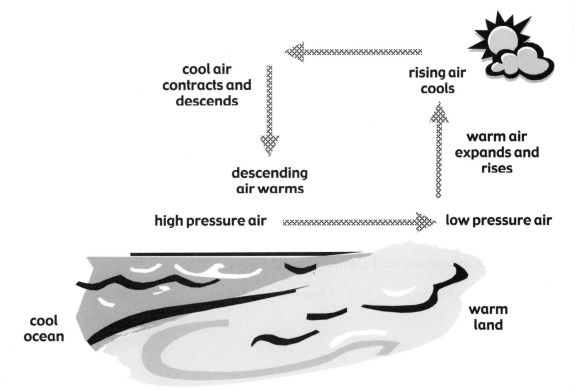

1. **Pressure and lateral air movement**

   a) The weather balloon is between a region of high pressure air and a region of low pressure air. With an arrow show the direction the balloon will travel and explain why. (see Making Sense Discussion)

b) The second picture shows the natural flow of air around the high and low pressure systems. Now predict the balloon's travel. Use an arrow to show the direction in which it will travel and explain why.

  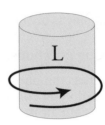

c) The temperature of the air over the land increases on a sunny day. What happens to the volume of the air?

d) Why is the pressure lower over the land compared with the ocean?

e) Why do afternoon sea breezes normally blow from the ocean across the land?

f) Why do you think the air moves *out* from the middle of a high pressure system and *in* towards the middle of a low pressure system? (see arrows in above diagram)

2. **Temperature and vertical air movement**

a) What happens to the density of the air as it warms

b) Why does warm air rise?

c) What happens to the temperature of the rising air when it reaches higher altitudes? Explain your thinking.

d) Air descending down a mountain slope contracts and warms. Do you predict a high or low pressure system when air is descending? Explain your thinking.

Making sense:
How do temperature and pressure affect air movement on the planet?

Unit 3: Weather

Investigation IV: Counting Matter

Contents of Investigation IV

Investigation IV Summary:

Counting Matter

Investigation IV consists of seven lessons that focus the amount of air (mass and number of particles). The investigation begins with an examination of the atmosphere and a discussion of how a barometer is used to measure the amount of air above you. Students learn that pressure depends on density. In the second lesson, students are introduced to Avogadro's hypothesis, and use it to determine the number of gas particles in a specific volume of gas. They find out that air pressure can be determined from the number of gas particles, regardless of their identity. In the third lesson, the mole is used as a counting unit. Students determine the number of moles in a breath in the fourth lesson. The amount of water vapor in the air is discussed in the next two lessons. The final lesson is a review that integrates gas laws, phase changes, and weather forecasting

In Investigations I, II, and III, students explored volume, density, phase, temperature, heat, and air pressure. This led to discussions of average amounts of rainfall, average temperatures in the United States, regions of high and low pressure, and wind. In Investigation IV, students learn about the importance of the number of gas particles. This allows them to think about the variable water content in the atmosphere. They can explain humidity, predict rain, and understand what sweating has to do with humidity and temperature.

Lesson 1 – Tower of Air. So far in the weather unit gases have been described by their volume, temperature, and pressure. In this investigation, we turn our attention to the amount of gas (mass and number of molecules). We begin in this lesson by exploring how the density of the air is related to the pressure. Students examine density changes of air with altitude and consider how the weight of a column of air is related to the pressure you feel if you stand below it. Students are introduced to how mercury barometers are used to measure pressure.

Lesson 2 – Lighter Than Air. In this activity students begin by observing three balloons of equal volume containing three different gases. The helium (He) balloon rises, the nitrogen (N_2) balloon falls slowly, and the carbon dioxide (CO_2) balloon falls rapidly. Students speculate on what accounts for these observations. Avogadro's hypothesis is introduced. It states that equal volumes of gas contain equal numbers of gas particles. Students investigate this hypothesis, and use it to understand why the densities of the balloons are different (why some balloons float and others sink).

Lesson 3 – More Than a Trillion. In the previous lesson, students learned that there are 6.02×10^{23} gas particles in 22.4 L at STP. This is a very large number of particles. In this lesson, students explore this number further. They are introduced to a counting unit called a mole, which chemists use to keep track of these large numbers of molecules. Students solve problems that relate moles to numbers of molecules and to numbers of atoms. The purpose of this lesson is to lay a foundation to relate moles to volume, temperature, and pressure and introduce the ideal gas law in the next lesson.

Lesson 4 – Take a Breath. In the previous lesson, students learned that chemists use a counting unit called a mole. In this lesson, students are introduced to the ideal gas law, $PV = nRT$. In this equation, n stands for number of moles of gas particles. In this activity students consider how pressure is related to the number of moles of particles in a gas. The activity begins with an experiment to determine the volume of one breath of air. This volume is then used to determine the number of moles of air in a breath at sea level and on a mountaintop. Students discuss why it is harder to breathe on a mountaintop.

Lesson 5 – Up in the Clouds. In this lesson, students explore the variable water vapor content in the atmosphere. Meteorologists refer to the amount of water vapor in the air as humidity. During the activity students create their own miniature cloud in a bottle. They consider how the moles of water vapor, the pressure, and temperature determine whether a cloud will form or not. Humidity is defined as the number of moles of water vapor per liter of air.

Lesson 6 – Rain in the Forecast. In this lesson students explore how the amount of water vapor in the air varies with temperature, and how this variation affects the weather. First they examine a graph of the maximum number of moles of water vapor per liter of air at a given temperature. This graph is then used to predict if it will rain, if dew will form, and at what altitude clouds will form depending on the moles of water vapor per liter of air. This is followed by a discussion of the interplay between temperature and humidity in determining how hot you feel.

BEFORE CLASS...

LESSON 1 – Tower of Air

Key Ideas:

The atmosphere is a large envelope of gas particles around the planet. About 99% of the air on the planet is located below 30,000 meters in altitude. As altitude increases, the density of the gas particles decreases. Mercury is a very dense liquid. It is so dense that a column of mercury 0.76 meters high (30 inches high) can offset the pressure in 30,000 meters of air. Mercury is commonly used in barometers to measure air pressure.

What Takes Place:

Students will observe a demonstration at the beginning of class that show the force of the pressure of the atmosphere. Then they are quickly introduced to the instrument most commonly used to measure air pressure – the barometer. They complete a worksheet that allows them to compare the pressure exerted by different substances by virtue of their densities. This leads students to understand why mercury works well as a substance to measure air pressure.

Materials: (per class)

- Student worksheet
- 2 full sheets of newspaper
- 1 wooden or plastic ruler

Investigation IV – Counting Molecules

LESSON 1 – Tower of Air

So far in the weather unit gases have been described by their volume, temperature, and pressure. In this investigation, we turn our attention to the amount of gas (mass and number of molecules). We begin in this lesson by exploring how the density of the air is related to the pressure. Students examine density changes of air with altitude and consider how the weight of a column of air is related to the pressure you feel if you stand below it. Students are introduced to how mercury barometers are used to measure pressure.

Exploring the Topic   (5–10 min)

1. Introduce the ChemCatalyst exercise.

Write the following exercise on the board for students to complete individually.

- What is the atmosphere? What is it made of?
- How big is the atmosphere? How do we measure it?

2. Discuss the ChemCatalyst exercise.

Use the discussion to get a sense of students' initial ideas.

<u>Discussion goals:</u>
Assist students in sharing their ideas about the composition and size of the atmosphere.

Sample questions:
   What does the atmosphere consist of?
   How big is the atmosphere?
   How do we measure the atmosphere?
   Why does air pressure change with altitude?

3. Complete the demonstration.

You may wish to have student volunteers assist you with this demonstration.

Materials:
Wooden or plastic ruler
Four full sheets of newspaper

Suggested demonstration:
Place the ruler on a tabletop with the end of it sticking out over the edge approximately two to three inches. Lay two sheets of newspaper on top of the ruler – the paper should be completely unfolded. Ask students what will happen if you strike the overhanging end of the ruler with a small amount of force. After they predict, go ahead and complete this step. Then set the ruler up again, and

place the other two sheets of newspaper over the ruler, this time with the sheets of newspaper folded three times (it should be one-eighth the size of the full newspaper). Ask them what will happen this time if you strike the end of the ruler. Repeat as needed.

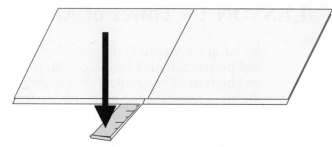

The air around us has mass and presses down on everything. The unfolded newspaper had a much greater surface area for the air to press down on. More molecules of air were above the unfolded newspaper. In fact, since the surface area of the unfolded paper was eight times larger than the folded paper, the unfolded paper has eight times the air pressure on it.

Discussion goals:
Assist students in sharing their ideas about what happened in the demonstration.

Sample questions:
Is the weight of the paper the same in both cases?
Why wasn't the unfolded paper as easy to move as the folded paper?
What effect did the atmosphere have on the outcome?
Can you feel the pressure of the air on your body? Why or why not?

4. Introduce a barometer to the class.

Draw a picture of a simple mercury barometer on the board.

mercury is pushed up

Points to cover:
A mercury barometer is a common tool of the meteorologist. It measures the atmospheric air pressure. A sealed glass tube is filled with mercury. There is no air in the tube at all. The tube is then inverted in a dish of mercury. The air pressure on the outside of the tube supports the mercury. When the air pressure decreases, the mercury goes down in the tube. When the air pressure increases the mercury goes back up the tube. By noting when the barometer is rising or falling, and measuring the height of the column of mercury, meteorologist can tell when a low or a high pressure area is in the region. Today's activity will explore how a column of mercury can be used to measure the air pressure of the earth's atmosphere.

air pushes down

5. Explain the purpose of the activity.

If you wish you can write the main question on the board.

Points to cover:

Tell students they will be exploring how the atmosphere is measured. They will be answering the question, "How does a column of mercury measure the air pressure on the earth?"

Activity – Tower of Air   (15 min)

6. Pass out the worksheet. (Worksheet)

Tell students they will be considering the pressure exerted by different substances.

Answer the following questions:

1. The figure shows the height of the atmosphere above sea level. Two columns of air are shown, one beginning at sea level and the other beginning on a mountaintop. The columns end at 30,000 m because 99% of the atmosphere is below this altitude.

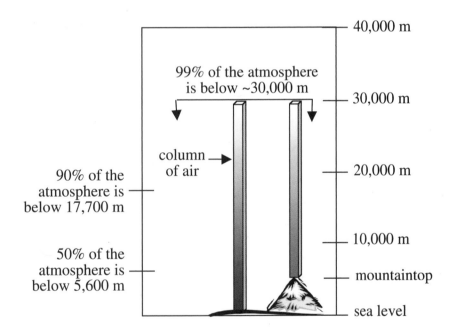

a) What percent of the atmosphere is above 5,600 m? (50%)

b) What is the air pressure in atmospheres at the top of the mountain? (0.5 atm)

c) What is the height in meters of the column of air above 5,600 m? (30,000 – 5,600 = 24,400 m)

d) What percent of the atmosphere is above 17,700 m? (10%)

e) What is the air pressure in atmospheres at 17,700 m? (0.1 atm)

2. **Air.** The table gives the height of various columns of air, and the pressure they exert.

Substance	Altitude	Height of the air in m	Height of the air in ft	Density of the air above	Air pressure
air	sea level	30,000 m	99,000 m	0.00034 g/cm^3	1.0 atm
air	5,600 m	24,400 m	80,500 ft	0.00022 g/cm^3	0.5 atm
air	11,000 m	19,000 m	62,700 ft	0.00013 g/cm^3	0.25 atm
air	17,700 m	12,300 m	40,600 ft	0.00008 g/cm^3	0.1 atm

a) What happens to the density of the air as the altitude increases? Explain why. (the density decreases – there are less gas particles per liter of air)

b) Using the table give two reasons why the air pressure decreases as the altitude increases. (The column of air above is shorter and the air is less dense.)

3. **Water.** The table gives the height of various columns of water, and the pressure they exert.

Substance	Height of the water in m	Height of the water in ft	Density	Pressure
water	10.3 m	34.0 ft	1.0 g/cm^3	1.0 atm
water	20.6 m	68.0 ft	1.0 g/cm^3	2.0 atm
water	103 m	340 ft	1.0 g/cm^3	10.0 atm

a) If you have a column of air above you that is 30,000 m, the pressure is 1.0 atm. What is the height of a column of water that exerts the same pressure? (10.3 m)

b) Explain why a column of air that exerts 1.0 atm pressure is not the same height as a column of water that exerts the same pressure. (water is denser so there is more mass in a shorter column)

c) If you were 10.3 m deep in the ocean below sea level, the pressure would be 2.0 atm. Explain why. (10.3 m of water exerts 1.0 atm plus there is a column of air above the water exerting 1.0 atm – the total is 2.0 atm)

d) The average depth of the ocean is 13,200 ft. What is the pressure at this depth? (1 atm is 34.0 ft, so the pressure at 13,200 ft is 13,200/34.0 = 388 atm)

4. **Mercury.** Atmospheric pressure is often measured by determining the height of a column of mercury. The weight of the atmosphere pushes down on the liquid in the container, which pushes mercury up the tube as shown in the figure. The table gives the height of a column of mercury, and the pressure it exerts.

Substance	Height of the mercury in m	Height of the mercury in ft	Density	Pressure
mercury	0.76 m	2.5 ft	13.6 g/cm^3	1.0 atm

a) What is the height of the column of mercury in meters if the pressure is 1.0 atm? (0.76 m)

b) What is the height of the column of mercury in inches if the pressure is 1.0 atm? (30.0 inches)

c) If the weather report gives an air pressure of 29.5 inches of mercury at sea level, is the air pressure high or low? Explain. (low because this is less than 1.0 atm)

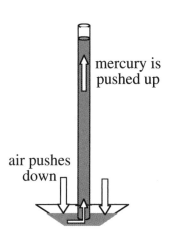

mercury is pushed up

air pushes down

Making sense question:
Why does the density of the air decrease as altitude increases?
Why isn't water used in a barometer?

If you finish early...
Explain how it might be possible to use a barometer to figure out how high above sea level a geographic location is.

Making Sense Discussion   (15 min)

Major goals: In this discussion students should consolidate their understanding of a mercury barometer and how it can be used to measure air pressure. In addition students should begin to focus on the number of molecules in the air, rather than just the mass of each particle. The notion that density can be thought of as number of particles per unit of volume as well as mass per unit volume should be presented. Finally, the composition of the earth's atmosphere should be discussed.

7. Discuss how pressure is measured.

Sketch a mercury barometer on the board.

<u>Discussion goals:</u>
Assist students in sharing how a mercury barometer works.

Suggested questions:

How is a column of mercury used to measure air pressure?

What height of air is being offset by a column of mercury 30.0 inches high? (all of the atmosphere, 30,000 meters)

When the air pressure is 0.5 atm, how high will the column of mercury be? (15 inches, 0.38 meters)

Why is mercury used instead of water to measure air pressure? (mercury has a higher density – it would take a lot more water)

How big would a water barometer have to be to measure air pressure? (~34 feet)

Why is it only necessary to measure the height and not the volume of a column of mercury? (Hint: Pressure is a force per unit area.)

Points to cover:

The mercury barometer was developed in the 17th century. The word barometer is derived from the Greek words "baros" meaning weight and "metron" meaning measure. An Italian scientist named Evangelista Torricelli (1608-1647) is credited with designing the first barometer. Torricelli was convinced that weather changes were associated with changes in air pressure. He built on the work of Galileo, who was interested in proving that a vacuum (a space with nothing in it) could exist.

Torricelli used water in his first barometer, which was in the shape of a large 34 foot tube sticking out of his house. Remember, the reason the tube was so large is because the pressure of the atmosphere is able to hold up a column of water about 34 feet high. However, Torricelli's neighbors were concerned that he was up to some sort of sorcery or witchcraft. Torricelli was interested in avoiding any problems with church authorities. Torricelli decided to find a liquid that would allow him to be a bit more secretive about his experiment. He decided that mercury would have enough density to allow for a much shorter tube than the water. The density of mercury is 13.5 grams/cm2. The density of water is 1.0 grams/cm2. Thus, the mercury barometer should be approximately one thirteenth the size of the water barometer. This is true. If we divide 34 feet by 13.5 we get 2.5 feet. This is the size of a mercury barometer.

Barometers are usually read in millimeters of mercury or inches of mercury (not feet). One atmosphere of pressure is equal to 760 mm of mercury or 29.92 inches of mercury. These units are written as shown below: Many gas law problems will report air pressure in millimeters of mercury.

$$1 \text{ atm} = 760 \text{ mm Hg} = 29.92 \text{ in. Hg} = 14.7 \text{ lbs/ in}^2 \text{ of pressure.}$$

8. Discuss how the amount of air is related to air pressure.

Have students draw a picture of how the density of air changes with altitude?

Discussion goals:

Assist students in thinking about density in terms of numbers of particles.

Sample questions:
  Does the density of a solid change with altitude? Explain.
  How does the density of the air change with altitude? Draw a picture to
    illustrate.
  Why is air at high altitudes called "thin air"?
  Air that is less dense is harder to breathe. Explain why.
  When you think about gas density are you considering the mass of the
    molecules or the number of gas particles?

Points to Cover:
There are two ways to look at the density of a substance. We can either consider
the mass per volume or the number of particles per volume. This second way of
looking at density is sometimes referred to as **number density.** During this
activity we have used the term density in both ways. Sometimes we have referred
to the density of the actual element or compound, like mercury
or water. Other times we have referred to the density of the
atmosphere. Apparently, the actual mass of the individual gas
molecules is not changing with altitude. But, the number of gas
particles is changing. Remember that when we heated water it
expanded. Thus, its density changed by virtue of the fact that
the molecules were farther apart. Recall that this is how a
thermometer works. Gas molecules are even more free to
move away from each other. There is a lot of space between
them, unlike liquids and solids.

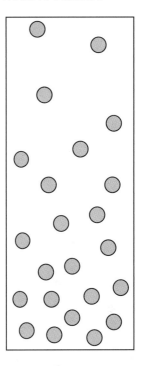

Note that in the picture we have drawn, the number of gas
particles in a certain space seems an easy way to think about
the density of the air at any particular altitude. Gas particles
are very small and difficult to count. Nevertheless, chemists
have figured out how to keep track of the number of gas
molecules (referred to as "n") in a certain space. We will be
learning about "n" in the next few lessons.

9. Discuss the composition of the atmosphere.

Points to cover:
The earth's atmosphere has many different gases in it. The most important gases,
in terms of their effects on the health of the earth, are nitrogen, oxygen, water
vapor, carbon dioxide, methane, nitrous oxide, and ozone. Nitrogen and oxygen
make up 99% of the dry atmosphere, with nitrogen being the most abundant gas at
78%. The atmosphere also contains argon, neon, helium, and hydrogen gases.
Obviously, because we drive a lot of cars, burn a lot of fossil fuels in power
plants, and release substances from factories, there is also **particulate matter** in
the air. Particulate matter refers to tiny particles that are not gases, but are small
enough to be airborne. These include carbon, sulfates, nitrates, metals, acids and

other compounds. Because of their small size, airborne particles can remain in the atmosphere for weeks or months and may be transported thousands of miles.

Some of the substances in the air are considered **pollutants.** They are harmful to humans and to life on the planet. Many air pollutants are regulated by the federal government. These pollutants are measured and the results are reported to the public. The Air Quality Index (AIQ) has become a part of many weather forecasts. This index tells you how clean or dirty the air is on a given day and advises high risk people when to restrict their physical activities.

Check-in   (5 min)

10. Complete the Check-in exercise.
Write the following question on the board for students to complete individually.

- Why is mercury used in a barometer and not alcohol or water or some other liquid?

11. Discuss the Check-in exercise.
Get a sense of the level of understanding by asking students to defend their choices.

Discussion goals:
Make sure students understand how a barometer measures air pressure.

Suggested questions:
  What is it about mercury that makes it a good substance for measuring air pressure?

12. Wrap-up
Assist the students in summarizing what was learned in this class.
- A mercury barometer is used to measure the air pressure of the atmosphere because of its high density.
- The atmosphere becomes less dense with altitude. There are less gas particles per volume as altitude increases.
- The atmosphere consists mostly of nitrogen and oxygen gases.

Homework

13. Assign the following for homework.
Use the homework provided with the curriculum or assign your own.

Homework – Investigation IV – Lesson 5

1. If 1 atmosphere = 760 mm Hg, figure out the values of each of these in mm Hg:

    a. 0.5 atm

    b. 0.1 atm

    c. 0.75 atm

    d. 0.2 atm

2. Do some research – either on the internet or in a book. Find out the names of the different layers of the earth's atmosphere. Answer the following:

    a. What is the name of each layer?

    b. How thick is each layer?

    c. What are the major differences between these atmospheric layers?

    d. Which layer or layers contain most of the earth's atmosphere? Explain.

Tower of Air

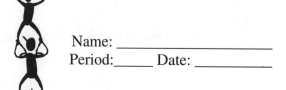

Name: _____

Period:_____ Date: _____

Purpose: This lesson allows you to explore why mercury is used in barometers to measure air pressure.

Answer the following questions:

1. The figure shows the height of the atmosphere above sea level. Two columns of air are shown, one beginning at sea level and the other beginning on a mountaintop. The columns end at 30,000 m because 99% of the atmosphere is below this altitude.

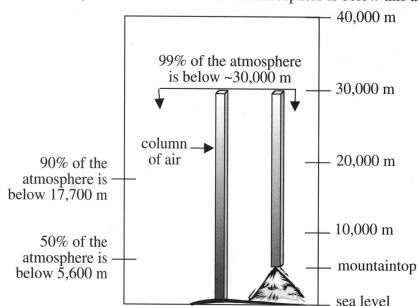

a) What percent of the atmosphere is above 5,600 m?

b) What is the air pressure in atmospheres at the top of the mountain?

c) What is the height in meters of the column of air above 5,600 m?

d) What percent of the atmosphere is above 17,700 m?

e) What is the air pressure in atmospheres at 17,700 meters?

2. **Air.** The table gives the height of various columns of air, and the pressure they exert.

Substance	Altitude	Height of the air in m	Height of the air in ft	Density of the air above	Air pressure
air	sea level	30,000 m	99,000 m	0.00034 g/cm^3	1.0 atm
air	5,600 m	24,400 m	80,500 ft	0.00022 g/cm^3	0.5 atm
air	11,000 m	19,000 m	62,700 ft	0.00013 g/cm^3	0.25 atm
air	17,700 m	12,300 m	40,600 ft	0.00008 g/cm^3	0.1 atm

Weather © UC Regents, LHS Living by Chemistry, 2003.

a) What happens to the density of the air as the altitude increases? Explain why.

b) Using the table give two reasons why the air pressure decreases as the altitude increases.

3. **Water.** The table gives the height of various columns of water, and the pressure they exert..

Substance	Height of the water in m	Height of the water in ft	Density	Pressure
water	10.3 m	34.0 ft	1.0 g/cm^3	1.0 atm
water	20.6 m	68.0 ft	1.0 g/cm^3	2.0 atm
water	103 m	340 ft	1.0 g/cm^3	10.0 atm

a) If you have a column of air above you that is 30,000 m, the pressure is 1.0 atm. What is the height of a column of water that exerts the same pressure?

b) Explain why a column of air that exerts 1.0 atm pressure is not the same height as a column of water that exerts the same pressure?

c) If you were 10.3 m deep in the ocean below sea level, the pressure on you would be 2.0 atm. Explain why.

d) The average depth of the ocean is 13,200 ft. What is the pressure at this depth?

4. **Mercury.** Atmospheric pressure is measured by determining the height of a column of mercury. The weight of the atmosphere pushes down on the liquid in the container, which pushes mercury up the tube as shown in the figure. The table gives the height of a column of mercury, and the pressure it exerts.

Substance	Height of the mercury in m	Height of the mercury in ft	Density	Pressure
mercury	0.76 m	2.5 ft	13.6 g/cm^3	1.0 atm

a) What is the height of the column of mercury in meters if the pressure is 1.0 atm?

b) What is the height of the column of mercury in inches if the pressure is 1.0 atm?

c) If the weather report gives an air pressure of 29.5 inches of mercury at sea level, is the air pressure high or low? Explain.

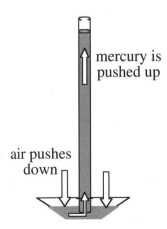

mercury is pushed up

air pushes down

Making sense question:

Why does the density of the air decrease as altitude increases?

Why isn't water used in a barometer?

If you finish early…
Explain how it might be possible to use a barometer to figure out how high above sea level a geographic location is.

BEFORE CLASS…

LESSON 2 – Lighter Than Air

Key Ideas:

An Italian scientist, Amadeo Avogadro, hypothesized that equal volumes of gases contain equal numbers of gas particles. This became known as Avogadro's Hypothesis. At a standard pressure of 1 atmosphere and a standard temperature of 273 K, 22.4 liters of *any* gas will contain 6.02×10^{23} gas particles. This is known as Avogadro's Number. One atmosphere of pressure and 273 K are referred to as standard temperature and pressure for a gas, and represented by the notation STP.

What Takes Place:

Students observe the behavior of three different gases in balloons of equal volume. They speculate on what causes one of the balloons to float and the others to fall. Avogadro's Hypothesis is introduced. Then a worksheet is distributed and students examine data for several gases.

Materials:

* Student worksheet
* 3 balloons
* Nitrogen gas, helium gas, carbon dioxide gas (air can be substituted for nitrogen gas and carbon dioxide can be generated from the reaction of baking soda and vinegar)

Investigation IV – Counting Molecules
LESSON 2 – Lighter Than Air

In this activity students begin by observing three balloons of equal volume containing three different gases. The helium (He) balloon rises, the nitrogen (N_2) balloon falls slowly, and the carbon dioxide (CO_2) balloon falls rapidly. Students speculate on what accounts for these observations. Avogadro's hypothesis is introduced. It states that equal volumes of gas contain equal numbers of gas particles. Students investigate this hypothesis, and use it to understand why the densities of the balloons are different (why some balloons float and others sink).

Exploring the Topic   (5–10 min)

1. Introduce the ChemCatalyst exercise.

Write the following exercise on the board for students to complete individually.

- Why do you suppose meteorologists use helium and hydrogen for weather balloons?
- Which gas would cause the weather balloon to rise faster? Explain the reasoning behind your answer.

2. Discuss the ChemCatalyst exercise.

Use the discussion to get a sense of students' initial ideas.

Discussion goals:
Assist students in sharing their initial ideas about differences between gases.

Sample questions:
What makes helium and hydrogen good for weather balloons?
Which gas would cause the weather balloon to rise faster? Explain.
What things are different about a liter of helium gas and a liter of hydrogen gas?
If the volume, temperature, and pressure are the same for both gases, which weather balloon will have more mass? Explain your thinking.
Which weather balloon contains more gas particles? (Assume the volume, temperature, and pressure are identical.) Explain your answer.
Would carbon dioxide gas work well for a weather balloon? Why or why not?

Students will probably say that the He and H balloons float because they are lighter than air. It is important to check out what "lighter than air" means for the students. Students may mention that hydrogen and helium have different densities. They may also mention differences in the masses of individual gas particles or differences in the numbers of gas particles, or both. (Note: Technically, floating and sinking have to do with density (mass per volume), not just mass. However, since the volumes are the same, we can talk about mass to simplify the discussion.)

3. Complete the balloon demonstration.

You will need to have 3 balloons available for a demonstration.

Suggested demonstration:
Fill three party balloons with equal volumes of three different gases – helium, nitrogen, and carbon dioxide. Inform students that the three balloons have the same volume, pressure, and temperature. You may wish to label each balloon with a permanent marker to show its contents. Release the balloons to show how they rise or fall. The helium balloon will rise, the nitrogen balloon will fall slowly, and the carbon dioxide balloon will fall quickly.

[Note: The three balloons do not need to be exactly the same volume, they simply need to look like they are the same volume. Air can be substituted for pure nitrogen. It is also okay to omit the carbon dioxide balloon, although it is useful for students to see how quickly it falls. A carbon dioxide balloon can be made by reacting baking soda and vinegar in a small bottle with a balloon attached; the carbon dioxide gas produced will inflate the balloon.]

Discussion goals:
Assist students in articulating their explanations for the behavior of the three balloons.

Sample questions:
 What happened when the balloons were released?
 What do you think accounts for the different behaviors of the three balloons?

4. Introduce Avogadro's hypothesis.

Points to cover
In 1811, Amadeo Avogadro, building on the work of Gay-Lussac, hypothesized that equal volumes of gases at the same temperature and pressure contain equal numbers of particles. In this case the term particle refers to either an individual gas atom or a gas molecule. **Avogadro's Hypothesis,** as it came to be called, was not truly embraced by the scientific community for another fifty years. This is because it was not easy to prove. Gas particles are too small and too numerous to count directly. Avogadro's Hypothesis is quite useful in extending understanding of the behavior of gases.

If we apply Avogadro's Hypothesis to the situations we have been considering then all of the balloons we've talked about today have the same number of gas particles. This is because they all have the same volume. Remember, the nitrogen balloon will contain molecules with two atoms because nitrogen gas is N_2. The helium balloon, on the other hand, will contain individual He atoms. If the volumes of both balloons are identical, then the two balloons will have exactly the same number of gas particles. To state another way: in two balloons of equal volume # of N_2 molecules = # of He atoms.

> **Avogadro's Hypothesis:** Equal volumes of gases at the same temperature and pressure contain equal numbers of gas particles (atoms or molecules).

5. Explain the purpose of the activity.

If you wish you can write the main question on the board.

Points to cover:
Tell students they will apply Avogadro's Hypothesis in order to determine the relationship between the number of gas particles and the mass, volume, and identity of the gas. They will try to answer the following question: "What is the relationship between the number of gas particles, the mass, and volume of different gases?"

Activity – Lighter Than Air   (15 min)

6. Pass out the worksheets. (Worksheet)

Answer the following questions:

Consider these 5 balloons. They are filled with helium (He), nitrogen (N_2), and carbon dioxide (CO_2). The pressure for all 5 balloons is 1.0 atm and the temperature is 273 K.

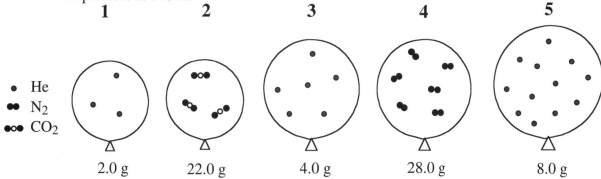

1. Which balloon(s) has/have the most gas particles? (Balloon 5)
2. Which balloon(s) has/have the most total atoms? (Balloons 4 and 5)
3. The volumes of Balloon 3 and Balloon 4 are the same. Explain why. (same number of particles)
4. The masses of Balloon 3 and Balloon 4 are different. Explain why. (the particles have different masses)

5. The volume of Balloon 2 is the same as Balloon 1, but smaller than Balloon 5. Explain why. (the number of particles are the same in Balloon 1 and 2, so they have the same volume)

6. The mass of Balloon 2 is larger than both Balloon 1 and Balloon 5. Explain why. (because CO_2 has more mass than He)

7. How could you have a helium balloon with the same mass as Balloon 2?

Use Avogadro's Hypothesis to complete the table below:

gas	# of particles	mass	volume	pressure	temperature
He	6.02×10^{23}	4.0 g	22.4 L	1.0 atm	273 K
He	12.04×10^{23}	8.0 g	44.8 L	1.0 atm	273 K
He	3.01×10^{23}	2.0 g	11.2 L	1.0 atm	273 K
N_2	6.02×10^{23}	28.0 g	22.4 L	1.0 atm	273 K
N_2	3.01×10^{23}	14.0 g	11.2 L	1.0 atm	273 K
N_2	6.02×10^{23}	28.0 g	11.2 L	2.0 atm	273 K
CO_2	6.02×10^{23}	44.0 g	22.4 L	1.0 atm	273 K
CO_2	3.01×10^{23}	22.0 g	11.2 L	1.0 atm	273 K

8. When you have a balloon that has a volume of 22.4 L at 1.0 atm and 273 K, how many particles does it have? (6.02×10^{23} particles)

9. What is the relationship between the volume of a particular gas and its mass? (proportional, when one doubles the other doubles)

10. What is the relationship between the mass of a particular gas and the number of gas particles? (proportional, when one doubles the other doubles)

11. Does the identity of the gas change the number of particles in 22.4 liters?

12. How would you write 6.02×10^{23} as a whole number instead of in scientific notation? (602,000,000,000,000,000,000,000)

13. Three balloons have the same volume, pressure, and temperature. A helium (He) balloon has a mass of 4.0 g, a nitrogen (N_2) balloon has a mass of 28.0 g, and a carbon dioxide (CO_2) balloon has a mass of 44.0 g. How do these masses relate to the atomic masses given on the periodic table? (The mass of He is 4.0 amu. The mass of N_2 is 2(14.0) amu = 28.0 amu. The mass of CO_2 is 2(16.0) + 12.0 = 44.0 amu)

14. Suppose you want to make an air mixture that has 4 nitrogen (N_2) molecules for every 1 oxygen (O_2) molecule.

   a) If you have 6.02×10^{23} O_2 molecules, how many N_2 molecules will you need? (4 times as many = 2.408×10^{24})

   b) If you have 100 L of N_2, how many liters of O_2 will you need? (one fourth as much = 25 L at 1.0 atm and 273 K)

Making sense question:
You have: 5.0 L of methane (CH_4) at 30°C and 1.0 atm, and
       5.0 L of oxygen (O_2) at 30°C and 1.0 atm.
List at least three things that are the same. (temperature, pressure, volume, number of particles)
List at least three things that are different. (mass of one particle, density, identity of the gas particles)
(Consider the volume, temperature, pressure, number of gas particles, identities of the gas particles, mass, and density.)

If you finish early…
Suppose you have 100 L of humid air at 30°C, and 100 L of dry air at 30°C. Which is denser? Explain your reasoning.

Making Sense Discussion   (15 min)

Major goals: The main goal of this discussion is to articulate the implications of Avogadro's Hypothesis for gases. Students should clearly understand that if two gases have the same pressure, volume, and temperature, then they have the same number of gas particles independent of the identity of the gases. The concept of standard temperature and pressure (STP) should be introduced, as well as Avogadro's number. Finally, students should consider why the densities of different gases of equal volume are different.

7. Discuss the numbers of gas particles.
This discussion should lead to an introduction of Avogadro's number. You will probably want to write Avogadro's number on the board.

Discussion goals:
Discuss the numbers of gas particles in 22.4 L at 1 atm and 273 K.

Sample questions:
   How many gas particles are in balloons that are 22.4 liters in volume if they are at 1 atm, and 273 K? (6.02×10^{23})
   Is 6.02×10^{23} a large number or a small number? (very large – 602,000,000,000,000,000,000,000
   What is inaccurate about the sketches showing gas particles in the balloons? (the number of particles shown is way too small)

Does the identity of the gas change the number of gas particles in 22.4 L? Explain.

Do you think 22.4 L of liquid water has more or less particles than 22.4 L of helium gas? Explain.

Points to cover

If the volume, pressure, and temperature of two gases are the same, then they have the same number of particles. Thus, it is not necessary to know the identity of the gas to determine the number of gas particles. This is because the gas particles are so far apart from one another that their individual sizes do not change the total volume. This is not true for a liquid or solid because the individual atoms are packed together so that their sizes do affect volume.

It is very useful to know that equal volumes of gases at equal temperatures and pressures contain the same number of gas particles. Once you know this, it is possible to count gas molecules simply by knowing the relationship between number, volume, temperature, and pressure. If you have 22.4 L of a gas at 1 atm and 273 K, then there will be 6.02×10^{23} gas particles present, *regardless of the identity of the gas*. This number, 6.02×10^{23} is also known as **Avogadro's number.**

This is a very large number, equivalent to 602,000,000,000,000,000,000,000 gas particles. Note that the sketches of the balloons on the worksheet did not show the correct total number of gas particles. However, the proportions of particles to each other are correct. That is, if one balloon has 3 particles and another has 6 particles, then there are twice as many particles in the second balloon.

8. Introduce standard temperature and pressure, STP.

Points to cover:

You may have noticed that we keep referring to one atmosphere of pressure and 273 Kelvin. In order to be consistent in comparing gases, scientists decided to set a standard set of conditions under which gases could be measured and compared. These conditions came to be known as **standard temperature and pressure, or STP.** In the future whenever we refer to STP in a gas problem, the conditions will be 1 atm and 273 K.

> **Standard temperature and pressure, STP,** is 1 atm and 273 K. At STP, 6.02×10^{23} gas particles occupy 22.4 L. This is true for *any* gas.

9. Review orders of magnitude.

Optional: You may wish to take the time to make sure students know what exponential numbers represent and how to use their calculators with this type of notation.

Discussion goals:
Assist students in understanding and translating exponential numbers.

Sample questions:
  Which is larger, 1000 or 10^6? (10^6)
  How much is 10^6? Write it out. (1,000,000 or a million)
  Which is larger, 10^4 or 10^5? (10^5 = 100,000)
  Which is larger, 10^6 or 10^{-12}? (1,000,0000 vs. 0.000000000012)
  Which is larger, 1.204×10^{24} or 6.02×10^{23}? (1.204×10^{24} = 12.04×10^{23})
  Which is smaller, 10^{-3} or 10^{-4}? (10^{-3} = 0.001)
  How to do you enter 6.02×10^{23} in your calculator?
  What is the product of $4 \times 6.02 \times 10^{23}$? ($2.4 \times 10^{24}$) Is the product bigger
    or smaller?

Take the time necessary to ensure that your students can use their calculators to translate back
and forth between the exponential notation and the number written out. Circulate around the
room and have the students help each other to figure out their own calculators.

10. Revisit the ChemCatalyst and demonstration.

Discussion goals:
Assist students in applying the Avogadro hypothesis to the earlier
balloon demonstration.

Sample questions:
  Now that we know that the three balloons at the beginning of class all
    contain the same number of particles, what accounts for the different
    floating and falling behavior?
  Explain how two gases can have the same number of particles and volumes
    but different densities.
  Will a hydrogen (H_2) balloon (at the same volume, temperature, and
    pressure as the other balloons) float or sink? What about a xenon (Xe)
    balloon? (hydrogen will float, xenon will sink)
  Predict what a methane (CH_4) balloon would do, float or sink. Explain.
    (float)
  List three gases that you might use in a weather balloon if you want the
    balloon to rise.

Points to cover:
Different gases at the same volume, temperature, and pressure have the same
number of particles. However, the densities of different gases are not the same
because the individual gas particles have different masses. If the density of a
gas is less than that of air, then a balloon filled with the gas will rise. (Air is
mainly nitrogen (N_2).) If the density of a gas is greater than that of air, then
the balloon will sink.

Check-in   **(5 min)**

11. Complete the Check-in exercise.

Write the following exercise on the board for the students to complete individually.

One balloon has 22.4 L of Ar and another balloon has 22.4 L of Ne gas. Both balloons are at STP.

- Are the balloons the same volume?
- Do the balloons contain the same number of particles? Why or why not?
- Will the balloons have the same mass? Why or why not?

12. Discuss the Check-in exercise.

Get a sense of the level of understanding by asking students to defend their choices.

<u>Discussion goals</u>
Check to see that students understand Avogadro's Hypothesis

Suggested questions
   If the volumes are the same, what does Avogadro's Hypothesis suggest
      about the numbers of gas particles?
   How does the mass of a molecule of Ar differ from Ne?

If both balloons have equal volumes, pressures, and temperatures, then both have the same number of gas particles. However, the mass will not be the same because Ar has a higher atomic mass compared with Ne.

13. Wrap-up

Assist the students in summarizing what was learned in this class.

- Avogadro's hypothesis states that equal volumes of gases contain the same number of molecules if they are at the same temperature and pressure, independent of the identity of the gas.
- Standard temperature and pressure is defined as 1 atmosphere and 273 K.

Homework

14. Assign the following for homework.

Use the homework provided with the curriculum or assign your own.

Homework – Investigation IV – Lesson 2

1. Which has more particles, 8.0 g of He or 40.0 g of Ar? Explain your reasoning.

2. If you have 22.4 L of the following gases at STP, which is the most dense: Ne, Ar, or Xe? Explain your reasoning.

3. Which has more particles, a balloon filled with 10 L of oxygen (O_2) gas or a balloon filled with 15 L of helium (He) gas? Explain your reasoning.

4. At 25°C, which balloon has the greater volume, an oxygen (O_2) balloon at 1.2 atm with a mass of 16.0 g, or a helium (He) balloon at 1.2 atm with a mass of 2.0 g?

5. Why is it useful to have a "standard temperature and pressure" for gases?

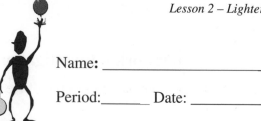

Lighter Than Air

Name: _____

Period: _____ Date: _____

Purpose: The purpose of today's lesson is to explore the number of gas particles in a specified volume of gas. You will need Avogadro's Hypothesis to help you answer the questions.

Avogadro's Hypothesis: Equal volumes of gases at the same temperature and pressure contain equal numbers of gas particles. A gas particle refers to either a single atom or a single molecule that is separated from other molecules or atoms.

Consider these 5 balloons. They are filled with helium (He), nitrogen (N_2), and carbon dioxide (CO_2). The pressure for all 5 balloons is 1.0 atm and the temperature is 273 K.

[Note: These drawings do not show the exact number of gas particles, they simply represent the gas particles in correct proportion to one another.]

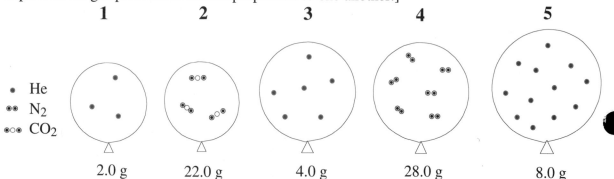

1. Which balloon(s) has/have the most gas particles?

2. Which balloon(s) has/have the most total atoms?

3. The volumes of Balloon 3 and Balloon 4 are the same. Explain why.

4. The masses of Balloon 3 and Balloon 4 are different. Explain why.

5. The volume of Balloon 2 is the same as Balloon 1, but smaller than Balloon 5. Explain why.

6. The mass of Balloon 2 is larger than both Balloon 1 and Balloon 5. Explain why.

7. Imagine you want to create a helium balloon with the same mass as Balloon 2. How would you do that? What would a drawing of the balloon look like?

Use Avogadro's Hypothesis to complete the table below:

gas	# of particles	mass	volume	pressure	temperature
He	6.02×10^{23}	4.0 g	22.4 L	1.0 atm	273 K
He		8.0 g	44.8 L	1.0 atm	273 K
He			11.2 L	1.0 atm	273 K
N_2	6.02×10^{23}	28.0 g	22.4 L	1.0 atm	273 K
N_2	3.01×10^{23}			1.0 atm	273 K
N_2	6.02×10^{23}	28.0 g	11.2 L		273 K
CO_2	6.02×10^{23}	44.0 g	22.4	1.0 atm	273 K
CO_2		22.0 g		1.0 atm	273 K

8. When you have a balloon that has a volume of 22.4 L at 1.0 atm and 273 K, how many particles does it have?

9. What is the relationship between the volume of a particular gas and its mass?

10. What is the relationship between the mass of a particular gas and the number of gas particles?

11. Does the identity of the gas change the number of particles in 22.4 liters? Explain.

12. How would you write 6.02×10^{23} as a whole number instead of in scientific notation?

13. Three balloons have the same volume, pressure, and temperature. A helium (He) balloon has a mass of 4.0 g, a nitrogen (N_2) balloon has a mass of 28.0 g, and a carbon dioxide (CO_2) balloon has a mass of 44.0 g. How do these masses relate to the atomic masses given on the periodic table?

14. Suppose you want to make an air mixture that has 4 nitrogen (N_2) molecules for every 1 oxygen (O_2) molecule. Answer the following:

    a) If you have 6.02×10^{23} O_2 molecules, how many N_2 molecules do you need?

    b) If you have 100 L of N_2, how many liters of O_2 do you need?

Making sense question:
You have: 5.0 L of methane (CH_4) at 30°C and 1.0 atm, and
            5.0 L of oxygen (O_2) at 30°C and 1.0 atm.

List at least three things that are the same.
List at least three things that are different.
(Consider the volume, temperature, pressure, number of gas particles, identities of the gas particles, mass, and density.)

If you finish early…
Suppose you have 100 L of humid air at 30°C, and 100 L of dry air at 30°C. Which is denser? Explain your reasoning.

BEFORE CLASS...

LESSON 3 – More Than a Trillion

Key Ideas:

Chemists keep track of large numbers of molecules or atoms by using a unit called a mole. The number of particles in 22.4 L of a gas at STP is 6.02×10^{23}. This is called Avogadro's Number and also is equivalent to a mole. A mole of O_2 (g) contains 6.02×10^{23} molecules of oxygen, or twice that many oxygen atoms.

What Takes Place:

Students are introduced to a counting unit called a mole at the beginning of class. Then they complete a worksheet that provides them with practice using the mole to count atoms, molecules, and particles in general.

Materials: (per pair of students)

• Student worksheet
• 24 small pieces of paper – index cards or small Post-Its ® work well

Investigation IV- Counting Molecules
LESSON 3 – More than a Trillion

In the previous lesson, students learned that there are 6.02 x 10²³ gas particles in 22.4 L at STP. This is a very large number of particles. In this lesson, students explore this number further. They are introduced to a counting unit called a mole, which chemists use to keep track of these large numbers of molecules. Students solve problems that relate moles to numbers of molecules and to numbers of atoms. The purpose of this lesson is to lay a foundation to relate moles to volume, temperature, and pressure and introduce the ideal gas law in the next lesson.

Exploring the Topic   (5–10 min)

1. Introduce the ChemCatalyst exercise.

Write the following exercise on the board for students to complete individually.

- Why might it be useful for a chemist to know there are 6.02 x 10²³ gas particles in a certain volume of gas?

2. Discuss the ChemCatalyst exercise.

Use the discussion to get a sense of students' initial ideas.

Discussion goals:
Assist students in sharing their initial ideas on counting atoms.

Sample questions:
Do you think chemists actually count atoms?
How do you think they figure out how much gas they have?
Why is it useful for a chemist to know how many atoms they have?
Why is 6.02 x 10²³ called Avogadro's Number?

From the previous lesson, students should know that there are 6.02 x 10²³ molecules of any gas in 22.4 L at STP.

3. Discuss counting units.

Discussion goals:
Solicit students' knowledge of counting units. Introduce the mole.

Sample questions:
What units do we use to count eggs? (dozens)
Can you think of any other counting units? (a case of soda, an hour, a mile)

Why do we measure driving speed in miles per hour rather than inches
per second?

Why do we use counting units?

Points to cover:

Chemists do not count individual molecules and atoms. That would be far too
difficult and time consuming. Nevertheless, they do have ways to keep track
of numbers of molecules. Chemists have a counting unit for molecules and
atoms called the **mole.** It is the standard unit for measuring quantities of
molecules and atoms. This number turns out to be 6.02×10^{23} particles.
Remember, "particles" refers to atoms or molecules. The quantity 6.02×10^{23}
is also referred to as **Avogadro's number** because it was derived from
Avogadro's hypothesis that equal volumes of a gas at STP have equal
numbers of particles. Just as a dozen is equal to twelve eggs, and a day is
equal to 43,200 seconds, a mole of molecules is equal to 6.02×10^{23}
molecules. That's a very large number - 602,000,000,000,000,000,000,000 to
be precise.

Although the mole as a counting unit was developed in relationship to gases, it
works equally well as a counting unit for particles of a liquid or a solid.

There are 6.02×10^{23} particles in a **mole.** This number of particles is also
called **Avogadro's number.**

---

4. Explain the purpose of the activity.

If you wish you can write the main question on the board.

Points to cover:

Tell students they will be working with counting units today. They will be
answering the question, "How is a mole used for counting particles in gases,
liquids, and solids?"

Activity – More Than a Trillion   (15 min)

5. Explain the procedure. (Worksheet)

Tell students they will be working in pairs on a worksheet.

Materials: (per pair of students)

24 small pieces of paper - index cards or small Post-Its ® work well

Procedure:

In Part II of the worksheet, each pair of students will need twenty-four pieces
of paper. They are to write the words "1 mole CHHO" on each piece. CH_2O is
the chemical formula for formaldehyde. The letters represent carbon (C),
hydrogen (H), and oxygen (O). CHHO represents 1 mole C to 2 moles H to

1 mole O. These pieces of paper will be useful in answering the questions on the worksheet, and in thinking about moles.

Part I: 1 mole = 6.02 x 10²³ particles

1. Look at the patterns and fill in the missing data.

Substance	# of moles	# of particles	total # of atoms
He (g)	1	6.02×10^{23}	6.02×10^{23}
He (g)	0.5	3.01×10^{23}	3.01×10^{23}
He (g)	2.0	1.204×10^{24}	1.204×10^{24}
H_2 (g)	1	6.02×10^{23}	1.204×10^{24}
H_2 (g)	0.5	3.01×10^{23}	6.02×10^{23}
H_2 (g)	2.0	1.204×10^{24}	2.408×10^{24}
Cu (s)	1	6.02×10^{23}	6.02×10^{23}
Cu (s)	0.1	6.02×10^{22}	0.602×10^{23}
H_2O (l)	1	6.02×10^{23}	1.806×10^{24}
H_2O (l)	0.5	3.01×10^{23}	9.03×10^{23}

2. How many particles are in 2 moles of a substance? (1.204×10^{24})

3. How many particles are in 10 moles of a substance? (6.02×10^{24})

4. How many particles are there in 2.0 moles of water? How many atoms? (1.204×10^{24} particles, 3.612×10^{24} atoms)

5. Name several collections of objects in your daily life that you might be able to count using moles. (atoms, gas molecules in the air, hair, cells, sand grains, stars)

6. Why do you think moles are useful as a counting unit for chemists? (so that they do not need to work with extremely large numbers all the time)

7. Which has more mass, 1 mole of He (g) or 1,000,000,000 atoms of He (one trillion)? Explain your reasoning. (one mole because it represents 6.02×10^{23} atoms of He which is a lot larger than one trillion)

Part II: Counting molecules vs. atoms

1. CH_2O is the chemical formula for formaldehyde.

   a) How many carbon atoms are there in 1 molecule of CH_2O? (one C atom)

b) How many carbon atoms are there in 1 mole of CH_2O?
(6.02 x 10^{23} C atoms)

c) How many hydrogen atoms are there in 1 molecule of CH_2O?
(two H atoms)

d) How many hydrogen atoms are there in 1 mole of CH_2O?
(1.24 x 10^{24})

e) How many oxygen atoms are there in 1 molecule of CH_2O?
(one O atom)

f) How many oxygen atoms are there in 1 mole CH_2O? (6.02 x 10^{23})

To answer the following questions, label 24 small pieces of paper with "1 mole CHHO."

2. How many moles of CH_2O are needed to have the same number of atoms as 1 mole of $C_6H_{12}O_6$? (Use the pieces of paper labeled "1 mole of CHHO" to check your answer.) (six)

3. Which has more mass: 1 mole of CH_2O (formaldehyde) or 1 mole of $C_6H_{12}O_6$ (sugar)? Explain your thinking. (1 mole sugar because each sugar molecule has more mass than each molecule of formaldehyde)

4. Suppose you have a container with 24 moles of CH_2O and another container with 4 moles of $C_6H_{12}O_6$. (Use the pieces of paper labeled "1 mole of CHHO" to check your answer.)

Formaldehyde
clear liquid
smells putrid

CH_2O
24 moles

Glucose
white solid
tastes sweet

$C_6H_{12}O_6$
4 moles

a) Is the total number of atoms in the two containers the same? Why or why not? (Yes, both containers have 24 moles of C atoms, 48 moles of H atoms, and 24 moles of O atoms)

b) Explain why 24 moles of CH_2O has the same mass as 4 moles of $C_6H_{12}O_6$. (Both have the same number s of the same types of atoms.)

c) Which has more molecules, 24 moles of CH_2O or 4 moles of $C_6H_{12}O_6$? Explain your thinking. (There are more molecules in 24 moles of CH_2O because 24 moles has 24 x 6.02 x 10^{23} while formaldehyde just has 4 x 6.02 x 10^{23}.)

Making sense question:

A company has a history of releasing NO_2 gas into the atmosphere, which forms smog. In order to reduce their pollution, they figure out how to release N_2O_4 instead. For every 1.0 mole of NO_2, they now release 0.75 moles of N_2O_4.

- Are there fewer gas particles with the release of 0.75 moles of N_2O_4 instead of 1.0 moles of NO_2? Explain. (yes, because 0.75 moles of N_2O_4 is less than 1.0 moles NO_2)

- Are there fewer N atoms being released? Explain. (no, because there is 1.0 mole of N atoms in 1.0 mole NO_2, but there are 1.5 moles of N atoms in 0.75 moles of N_2O_4)

- If the amount of smog depends on the number of N atoms, has the company reduced the amount of smog? (no)

If you finish early...

How many moles of acetic acid ($C_2H_4O_2$) are equivalent to 4 moles of $C_6H_{12}O_6$? (12 moles)

Making Sense Discussion   **(15 min)**

Major goals: The main goal of this making sense discussion is to make sure students clearly understand how to use moles for counting particles. In addition they should be clear on the relationships between molecules, numbers of atoms in those molecules, and moles.

6. Discuss how chemists use a mole for counting.

The following questions can be directed to the class as a whole or to teams of students to answer.

Discussion goals:

Give students some practice interpreting how moles are used for counting.

Sample questions:

How many particles are in 2 moles? (1.204×10^{23}) 4 moles? (2.408×10^{23})

Which has more mass, 1 mole of oxygen, O_2 (g), or 1 mole of ozone, O_3 (g)? (1 mole ozone)

Which has more atoms, a mole of oxygen or a mole of ozone? (1 mole ozone)

Which has more molecules, a mole of oxygen or a mole of ozone? (both have the same number of molecules)

Which has more mass, 1 mole of nitrogen, N_2 (g), or 1 mole of nitric oxide, NO_2 (g)? (1 mole of nitric oxide)

Which has more N atoms, a mole of nitrogen or a mole of nitric oxide? (1 mole nitrogen gas)

Which is denser, "clean" air (mainly N_2) or smoggy air (with NO_2)? Explain. (smoggy air because nitric oxide has more mass for equal numbers of gas particles)

Which has more mass, 1 mole carbon dioxide, CO_2 (g), or 1 mole aluminum, Al (s)? (1 mole carbon dioxide) Which has more total atoms? (1 mole carbon dioxide)

7. Focus on counting different types of particles.

Put the following on the board for the discussion.

Substance	Molecular formula
Formaldehyde (embalming liquid)	CH_2O
Acetic acid (vinegar)	$C_2H_4O_2$
Glucose (one form of sugar)	$C_6H_{12}O_6$
Sucrose (table sugar)	$C_{12}H_{22}O_{11}$

Discussion goals:

Assist students in refining their understanding of the relationship between moles and number of molecules, atoms, or particles.

Sample questions:

How many carbon atoms are in 1 mole of $C_2H_4O_2$? (1.206×10^{24} carbon atoms)

How many acetic acid molecules can you make from the atoms in 1 mole of CH_2O? (0.5 moles $C_2H_4O_2$)

Which has more carbon atoms, 1 mole of $C_6H_{12}O_6$ or 3 moles of CH_2O? (1 mole of $C_6H_{12}O_6$ has 6 moles of C whereas 3 moles of CH_2O only has 3 moles of C atoms)

How many moles of atoms are there in 2 moles of vinegar? (sixteen moles of atoms)

Explain how you would figure out how many atoms are in one mole of formaldehyde. (one mole of formaldehyde means four moles of atoms, then multiply by $6.02 \times 10^{23} = 2.408 \times 10^{24}$ total atoms.)

Points to cover:

A **molecular formula** gives the numbers of atoms that remain together as a molecule. Even though formaldehyde, acetic acid, and glucose all have the same kinds of atoms and the same ratio of C:H:O, the molecules contain different numbers of atoms. We know that the atoms are bonded into different size molecules because the properties of each are very different. Formaldehyde is a clear liquid that is toxic. Acetic acid is a clear liquid that tastes sour. Glucose is a white solid that tastes sweet. When considering moles of atoms in a substance it is important to pay attention to how many atoms of each kind are present in one molecule of the substance.

A mole is 6.02×10^{23} of whichever unit is specified. Here are some translations for the meaning of 1 mole of $C_6H_{12}O_6$, glucose.

one mole of sugar molecules	6.02×10^{23} molecules of $C_6H_{12}O_6$
6 moles of carbon atoms	12 moles of hydrogen atoms
3.612×10^{24} oxygen atoms	24 moles of atoms

Check-in   (5 min)

8. Complete the Check-in exercise.

Write the following exercise on the board for the students to complete individually.

You have 1 mole CH_4 (g) and 1 mole O_2 (g).

- Which has more atoms?
- Which has more molecules?
- Which has more mass?

9. Discuss the Check-in exercise.

Get a sense of the level of understanding by asking students to defend their choices.

Discussion goals:
Check to see that students understand the relationship between the mole, numbers of atoms, and mass.

Sample questions:
  Which has more atoms, one mole of methane or one mole of oxygen?
  Which has more molecules, one mole of methane or one mole of oxygen?
  Which has more mass?
  Why do we write 1 mole O_2 (g) rather than 1 mole O?
  How many moles of O atoms are in 1 mole O_2 (g)?

One mole of CH_4 (g) has more atoms than one mole of O_2 gas. Both have 6.02×10^{23} molecules. They will not have the same mass. The mass of C =12 amu and H =1 amu for a total of 16 amu. The mass of O = 16 amu for a total of 32 amu.

10. Wrap-up

Assist the students in summarizing what was learned in this class.
- A mole is 6.02×10^{23} units of whatever you are counting. This number is often referred to as Avogadro's number.

Homework

11. Assign the following for homework.

Use the homework provided with the curriculum or assign your own.

Homework – Investigation IV – Lesson 3

1. How many atoms are in a mole?

2. a) How many grams are in one mole of He? (HINT: use the periodic table)

    b) How many grams are in one mole of Ne?

3. For each of the following relationships, circle the side that represents MORE ATOMS. If the answer is neither, write neither:

    a) 1 mole of He vs. 1 mole of Ne

    b) 1 atom of He vs. 1 mole of Ne

    c) 1 atom of He vs. 1 atom of Ne

    d) 1 gram of He vs. 1 mole of Ne

    e) 1 atom of He vs. 1 gram of Ne

More Than a Trillion

Name: _____

Period: _____ Date: _____

Purpose: In this lesson, you will explore how to count using a new unit called the mole.

Part I: 1 mole = 6.02 x 10²³ particles
1. Look at the patterns and fill in the missing data.

Substance	# of moles	# of particles	total # of atoms
He (g)	1	6.02×10^{23}	6.02×10^{23}
He (g)	0.5	3.01×10^{23}	3.01×10^{23}
He (g)	2.0	1.204×10^{24}	
H$_2$ (g)	1	6.02×10^{23}	1.204×10^{24}
H$_2$ (g)	0.5	3.01×10^{23}	
H$_2$ (g)			2.408×10^{24}
Cu (s)	1		
Cu (s)	0.1	6.02×10^{22}	
H$_2$O (l)	1		1.806×10^{24}
H$_2$O (l)	0.5	3.01×10^{23}	

2. How many particles are in 2 moles of a substance?
3. How many particles are in 10 moles of a substance?
4. How many particles are there in 2.0 moles of water? How many atoms?

5. Name several collections of objects in your daily life that you might be able to count using moles.

6. Why do you think moles are useful as a counting unit for chemists?

7. Which has more mass, 1 mole of He (g) or 1,000,000,000 atoms of He (one trillion)? Explain your reasoning.

Part II: Counting molecules vs. atoms
1. CH$_2$O is the chemical formula for formaldehyde.
   a) How many carbon atoms are there in 1 molecule of CH$_2$O?
   b) How many carbon atoms are there in 1 mole of CH$_2$O?
   c) How many hydrogen atoms are there in 1 molecule of CH$_2$O?

  d) How many hydrogen atoms are there in 1 mole of CH_2O?

  e) How many oxygen atoms are there in 1 molecule of CH_2O?

  f) How many oxygen atoms are there in 1 mole CH_2O?

To answer the following questions, label 24 small pieces of paper with "1 mole CHHO."

2. How many moles of CH_2O are needed to have the same number of atoms as 1 mole of $C_6H_{12}O_6$? (Use the pieces of paper labeled "1 mole of CHHO" to check your answer.)

3. Which has more mass: 1 mole of CH_2O (formaldehyde) or 1 mole of $C_6H_{12}O_6$ (sugar)? Explain your thinking.

4. Suppose you have a container with 24 moles of CH_2O and another container with 4 moles of $C_6H_{12}O_6$. (Use the pieces of paper labeled "1 mole of CHHO" to check your answers.)

Formaldehyde
clear liquid
smells putrid

CH_2O
24 moles

$C_6H_{12}O_6$
4 moles

Glucose
white solid
tastes sweet

  a) Is the total number of atoms in the two containers the same? Why or why not?

  b) Explain why 24 moles of CH_2O weigh the same as 4 moles of $C_6H_{12}O_6$.

  c) Which has more molecules, 24 moles of CH_2O or 4 moles of $C_6H_{12}O_6$? Explain your thinking.

Making sense question:
A company has a history of releasing NO_2 gas into the atmosphere, which forms smog. In order to reduce their pollution, they figure out how to release N_2O_4 instead. For every 1.0 mole of NO_2, they now release 0.75 moles of N_2O_4 instead.

• Are there fewer gas particles with the release of 0.75 moles of N_2O_4 instead of 1.0 moles of NO_2? Explain.

• Are there fewer N atoms being released? Explain.

• If the amount of smog depends on the number of N atoms, has the company reduced the amount of smog that will be produced?

If you finish early…
How many moles of acetic acid ($C_2H_4O_2$) are equivalent to 4 moles of $C_6H_{12}O_6$?

BEFORE CLASS...

LESSON 4 – Take a Breath

Key Ideas:
The ideal gas law, PV = nRT, allows scientists to relate gas pressure, volume, moles of particles, and temperature. R is a constant and does not change – it is dependent on the units that are used. If all of these variables but one are known, the unknown can be calculated using this equation.

What Takes Place:
Students will determine the volume of one average breath of air from their lungs. They will blow air through a tube into a two-liter soda bottle, displacing an amount of water. They will use their measurement to calculate the volume of a single breath. Then, students will use the ideal gas law to calculate the number of moles of air in one breath at sea level and the number of moles of air in one breath at a higher elevation.

Materials: (per team of four students)
- Student worksheet
- 2 L plastic soda bottle with cap
- A tub or sink or other large container for water (at least 5 liters)
- Tap water
- 3 feet of flexible tubing
- 4 straws (to fit into the tubing as mouthpieces; you can cut one regular drinking straw into 3 or 4 pieces)
- 1 watercolor marker or overhead pen
- 1 graduated cylinder – 250 mL or 500 mL

Investigation IV – Counting Molecules
LESSON 4 – Take a Breath

In the previous lesson, students learned that chemists use a counting unit called a mole. In this lesson, students are introduced to the ideal gas law, $PV = nRT$. In this equation, n stands for number of moles of gas particles. In this activity students consider how pressure is related to the number of moles of particles in a gas. The activity begins with an experiment to determine the volume of one breath of air. This volume is then used to determine the number of moles of air in a breath at sea level and on a mountaintop. Students discuss why it is harder to breath on a mountaintop.

Exploring the Topic   (5–10 min)

1. Introduce the ChemCatalyst exercise.

Write the following exercise on the board for students to complete individually.

Mount Everest lies on the border between Nepal and Tibet. It is approximately 29,000 feet high. Those who climb Mount Everest usually pack along many tanks of oxygen to help them with breathing.

- Why do you think it is difficult to breathe at high altitudes?

2. Discuss the ChemCatalyst exercise.

Use the discussion to get a sense of students' initial ideas.

Discussion goals:
Assist students in sharing their initial ideas about how air pressure is related to the number of gas particles.

Sample questions:
Why is it harder to breathe at the top of Mount Everest?
Is there less oxygen and/or less air at higher altitudes? Explain your reasoning.
How does air pressure change as altitude increases?
Are there fewer moles of air per liter at the top of Mount Everest than there are where you live? Why or why not?
If you increase the number of moles of gas in a container, do the gas molecules collide with the walls of the container more? Explain.

Students will probably say that air pressure decreases with increasing altitude and that the number of moles of gas per liter decreases. They have probably heard references to the air "becoming thinner" at higher altitudes. Less molecules means less collisions and thus less pressure. By the way, the local people have two names for Mount Everest. The Tibetan people call it Chomolungma, which means Mother Goddess of the Universe. The Nepalese call the mountain Sagamartha, which means goddess of the Sky.

3. Introduce the ideal gas law.

At the appropriate time, write the ideal gas law on the board.

<u>Discussion goals:</u>
Assist students in sharing their initial ideas about how moles of gas relate to volume and pressure.

Sample questions:

As the number of moles of gas increases, the volume of a gas in a flexible container, like a balloon, increases. Explain why.

As the number of moles of gas increases in a container with fixed volume, like a steel tank, the pressure increases. Explain why.

You cannot change the number of moles by changing the temperature at fixed volume and pressure. Explain why.

Suggested points to cover:
Previously, when we applied the combined gas law, we always assumed that the number of particles of gas stayed the same. In other words, we used the equation $\dfrac{P_1V_1}{T_1} = \dfrac{P_2V_2}{T_2}$ to determine the volume (V), temperature (T), and pressure (P) for a fixed number of moles of gas. For each quantity of gas, there is a different ratio of PV/T.

[Note: From this information it is possible to come up with the equation PV/T = nR, which is simply the ideal gas law rearranged. However many students may not understand the mathematical subtleties here.]

However, there is another gas law that allows us to relate volume, temperature, and pressure of a gas to the number of gas particles. This is called the **ideal gas law.** The equation for the ideal gas law is:

$$PV = nRT$$

We already know what P, V, and T stand for. The variable n stands for the number of moles of gas particles. This leaves "R". It turns out that R is a constant – a number that doesn't change. When P is measured in atmospheres, V is measured in liters, T is measured in Kelvin, and n is measured in moles, the value of R is equal to 0.082. Its units sound complex, but the units match on both sides of the equation. R = 0.082 liter atmospheres per mole Kelvin, or 0.082 L-atm/mole-K.

The **ideal gas law** relates volume (V), temperature (T), pressure (P), and moles (n): PV = nRT, where R = 0.082 L-atm/mole-K.

Thus, if the pressure, volume, and temperature of a gas are known, the number of moles of gas can be calculated using this equation. When doing gas law problems it is best to stick with this one set of units (atmospheres, liters, moles, Kelvin). If you get a problem that is expressed in other units, it will be necessary to convert to these units, otherwise the value we are using for R will be incorrect.

4. Explain the purpose of the activity.

If you wish you can write the main question on the board.

Points to cover:
Tell students that the purpose of today's lesson is to explore how the ideal gas law can be used to figure out the number of moles of gas molecules in the air. Specifically, they will be gathering information to help them answer the question: "Why is it so difficult to breathe at high altitudes?"

Activity – Take a Breath   (15 min)

5. Introduce the activity. (Worksheet)

The activity has two parts. In the first part, students will determine the volume of a normal breath of air. In the second part, students will use the volume of one breath to determine how many moles of air they breathe at sea level and how many moles of air they breathe on a mountaintop.

Materials: (per team of four students)
2 L plastic soda bottle with cap
a tub or sink or other large container for water (at least 5 liters)
tap water
3 feet of flexible tubing
4 straws (to fit into the tubing)
1 watercolor marker or overhead pen
1 graduated cylinder – 250 mL or 500 mL

Part I: Volume of a breath of air
The goal of this part of the activity is to determine the volume of a normal breath of air. The outline for a procedure is given below. You will need to decide how many breaths to measure and how you will figure out the air volume.

1. Fill a larger container or tub about half full with tap water.
2. Fill a 2 L plastic soda bottle with tap water. Put the cap on loosely.
3. Carefully invert the bottle. Take care that you do not spill any water.
4. Put the bottle into the large container of water so that the mouth of the bottle is under water. Remove the cap.

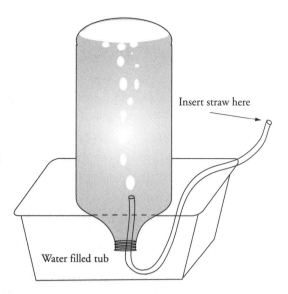

5. Feed the flexible tubing under the water so that one end goes inside the bottle.

6. Put your straw into the other end of the tubing. Do not share straws.

7. When it is your turn blow into the straw to collect the air of one or more breaths.

8. Mark the volume of air with a marking pen.

9. Figure out the volume of the air trapped inside the bottle. Record this volume.

Insert straw here

Water filled tub

Part II: Moles in a breath of air

Use the volume you determined for one breath to figure out the number of moles of air in one breath at sea level and in one breath on a mountaintop.

1. **Moles in a breath at sea level.** Suppose that you take a breath at sea level where the air pressure is 1.0 atm and the temperature is 25°C. Use the ideal gas law to determine the moles of air in one breath. (Outcomes will vary - if student's breath volume is 0.5 L, answer is 0.020 moles of air.)

2. **Moles in a breath on a mountaintop.** Suppose that you take a breath on a mountaintop where the air pressure is 0.75 atm and the temperature is 25°C. Use the ideal gas law to determine the moles of air in one breath. (answer should be around 0.015 moles of air)

3. Explain how you could figure out exactly how many gas particles are in a breath at sea level. (multiply number of moles by Avogadro's number)

4. Calculate the number of gas particles in a breath at sea level. Calculate the number of gas particles in a breath on a mountaintop.

5. Why is the air in airplanes pressurized? (so that we can breathe up there)

6. The air we breathe is mainly nitrogen gas, N_2. Oxygen is only 20% of the total number of gas molecules in the air. Determine how many moles of oxygen you breathe at sea level and on a mountaintop.

Making sense question:

Use your mole calculations to explain why you breathe faster at higher altitudes.

If you finish early...

Use the ideal gas law to figure out how many moles of air there would be in one breath at the top of Mount Everest. Air pressure at 29,000 feet is 0.3 atm.

The temperature at the summit at the warmest time of the year is –19 °C.
(0.007 moles of air)

Making Sense Discussion   (15 min)

Major ideas: The first goal of this discussion is to allow students to share the process
they went through completing the activity. In particular they should share how they
determined the volume of one breath, reasons for variations, and possible sources of
error. Next students should be guided through an ideal gas law problem to make sure
they are clear about how to complete a calculation. Finally, the effect of air pressure
fluctuations on our daily lives is discussed.

6. Discuss how to determine the volume of a breath.

Ask groups of students to write their results for the volume of one breath on
the board.

Discussion goals:
Allow students to share their experiences of the activity.

Sample questions:
  What are some of the reasons that the volumes differ from group to group?
  Do you think it is better to measure the volume of one breath or several
    breaths and then determine the average? Explain.
  How did you determine the volume of one breath of air?
  What are some of the possible causes of error?

The volumes may vary considerably depending on lung volume, how deep a breath was taken,
how hard the student exhaled, etc. Since each breath may not be the same as the next, it is
useful to average over several breaths. One way to determine the air volume is to calibrate the
2-L plastic bottle by putting in known quantities of water and marking the side of the bottle.

7. Discuss how to use the ideal gas law.

You may wish to guide the class through the last question on the worksheet.
Ask student volunteers to help you up at the board.

Discussion goals
Discuss how to use the ideal gas law to determine the number of
moles of gas and the number of moles of gas per liter.

Sample questions:
  How did you determine the number of moles in one breath at sea level?
  What is the number of moles of air per liter in one breath at sea level?
  What is the number of moles of air per liter in one breath on the
    mountaintop?
  Why is the air pressure lower on the mountaintop?
  Describe how you would figure out the number of moles of air in a breath at
    the top of Mount Everest.

Points to cover:

The last problem on the worksheet asks you to figure out the number of moles of air in a breath on top of Mount Everest. Insert the values for P, V, and T into the equation and solve for n. (We assume V= 0.5 L here.)

$$PV = nRT \qquad (0.3 \text{ atm}) (0.5 \text{ L}) = n (0.082 \text{ atm-L/mole-K}) (254 \text{ K})$$

$$n = 0.15 / 20.83 = 0.007 \text{ moles of air}$$

This means there are 0.014 moles per liter of air

Check-in   (5 min)

8. Complete the Check-in exercise.

Write the following exercise on the board for the students to complete individually.

You fill a 1.0 L plastic bottle with 1.0 mole of air on a mountaintop where the air pressure is 0.5 atm.

- Why does the plastic bottle become crushed when you bring the bottle to sea level?
- What is the volume of the bottle at sea level?
- How many moles per liter are there at sea level?

9. Discuss the Check-in exercise.

Get a sense of the level of understanding by asking students to defend their choices.

Discussion goals

Make sure that students understand the relationship between pressure and moles per volume.

Suggested questions

How is pressure related to moles per volume? (they are proportional)

What is the volume at sea level? (0.5 L)

Does the number of moles change? (no, the bottle is closed)

How many moles per liter are there at sea level? (0.5 moles per liter)

What do you need to assume about temperature to solve the problem? (stays constant)

Since the air pressure on the outside of the bottle is higher, the plastic bottle will become crushed. This assumes that the temperature stays constant. The number of moles stays the same, but the volume decreases by half. Thus, the number of moles per liter increases by a factor of two (same as the pressure).

10. Wrap-up

Assist the students in summarizing what was learned in this class.

- The ideal gas law relates volume, pressure, temperature, and the number of moles: $PV = nRT$, where $R = 0.082$ L-atm/mole-K.

Homework

11. Assign the following for homework.
Use the homework provided with the curriculum or assign your own.

Homework – Investigation IV – Lesson 4

1. How many moles of hydrogen gas are contained in 2 liters at 280 K and 1.5 atm?

2. What volume would 1.5 moles of nitrogen gas occupy at standard temperature and pressure?

3. Find the volume of 3.40 moles of gas whose temperature is 40.0 °C and whose pressure is 2.00 atm.

4. If the number of moles of a gas is doubled at the same temperature and pressure, will the volume increase or decrease?

5. How many moles of helium gas are contained in a 10,000 L weather balloon at 1 atm and 10 ˚C?

Take a Breath

Name: _____

Period: _____ Date: _____

Purpose: This activity will give you practice using the ideal gas law. You will figure out the number of moles of air in an average breath.

Part I: Volume of a breath of air

The goal of this part of the activity is to determine the volume of a normal breath of air. The outline for a procedure is given below. You will need to decide how many breaths to measure and how you will figure out the air volume.

1. Fill a larger container or tub about half full with tap water.

2. Fill a 2 L plastic soda bottle with tap water. Put the cap on loosely.

3. Carefully invert the bottle. Take care that you do not spill any water.

4. Put the bottle into the large container of water so that the mouth of the bottle is under water. Remove the cap.

5. Feed the flexible tubing under the water so that one end goes inside the bottle.

6. Put your straw into the other end of the tubing. Do not share straws.

7. When it is your turn blow into the straw to collect the air of one or more breaths.

8. Mark the volume of air with a marking pen.

9. Figure out the volume of the air trapped inside the bottle. Record this volume.

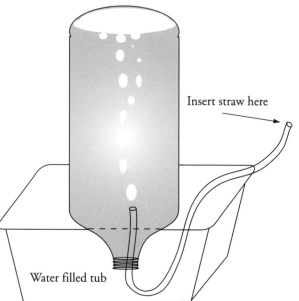

Insert straw here

Water filled tub

Part II: Moles in a breath of air

Use the volume you determined for one breath to figure out the number of moles of air in one breath at sea level and in one breath on a mountaintop.

1. **Moles in a breath at sea level.** Suppose that you take a breath at sea level where the air pressure is 1.0 atm and the temperature is 25°C. Use the ideal gas law to determine the moles of air in one breath.

2. **Moles in a breath on a mountaintop.** Suppose that you take a breath on a mountaintop where the air pressure is 0.75 atm and the temperature is 25°C. Use the ideal gas law to determine the moles of air in one breath.

3. Explain how you could figure out exactly how many gas particles are in a breath at sea level.

4. Calculate the number of gas particles in a breath at sea level. Calculate the number of gas particles in a breath on a mountaintop.

5. Why is the air in airplanes pressurized?

6. The air we breathe is mainly nitrogen gas, N_2. Oxygen is only 20% of the total number of gas molecules in the air. Determine how many moles of oxygen you breathe at sea level and on a mountaintop.

Making sense:
Use your mole calculations to explain why you breathe faster at higher altitudes.

If you finish early...
Use the Ideal Gas Law to figure out how many moles of air there would be in one breath at the top of Mount Everest. Air pressure at 29,000 feet is 0.3 atm. The temperature at the summit at the warmest time of the year is –19 °C.

BEFORE CLASS...

LESSON 5 – Up In the Clouds

Key Ideas:

Water vapor forms when water evaporates from bodies of water on the planet. In order for water vapor to condense and form water droplets, the temperature in the air must decrease. According to Gay-Lussac's law, when the air pressure drops the temperature of the air also decreases. Under these conditions, water vapor condenses and forms clouds.

What Takes Place:

Students work in pairs or groups of four to create miniature clouds in a soda bottle. They try to create a cloud under three different conditions – a bottle with cold water, a bottle with hot water, and a dry bottle. They compare the results and speculate on the conditions that lead to cloud formation.

Materials: (for every 2–4 students)

- Student worksheet
- 2 L bottles with cap
- Dry 2 L bottle with cap (this can be shared by the whole class)
- Long matches
- Tap water
- Hot water (~80 °C)

Investigation IV – Counting Molecules
LESSON 5 – Up in the Clouds

In this lesson, students explore the variable water vapor content in the atmosphere. Meteorologists refer to the amount of water vapor in the air as humidity. During the activity students create their own miniature cloud in a bottle. They consider how the moles of water vapor, the pressure, and temperature determine whether a cloud will form or not. Humidity is defined as the number of moles of water vapor per liter of air.

Exploring the Topic   (5–10 min)

1. Introduce the ChemCatalyst exercise.

Write the following exercise on the board for students to complete individually.

- What is a cloud?
- How do you think clouds form?

2. Discuss the ChemCatalyst exercise.

Use the discussion to get a sense of students' initial ideas.

Discussion goals:
Assist students in sharing their initial ideas about why clouds form. Encourage them to use what they have learned in the unit.

Sample questions:
  What is a cloud?
  How do you think clouds form?
  How does water vapor get in the air? Why does water vapor rise?
  What causes water vapor to condense to form clouds?
  Where would you expect to find clouds, in a high pressure region or a low
    pressure region? Explain your reasoning.
  Do you think clouds are associated with warm or cool temperatures?
    Explain.

Students may be divided on whether clouds are associated with high or low pressure regions. There are also several ways to think about the relationship between clouds and air temperature. There can be more moisture in warm air, but the air must cool in order for water vapor to condense. Listen to students' ideas without judgment. Encourage them to use their understanding of gases, gas laws, and phase changes.

3. Explain the purpose of the activity.

If you wish you can write the main question on the board.

Points to cover:

Tell students they will be examining the factors that influence cloud formation by creating their own miniature clouds. They will be exploring the question: "What causes clouds to form?"

Activity – Up In The Clouds   **(15 min)**

4. Explain the procedure. (Worksheet)

Students can work in teams of 2 to 4 students depending on the materials available. Explain to them that they will be trying to create a cloud inside a two-liter bottle. They will try three different sets of conditions.

Materials: (for groups of 2–4 students)
2 L bottle with cap
dry 2 L bottle with cap (this can be shared by the whole class)
Long matches
Tap water
Hot water

Procedure:
1. Put a small amount (about 10 mL) of water into a two-liter bottle.
2. Light a match. Blow it out and then hold it inside the bottle to collect some smoke. Hold the bottle with the open end down and the match underneath.
3. Quickly remove the match and put the lid on the bottle.
4. Shake the bottle to add moisture to the air inside the bottle.
5. Squeeze the bottle, then release it quickly. Observe what happens.
6. Squeeze and release several times. Record your observations.
7. Repeat the experiment, but this time add 10 mL of hot water (above ~80°C)
8. Repeat the experiment with a dry bottle. Do not add water, just create smoke, close the bottle, and squeeze and release. Record you observations.

The first time that the students release the bottle, a fog-like cloud fills the bottle. The effect becomes more impressive as they continue to squeeze and release the bottle. Each time they squeeze the bottle, the cloud completely disappears and each time they release the bottle the cloud reforms. The effect is larger if the water is at a higher temperature. A cloud is not formed at all under dry conditions.

[Note to the teacher: If the cloud is not very visible, tell students to try to collect more smoke in the bottle. They need to hold the bottle with the open end down and the match underneath. They can even hold the lit match in the bottle. It will extinguish on its own.]

Answer the following questions:
1. What did you observe inside the bottle as you squeezed and released? (A cloud forms each time that you release the bottle and disappears each time you squeezed the bottle.)

2. Why do you think we shook the bottle at the beginning of the experiment? (in order to put more water vapor into the air)

3. When you *squeezed* the bottle what happened to the volume of the container? (It decreased.)

4. What happened to the pressure inside the container as the result of the volume change when you squeezed the bottle? (pressure increased)

5. Which gas law and equation relates gas volume to gas pressure? (Boyle's law, $P_1V_1 = P_2V_2$)

6. What did *releasing* the bottle do to the volume occupied by the air? (increased the volume)

7. What effect did *releasing* the bottle have on the air pressure? Explain why. (decreased the air pressure because less volume, n did not change, more space for the same number of molecules)

8. Which gas law and equation relate pressure to temperature? (Gay-Lussac's, $\dfrac{P_1}{T_1} = \dfrac{P_2}{T_2}$)

9. According to Gay-Lussac's law what happens to the gas temperature when the pressure suddenly decreases? (The temperature decreases because the pressure decreases.)

10. In order to form a cloud, what has to happen to some of the water vapor? (it must condense into water)

11. What did you observe when you used the dry bottle? Explain the outcome. (You need water vapor in the air to form a cloud. A cloud does not form or only a very tiny cloud forms from the humidity in the air when the bottle is dry.)

12. Which bottle formed the biggest cloud – the dry bottle, the bottle with room temperature water, or the hot water bottle? Explain why. (The cloud was more noticeable when hot water was used. This indicates that more water vapor was in the air. This makes sense because we might expect more water to evaporate for a higher water temperature.)

Making sense:
Explain how a cloud was formed in this experiment.
What do you think pressure and temperature have to do with cloud formation?

If you finish early...
Explain how the weather where you are might affect the outcome of this experiment.

Making Sense Discussion   **(15 min)**

Major goals: This discussion allows the students to debrief the experiment and review the gas laws that are associated with cloud creation. It is important to go over the formation of the cloud in the bottle step-by-step so that students follow the changes that occurred and tie these to the various gas laws. Then, cloud formation in the atmosphere should be discussed. Humidity is introduced at the end of the discussion.

5. Debrief the experiment.

Go over the experiment step-by-step. You may wish to draw two soda bottles on the board labeled "squeeze" and "release." In addition you can write V, P, and T below each bottle to track the changes in these variables.

Discussion goals:
Assist students in sharing their ideas about volume, temperature, and pressure as they relate to the cloud in a bottle activity.

Sample questions:
What variables did you change by squeezing the bottle?
When you released the bottle, what happened to V? P? T?
The temperature of the air in the bottle decreases when the bottle is released. Explain why.
What was the purpose of shaking up the bottle beforehand?
Do you think the water vapor in the air in the room had any effect on the cloud formation? (Yes, if there's already water vapor in the air, it will increase the chances of a cloud forming.

Points to cover:
Students should realize that upon squeezing the bottle, the volume decreases, and the temperature and pressure increase. Then when the bottle is released, the volume increases, and the temperature and pressure decrease. The decrease in temperature causes the water vapor to condense in the bottle. The smoke provides some particles in the air for the water droplets to cling to or form around. Dust particles serve this purpose in the atmosphere.

6. Discuss cloud formation in the earth's atmosphere.

Discussion goals:
Assist students in extrapolating from the cloud in a bottle to clouds in the earth's atmosphere.

Sample questions:
How did you make a cloud form in today's activity? (by manipulating the volume of the container)
Is the air in our atmosphere in a container? Explain.

What is the first step in the formation of clouds on the planet? (evaporation of water)

Why does water vapor rise?

What happens to the temperature and pressure of the water vapor as it rises?

Do you expect clouds to form at high or low temperature?

Do you expect clouds to form over a desert or a rain forest? Explain your thinking.

Why do some clouds form near the ground and others at very high altitudes?

Points to cover:

Water vapor enters the atmosphere due to evaporation from bodies of water. When the water is warmer, more water evaporates. This is one of the reasons why warm, tropical areas have lots of rainfall. Since there is no "volume" or container associated with the earth's atmosphere, it is easier to explain weather by focusing on pressure and temperature changes.

Warm air rises because it is less dense than cold air. As it rises the temperature and pressure decrease. As the water vapor cools, it condenses into droplets, forming clouds.

Enough water vapor must be present in the air in order for clouds to form. This is why more clouds form over the rainforest compared with the desert. Fog is common near bodies of water. On warm days, large puffy clouds are observed at lower altitudes. On cold days, if there are clouds at all, they tend to be wispy and high in the sky.

7. Define humidity.

Discussion goals:

Assist students in understanding the concept of humidity.

Sample questions:

What do you think the term "humidity" means?

What is the weather like when there is high humidity in the air?

What do you think the humidity of the air is when it is raining?

How can it get really humid on hot summer days and not rain?

Points to cover:

Humidity refers to the amount of water vapor in the air. Meteorologists use the term in more than one way. They talk about **absolute humidity** and **relative humidity.** Absolute humidity is simply the number of moles of water vapor per liter of air. The absolute humidity depends on how much water has evaporated. As the temperature increases, it is possible to have more moles of water vapor per liter of air. Meteorologists rarely use absolute humidity in their forecasts to the public. The data most often broadcast to the public is the relative humidity.

As the air gets warmer, the maximum amount of water vapor that can be in the air increases. Scientists have measured the maximum amount of water vapor contained in air at different temperatures. At 10 °C, the maximum amount is 9 grams of water vapor per cubic meter of air. For warmer air, at 30°C, the maximum amount is 30 grams of water vapor per cubic meter. When air has the maximum amount of water vapor possible for a given temperature, we say that the air is **saturated** or that it has reached its **saturation point.**

Relative humidity is the amount of water vapor in the air compared to the maximum amount of water vapor possible at the current temperature. Thus, relative humidity describes how close the air is to the saturation point. Relative humidity is expressed in percent. Thus, when a meteorologist tells you the air is at 30% humidity, it means that the air already contains 30 percent of the total water vapor possible at the current temperature. Students may wonder whether "saturation" will lead to rainfall. This will be discussed in the next lesson.

Check-in   (5 min)

8. Complete the Check-in exercise.

Write the following exercise on the board for the students to complete individually.

- What information would you want to know to be able predict if clouds will form?

9. Discuss the Check-in exercise.

Get a sense of the level of understanding by asking students to defend their choices.

Discussion goals:
Check to see that students understand the conditions associated with cloud formation.

Sample questions:
Why is it important to know the humidity of the air if you are predicting the weather?
What might the temperature tell you about the possibility of rain?

At this point, students should realize that clouds do not form if the absolute humidity is low. The absolute humidity is low when the temperature is low or in dry areas.

10. Wrap-up.

Assist the students in summarizing what was learned in this class.

　　　　　　　　Weather © UC Regents, LHS Living by Chemistry, 2003.

- Water vapor condenses and forms clouds of water droplets when the temperature drops. Temperature decreases occur in gases when there is a decrease in pressure.
- Absolute humidity is a measure of the number of moles of water vapor per liter of air.
- Relative humidity is a measure of the amount of water vapor in the air compared to the maximum possible for a certain temperature. It is expressed in percent.

Homework

11. Assign homework.
Use the homework provided with the curriculum or assign your own.

Homework – Investigation IV – Lesson 5

1. What evidence have you seen to support this statement: A higher humidity is possible at higher temperatures?

2. What do you think happens to the moles of air per liter in a region where clouds have just formed?

3. What does it mean when the relative humidity is 25%?

4. What does it mean when the relative humidity is 100%?

Up in the Clouds

Name: _____

Period: _____ Date: _____

Student Worksheet

Purpose: This activity allows you to create a tiny cloud inside a soda bottle and examine the forces that contribute to cloud formation.

Materials
Two 2 L bottles with caps. (You will need one that is dry.)
Long matches
Tap water
Hot water

Procedure:

1. Put a small amount (about 10 mL) of water into a two-liter bottle.

2. Light a match. Blow it out and then hold it inside the bottle to collect some smoke. Hold the bottle with the open end down and the match underneath.

3. Quickly remove the match and put the lid on the bottle.

4. Shake the bottle to add moisture to the air inside the bottle.

5. Squeeze the bottle, then release it quickly. Observe what happens.

6. Squeeze and release several times. Record your observations.

7. Repeat the experiment, but this time add 10 mL of hot water (above ~80°C)

8. Repeat the experiment with a dry bottle. Do not add water, just create smoke, close the bottle, and squeeze and release. Record you observations.

Answer the following questions:

1. What did you observe inside the bottle as you squeezed and released?

2. Why do you think we shook the bottle at the beginning of the experiment?

3. When you *squeezed* the bottle what happened to the volume of the container?

4. What happened to the pressure inside the container as the result of the volume change?

5. Which gas law and equation relates gas volume to gas pressure?

6. What did *releasing* the bottle do to the volume occupied by the air?

7. What effect did *releasing* the bottle have on the air pressure? Explain why.

8. Which gas law and equation relate pressure to temperature?

9. According to Gay-Lussac's law, what happens to the gas temperature when the pressure suddenly decreases?

10. In order to form a cloud, what has to happen to some of the water vapor?

11. What did you observe when you used the dry bottle? Explain the outcome.

12. Which bottle formed the biggest cloud – the dry bottle, the bottle with room temperature water, or the hot water bottle? Explain why.

Making sense:
Explain how a cloud was formed in this experiment.

What do you think pressure and temperature have to do with cloud formation?

If you finish early...
Explain how the weather where you are might affect the outcome of this experiment.

BEFORE CLASS...

LESSON 6 – Rain in the Forecast

Key Ideas:
The last lesson introduced the concept of absolute humidity – a measure of the amount of water vapor in the air. For a given temperature, there is a maximum absolute humidity. When the absolute humidity reaches the maximum amount, water vapor will condense out of the air. This is when rain and dew occur. The dew point is the temperature that must be reached before water vapor will condense. When sweat evaporates from your body, heat is transferred from your skin to the water and you feel cooler.

What Takes Place:
Students complete a worksheet that includes a graph of the maximum absolute humidty vs. temperature. They explore the conditions necessary for rain to form. In addition they explore the relationship between humidity, temperature, and how hot you feel.

Set-up:
Before class you may wish to prepare the droppers. Half should contain a small amount of alcohol. The other half should contain a small amount of water. You may label them as you see fit (with masking tape or a marking pen). These droppers will be passed around during the second portion of the activity. Students will place 1-2 drops on their skin in order to determine how they feel when the liquid evaporates.

Materials: (per class)
- Student worksheet
- Rubbing alcohol (approximately 50 mL)
- Tap water
- Disposable droppers – approximately 8–10

Investigation IV – Counting Molecules
LESSON 6 – Rain in the Forecast

In this lesson students explore how the amount of water vapor in the air varies with temperature, and how this variation affects the weather. First they examine a graph of the maximum absolute humidity vs. temperature. This graph is then used to predict if it will rain, if dew will form, and at what altitude clouds will form depending on the absolute humidity at a given temperature. This is followed by a discussion of the interplay between temperature and humidity in determining how hot you feel.

Exploring the Topic   (5–10 min)

1. Introduce the ChemCatalyst exercise.

Write the following exercise on the board for students to complete individually.

- Does it always rain when the humidity is high? Why or why not?

2. Discuss the ChemCatalyst exercise.

Use the discussion to get a sense of students' initial ideas.

Discussion goals:
Assist students in thinking about humidity and temperature, and how they are related to whether or not it rains.

Sample questions:
When is the humidity of the air high?
Do you expect rain if the absolute humidity is high? Explain.
Do you expect rain if the relative humidity is high? Explain.
Why does it rain when the relative humidity is 100%?
Suppose you have a lot of water in the air at 35°C. Do you expect clouds at low or high altitudes? Explain.

Listen to students' ideas without judgment. Students should be able to relate that humidity has to do with the amount of water vapor in the air. If the absolute humidity is high, there is a lot of water vapor per liter of air. This increases the possibilities for rain. If the relative humidity is high, this means that the air is getting close to the maximum absolute humidity. Again, it increases the likelihood of rain. If the temperature drops, this increases the relative humidity and the likelihood of rain.

3. Explain the purpose of the activity.

If you wish you can write the main question on the board.

Points to cover:

Tell students they will use a graph to determine the conditions for rain. They will consider how humidity and temperature together determine whether or not it will rain. In addition, they will explore how humidity and temperature relate to how hot you feel. The main questions is: "How do you know if it will rain?"

Activity – Rain in the Forecast   **(15 min)**

4. Pass out the worksheet. (Worksheet)

There are two parts to this activity. In the first part, students will examine a graph of the maximum absolute humidity vs. temperature. This graph will be used to predict whether or not it will rain. In the second part, students consider how the relative humidity and the temperature together determine how hot you feel.

Materials:

Rubbing alcohol in disposable droppers to pass around (about 50 mL total)
Water in disposable droppers to pass around

Part I: Maximum absolute humidity

The graph below shows the maximum absolute humidity vs. temperature. Use the graph to answer the questions below.

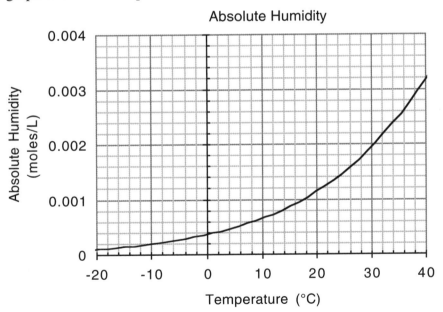

Answer the following questions:

1. Is it possible to have 0.001 moles of water vapor per liter of air at 10°C? Explain your answer. (No, this is above the maximum value.)

2. Is it possible to have 0.001 moles of water vapor per liter of air at 30°C? Explain your answer. (Yes, this is below the maximum value.)

3. When you have 0.001 moles of water vapor per liter of air at 18°C, it begins to rain. Explain why. (This is the maximum value at 25°C. Water begins condensing.)

4. Suppose the absolute humidity is 0.0015 moles of water vapor per liter of air at 35°C. It cools overnight to 25°C and you find drops of dew on the grass in the morning. Explain why. (At 25°C, 0.0015 mole/L is at the maximum value.)

For a given absolute humidity, meteorologists call the temperature at which the maximum absolute humidity is reached the **dew point.**

5. Lightly shade the area on the graph showing all the possible values for the absolute humidity. (Hint: The curve represents the *maximum* value for the absolute humidity.)

6. Why do you suppose meteorologists call the temperature at which the absolute humidity reaches the maximum value the dew point? (Because the moles/L on the curve at a specific temperature gives the conditions where dew will form.)

7. This table shows the temperature of the air as a function of altitude. Use the graph to assist you in answering questions about the table below.

Altitude	2,000 ft	4,000 ft	6,000 ft	8,000 ft	10,000 ft
Temperature	11°C	7.2°C	3.3°C	–1.1°C	–5.0°C

   a) What is the maximum absolute humidity at 4,000 ft? (~0.00055 moles/L)

   b) What is the maximum absolute humidity at 10,000 feet? (~0.00025 moles/L)

   c) Will water vapor condense to rain at 2,000 feet if the absolute humidity is 0.0007 moles per liter? (Yes. At 11°C, this is the maximum absolute humidity)

   d) As the absolute humidity in the air increases, do clouds form at lower or higher elevations? Explain your thinking. (Clouds form at lower elevations because the temperature does not need to drop as much to reach the dew point.)

8. Why is the relative humidity at the dew point always 100%? (Because the relative humidity is the absolute humidity divided by the maximum absolute humidity. When the absolute humidity = the maximum absolute humidity, then the ratio is 1, or 100%)

Part II: How hot you feel

How hot you feel depends on both the humidity and the temperature. The following questions will help you understand why.

Answer the following questions:

1. Put a drop of water on your skin. Spread it around a little. Put a drop of alcohol on your skin nearby. Spread it around a little. Blow on the spot. What do you feel? (They both feel cold, but the alcohol spot feels colder.)

2. What is happening with the alcohol and the water on your skin? Why does one feel colder than the other? (They are both evaporating. The alcohol evaporates quicker than the water, thus it feels cooler.)

3. Why do you think you feel cool when you get out of a swimming pool dripping wet? (water is evaporating)

4. Heat is required to evaporate liquids. Why does sweating cool you off? (Heat is transferred from your body to the water.)

5. If the relative humidity is 100%, will your sweat evaporate? Why or why not? (No, because the amount of water vapor in the air is already at the maximum amount.)

6. Explain why 40% humidity at 75°F feels cooler than 80% humidity at 75°F. (Water evaporates faster when there is less water vapor in the air.)

7. Explain why you feel cooler on a windy day. (Wind causes water to evaporate faster so you feel cooler.)

Making sense question:
What do you need to know to decide if it will rain?
Under what weather conditions does sweating work well to cool you off?

If you finish early…
Dry air is denser than air with water vapor in it. Show how this is true.

Making Sense Discussion   **(15 min)**

Major goals: The goal of this discussion is to make sure students understand the relationship between temperature and the maximum absolute humidity. They should be able to predict when it will rain if they know these two variables. The term dew point should be defined. Finally, students should understand the interplay between temperature and humidity in determining how hot you feel.

5. Discuss the maximum absolute humidity.

<u>Discussion goals:</u>
Assist students in articulating how the maximum absolute humidity curve helps them to predict when it will rain.

Sample questions:
There are 0.0014 moles of water vapor per liter in the air at 30°C. If it cools to 20°C overnight, do you expect dew to form? Explain your thinking. (yes)

Suppose you graph the humidity and temperature, and the point lies on the curve. Do you expect rain? Explain your thinking.

What is the relative humidity for points that are on the curve?

For points that lie below the line, are the conditions right for rain? Why or why not?

Points to cover:

The curve on the graph of maximum absolute humidity vs. temperature specifies the maximum amount of water vapor than can be in the air at a given temperature. Once this maximum value is reached, it is not possible for more water to evaporate to increase the absolute humidity further – instead, water begins to condense. The only way to increase the number of moles of water vapor in the air further is to raise the temperature. As the temperature increases, the maximum amount of water vapor that can be in the air increases.

If the absolute humidity lies below the curve for a given temperature, then dew, rain, and clouds are not expected. However, as the air cools, the maximum amount of water vapor than can be in the air decreases. If the air cools sufficiently so that the amount of water vapor in the air is the maximum amount for the new lower temperature, then the moisture in the air will condense. This is why dew forms when it cools overnight, and why clouds form when air rises to higher altitudes where it is cooler.

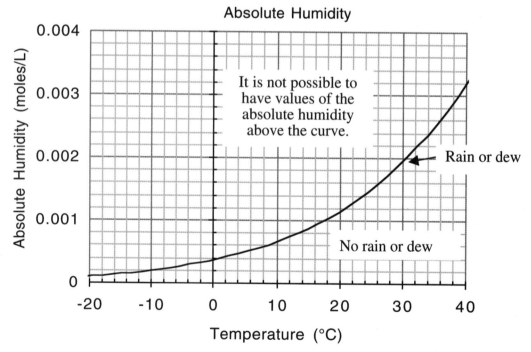

The dew point is expressed in degrees. A meteorologist may report that the dew point is 45° F. This means that for the current absolute humidity, water will condense out of the air when the temperature decreases to 45° F or lower.

Optional points to cover:

Why is there a maximum absolute humidity at a given temperature? It is tempting to say that the maximum value is the maximum amount of water vapor that the air can "hold." It turns out that this is not a good way to think about it. First of all, air does not "hold" water vapor. Moreover, this focuses our attention only on the water vapor whereas we need to thinking about both water vapor *and* liquid water.

Liquid water evaporates at a certain rate at a given temperature. The rate of evaporation decreases as the amount of water vapor in the air increases. Likewise, water vapor condenses at a certain rate at a given temperature. The rate of condensation increases as the amount of water vapor in the air increases. When the rate of condensation equals the rate of evaporation, liquid water and water vapor will co-exist. This means that the maximum absolute humidity has been reached. No more water can be put in the air because it will condense. The relative humidity is 100%. Because the water is condensing as quickly as it is evaporating, dew, rain, and clouds form under these conditions. Since the rates of evaporation and condensation depend on temperature (heat is required to evaporate water), the dew point depends on temperature.

6. Discuss conditions that make you feel hot.

Discussion goals:

Assist students in thinking about how both temperature and relative humidity affect how hot you feel.

Sample questions:

How did your skin feel when the alcohol evaporated?

Heat is required to evaporate liquids. Why does sweating making you feel cooler?

Why do you feel hotter when it is 95°F in the tropics compared with 95°C in the desert?

Explain why it often gets warmer when it rains. (Hint: Condensation is the opposite of evaporation.)

Points to cover:

Heat is required to evaporate water. This is because the water molecules in liquid water are attracted to one another. The heat is need to pull the molecules apart and set them free as individual water molecules in the gas phase. Your skin feels cool when liquids evaporate because your body transfers heat to the liquid to cause it to evaporate. This cools your body. Increasing the rate of water evaporation by blowing on your skin also feels cool for the same reason.

As the amount of water vapor increases at a given temperature, the rate of evaporation decreases and the rate of condensation increases. Hence, as there is more water in the air, beads of sweat on your body do not evaporate as quickly. This makes you feel hotter in the tropics compared with a desert, even if the temperature in the two locations is the same.

Condensation is the opposite of evaporation. Since heat is required to evaporate water, you might expect that heat is released in the opposite process. In fact, when it rains it often feels warmer because heat is released when water condenses.

Check-in   (5 min)

7. Complete the Check-in exercise.

Write the following exercise on the board for the students to complete individually.

- Explain how you can tell if it will rain, if you are given the absolute humidity and the temperature.

8. Discuss the Check-in exercise.

Get a sense of the level of understanding by asking students to defend their choices.

Discussion goals:
Encourage students to explain the relationship between humidity and temperature.

Sample questions:
How does knowing the absolute humidity and the temperature help you to know if it will rain?
Do you need to know anything else?

The absolute humidity is the amount of water vapor in the air. If you know the dew point and the temperature for the day's specific conditions, you can predict if it will rain. If the absolute humidity is above the dew point then water vapor will condense. It may take the form of dew, or rain, or simply the formation of clouds depending where you are in the atmosphere.

9. Wrap-up

Assist the students in summarizing what was learned in this class.
- Condensation of water (rain or dew or cloud formation) occurs when the relative humidity is 100%.
- The maximum amount of water vapor that can be in a liter of air increases as the temperature increases.

Homework

10. Assign the following for homework.

Use the homework provided with the curriculum or assign your own.

Homework – Investigation IV – Lesson 6

1. How does a damp rag or bandana around your neck help to cool you on a hot day?

2. 0°C is sometimes referred to as the **frost point.** Explain what you think this means.

3. Explain how there can be 100% humidity on a day that is 80°C, as well as on a day that is 50 °C.

4. Explain how sweating works.

5. What is the difference between the relative humidity and the absolute humidity?

6. Use absolute humidity and temperature to explain why water condenses on the outside of a glass of ice cold lemonade, even though the day is very hot.

Rain in the Forecast

Name: _____
Period:_____ Date: _____

Purpose: This lesson allows you to explore what conditions are necessary for water vapor to condense and form rain.

Part I: Maximum absolute humidity

The line on the graph below shows the maximum absolute humidity vs. temperature. Use the graphs to answer the questions below.

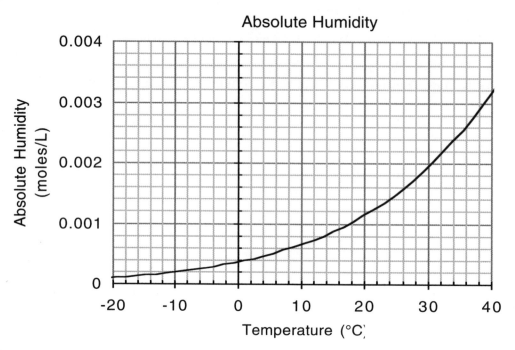

Answer the following questions:

1. Is it possible to have 0.001 moles of water vapor per liter of air at 10°C? Explain your answer.

2. Is it possible to have 0.001 moles of water vapor per liter of air at 30°C? Explain your answer.

3. When you have 0.001 moles of water vapor per liter of air at 18°C, it begins to rain. Explain why.

4. Suppose the absolute humidity is 0.0015 moles of water vapor per liter of air at 35°C. It cools overnight to 25°C and you find drops of dew on the grass in the morning. Explain why.

For a given absolute humidity, meteorologists call the temperature at which the maximum absolute humidity is reached the **dew point.**

5. Lightly shade the area on the graph showing all the possible values for the absolute humidity. (Hint: The curve represents the *maximum* value for the absolute humidity.)

        Weather © UC Regents, LHS Living by Chemistry, 2003.

6. Why do you suppose meteorologists call the temperature at which the absolute humidity reaches the maximum value the dew point?

7. The following table shows the temperature of the air as a function of altitude. Use the graph to assist you in answering questions about the table below.

Altitude	2000 ft	4000 ft	6000 ft	8000 ft	10000 ft
Temperature	11°C	7.2°C	3.3°C	–1.1°C	–5.0°C

a) What is the maximum absolute humidity at 4,000 feet?

b) What is the maximum absolute humidity at 10,000 feet?

c) Will water vapor condense to rain at 2,000 feet if the absolute humidity is 0.0007 moles per liter?

d) As the absolute humidity in the air increases, do clouds form at lower or higher elevations? Explain your thinking.

8. Why is the relative humidity at the dew point always 100%?

Part II: How hot you feel

How hot you feel depends on both the humidity and the temperature. The following questions will help you understand why.

Answer the following questions:

1. Put a drop of water on your skin. Spread it around a little. Put a drop of alcohol on your skin nearby. Spread it around a little. Blow on the area. What do you feel?

2. What is happening with the alcohol and the water on your skin? Why does one feel colder than the other?

3. Why do you think you feel cool when you get out of a swimming pool dripping wet?

4. Heat is required to evaporate liquids. Why does sweating cool you off?

5. If the relative humidity is 100%, will your sweat evaporate? Why or why not?

6. Explain why 40% humidity at 75°F feels cooler than 80% humidity at 75°F.

Making sense

What do you need to know to decide if it will rain?

Under what weather conditions does sweating work well to cool you off?

If you finish early…

Dry air is denser than air with water vapor in it. Show how this is true.

The Conservation Biolo
Molluscs

Proceedings of a Symposium held at the 9th International
Malacological Congress, Edinburgh, Scotland, 1986.

Edited by E. Alison Kay

Including a Status Report on Molluscan Diversity,
written by E. Alison Kay.

IUCN/SSC Mollusc Specialist Group.

The World Conservation Union   Species Survival Commission

WWF   Sultanate of Oman   Chicago Zoological Society

Contents

Foreword

The Mollusc Specialist Group is one of several specialist groups established to provide advice and data to the Species Survival Commission (SSC), and through it, to the International Union for Conservation of Nature and Natural Resources (IUCN). An Action Plan is mandated of each Specialist Group by the Species Survival Commission and is the means by which Specialist Groups provide input into an overall SSC Action Programme, which is in turn used to develop the IUCN "Conservation Programme for Sustainable Development," the thesis of which is that the conservation of resources relies on sustainable development.

Recognizing the importance of molluscs in the life of humankind and the significant roles they play in ecosystems, the Mollusc Specialist Group (MSG) believes that continuing loss of mollusc diversity is detrimental not only to ecosystems around the world, but, in the long run, to the welfare of humankind itself. In an effort to ameliorate the increasing loss of diversity suffered by molluscs worldwide, this volume has been developed to provide a resource on the conservation status of molluscs today and some suggestions for the conservation of molluscan diversity in the future. There are two parts: 1) a series of papers summarizing the current status of molluscs presented at a Symposium on Endangered Molluscs at the 9th International Malacological Congress, held in Edinburgh, in September 1986; and 2) a status report on molluscan diversity worldwide.

The Symposium on Endangered Molluscs was commissioned by Resolution of the 8th International Malacological Congress, held in Budapest in September 1983:

"Recognizing that all biotic diversity is changing in a dramatic manner as a result of increasing pressures of man, and recognizing the need for the enunciation of priorities if we are to develop a world strategy which will insure the survival of species and genetic diversity, be it resolved that the Unitas Malacologica encourage and support the activities of the Species Survival Commission on Invertebrates of the International Union for Conservation of Nature, and in particular the work of the Species Survival Commission on Mollusca.

Be it further resolved that the Unitas Malacologica encourage and support a climate for research and education in such areas of concern as those of economically important species like the giant clam *Tridacna*, of endangered species such as the achatinellid snails of the Hawaiian Islands, and of areas of high molluscan diversity such as in the Madeira Islands.

And, be it further resolved that a meeting on the conservation of molluscs be organized for the 9th International Congress in Edinburgh in 1986."

The eight papers and five abstracts from the symposium are arranged in Section 1 in four chapters: 1) the keynote address, a synthesis of what we know and what we do not know about current pressures on molluscs; 2) a group of papers that address the pressures on especially vulnerable groups of Mollusca, namely those found in island habitats; 3) several papers dealing with the current status of molluscs on continents; and 4) a final paper representing a major statement on the economics of the shell trade, a continuing source of pressure on marine molluscs.

Section 2 presents a report on molluscan diversity. This status report focuses on the diversity of molluscs on continents, on islands, in freshwater, on coral reefs, as economic resources, as alien species, and as model systems. Five major actions are proposed for the conservation of molluscan diversity:

1) the acquisition and management of threatened habitats on islands, in aquatic ecosystems, on continents and on coral reefs;

2) the development of a data base necessary for knowledge of molluscan diversity;

3) the prevention of the introduction of alien species that have negative impacts on native mollusc species and control and eradication of those exotic species where such introductions have already occurred;

4) the establishment of self-sustaining captive populations of endangered mollusc species and support of their eventual re-introduction into their native habitats;

5) the promotion of public awareness and concern for molluscan conservation programmes.

E. Alison Kay
Mollusc Specialist

Editors Note:
The publication of the Proceedings of the Symposium held at the 9th International Malacological Congress, Edinburgh, Scotland, on 31 August - 6 September 1986 was subject to a number of delays. Because of the lateness of publication, authors of the papers making up the report of the proceedings were given an opportunity to check their original text and correct errors which appeared in the orginal text (which may have come to light after the text was submitted). Authors were specifically asked to refrain from updating their text with new information, but were invited to refer to sources of updated information if they wished, in a separate section to be inserted just after their original text.

SECTION 1: PROCEEDINGS OF THE SYMPOSIUM

Chapter 1: Keynote address

Which molluscs for extinction?

E. Alison Kay

Department of Zoology, University of Hawaii, Honolulu, Hawaii, 96822, U.S.A.

Abstract

Molluscs, along with other animals and plants, are undergoing an unprecedented rate of extinction. Does the record show differentially threat-prone groups of molluscs among major taxonomic categories? A data base of about 1130 species (and subspecies) considered threatened, endangered, rare and/or recently extinct was compiled from sources around the world. Three patterns emerge. The list is essentially geographically restricted to North America (the United States), Australia-New Zealand, and Europe. Ninety-eight percent of the species are freshwater and terrestrial molluscs, and 61% of the list is from nine families. The common characteristics of these "threat-prone" molluscs include late maturity, relatively great longevity, low fecundity, restricted distribution, and specialized habits and habitats. In contrast, there are molluscs which are "successful": the giant African snail, *Achatina fulica*, the carnivorous snail *Euglandina rosea*, and the freshwater bivalve *Corbicula fluminea* have nearly legendary reproductive and dispersal potentials; they are opportunistic, rapidly exploiting vacant niches; and they adapt to a wide range of habitats. If these ecological successes are the only survivors of the present extinction crisis, will the world of molluscs eventually be reduced to a few common species?

Introduction

Molluscs are among the most ancient of animals on earth today. They appear in the oldest Cambrian deposits, more than 500 million years BP. Molluscs are also among the most successful of all animals, and are second only to insects in numbers of species. As with other organisms however, the fossil record does not show the continuous presence of all families and genera through time. Groups at various taxonomic levels have appeared, radiated and disappeared: the rudists, ammonites and belemnites are among the best known molluscs of the fossil record but all were extinct by Tertiary time. There are innumerable local records — in the Eocene and Miocene of the Paris Basin, in the Pleistocene of the eastern coast of North America, and in the Miocene and Plio-Pleistocene deposits of Pacific islands — of genera and species which are now extinct.

In recent years it has become increasingly apparent that molluscs along with other animals and plants are undergoing yet another period of extinction. The current extinction differs from that in geological time in that it is occurring much more rapidly and is largely the result of human activities rather than of natural causes. Where the Permian and Cretaceous extinctions occurred over periods of a million or more years, the present extinctions of species occur in time spans of less than ten years. In the Hawaiian Islands before human colonization, the extinction rate for molluscs may have been on the order of one species per million years. With settlement by the Polynesians, it increased to perhaps one species per 100 years. Since 1778, the year Captain Cook discovered Hawaii for the western world, the extinction rate for molluscs has reached a rate of between one and three species a year (Kay and Schoenberg-Dole 1990). On Moorea in French Polynesia, eight species and subspecies of *Partula* became extinct in a period of less than 10 years, following the introduction of the carnivorous snail *Euglandina rosea* (Clark, *et al.* 1984; Murray, *et al.* 1988).

The problem

There is now an enormous literature on the present period of extinction, much of that literature published within the last decade. There are many generalizations about organisms which appear to be extinction-prone, among them: 1) the "basket cases," animals and plants enroute to extinction as a result of natural causes; 2) k-selected species, that is, those with long lives and low fecundity; 3) species which live on islands; 4) species with small geographical ranges; 5) species near the top of the pyramid of biomass or at the end of a food chain; 6) species with little or no power of dispersal; 7) species with large body size; 8) species requiring climax vegetation; 9) species with small populations; and 10) species with specialized niches.

The listed characteristics, which emerge from a variety of studies of rare and endangered species, serve as a profile for each group of organisms. In this review I analyze the molluscs in terms of that profile. Does the record show differentially threat-prone groups among major taxonomic categories? If so, this selectivity may tell us a great deal about what will become extinct in the near future.

To answer the question, a data base of about 1130 species (and subspecies) was compiled from national and international sources of mollusc species considered threatened, endangered, rare and/or recently (within the last 200 years) extinct, and the molluscs on the

Table 1.1 Molluscan families with estimated numbers of threatened species and subspecies.

	Number of species threatened		Number of species threatened
GASTROPODA			
PROSOBRANCHIA		**STYLOMMATOPHORA**	
Aciculidae	2	Acavidae	1
Assimineidae	10	Achatinellinae*	51
Bithyniidae	1	Amastridae	13
Helicinidae	2	Ammonitellidae	1
Hydrobiidae	128	Arionidae	3
Hydrocenidae	1	Bradybaenidae	1
Melaniidae	2	Bulimulidae	73
Muricidae	1	Camaenidae	5
Neritidae	5	Caryodidae	2
Pleuroceridae	79	Cerionidae	1
Pomatiasidae	2	Charopidae	36
Pomatiopsidae	1	Clausiliidae	11
Potamididae	3	Cochliocopidae	1
Ranellidae	1	Diplommatinidae	9
Turbinidae	1	Elonidae	1
Valvatidae	3	Endodontidae	12
Viviparidae	5	Enidae	4
		Haplotrematidae	1
OPISTHOBRANCHIA		Helicarionidae	43
Corambidae	1	Helicidae	29
		Helicodiscidae	6
BASOMMATOPHORA		Helminthoglyptidae	48
Acroloxidae	1	Limacidae	4
Anyclidae	9	Megaspiridae	1
Glacidorbidae	3	Oleacinidae	1
Lymnaeidae	7	Oreohelicidae	13
Physidae	14	Partulidae	23
Planorbidae	20	Polygyridae	23
		Punctidae	12
BIVALVIA		Pupillidae	16
Hyatellidae	1	Rhytididae	56
Hyriidae	2	Sagdidae	1
Margaritiferidae	6	Streptaxidae	3
Mytilidae	1	Subulinidae	8
Pteriidae	2	Succineidae	5
Sphaeriidae	17	Testacellidae	1
Tridacnidae	7	Vallonidae	5
Unionidae	158	Vertiginidae	18
		Zonitidae	22
		* = Subfamily	

list are examined for taxonomic composition, geography and their biological characteristics. The list was derived from lists circulated by the International Union for the Conservation of Nature (IUCN), the United States Office of Endangered Species, individual states in the United States, individual countries in Europe, and from compilations such as those of Basch (1963), Bogan and Parmalee (1983), Coppois and Wells (1987), Clarke (1976), Hubricht (1981), Solem, *et al.* (1982), Stansberry (1971), and Taylor (1980).

The mollusc data base

The results of simple computerized sorting of the database suggest three patterns.

1) There is a noticeable geographical skew among the items in the data base (Table 1.1), and the list is virtually restricted to North America (the United States) (40% of the list), Australia and New Zealand (19%) and Europe (16%). About 33% of the molluscs are species from oceanic islands.

2) The list (Table 1.1) is biased toward non-marine molluscs: about half the list consists of freshwater molluscs (prosobranchs and bivalves), and half are land snails (Stylommatophora). Only 22 (2%) of the 1130 molluscs on the list are marine molluscs.

3) Taxonomic groups are affected differently (Table 1.1): 61 percent of the list is derived from nine families. Among the prosobranchs, the Hydrobiidae and the Pleuroceridae bear the greatest species burdens: 83% of the prosobranchs on the list are in these two families. In the Stylommatophora, 69% of the 62 families include threatened species. Except for the Helminthoglyptidae of western North America with 20% of the species listed, the families occurring on islands are among the most heavily encumbered, that is, the achatinelline, amastrid and partulid land snails of Pacific islands, the Bulimulidae of the Galapagos Islands, and the Rhytididae of New Zealand. Only eight families of bivalves are on the list, and 81% of the 197 bivalves are unionids.

Characteristics of threat-prone groups

The foregoing summaries indicate that threat-proneness does not occur randomly among molluscs but that it is associated with certain groups of molluscs. A survey of the characteristics of the threat-prone families shows the following:

1) The families on the list represent for the most part actively

evolving groups of molluscs averaging six species per genus.

2) Body size (Table 1.2) is relatively large in six of the seven groups. In the Bulimulidae, Rhytididae, and Unionidae body size is on the order of 100 mm in length; in the Helminthoglyptidae, shells are 20-30 mm in diameter. Only in the Hydrobiidae are the shells small, usually less than 10 mm in greatest dimension.

3) Virtually all species on the list have restricted distributions (Table 1.2). In the Hydrobiidae and in the Pleuroceridae, 62 of 85 (73%) and 67 or 82% listed from the United States are, respectively, known only from single states. In the Helminthoglyptidae, all 52 species listed are from a single state and most are from single localities, sometimes a single rock pile. The epitome of short range and restricted distribution is on islands. In the Pacific, the achatinellines and Amastridae of Hawaii, Partulidae of Tahiti and Guam, and Bulimulidae of the Galapagos are, for the most part, single island endemics, and in some cases found only on single mountain ridges or in a single valley.

4) The molluscs on the list are specialists in habitat and food habits (Table 1.2). The Hydrobiidae are found in single drainage basins, springs, caves and other subterranean habitats where there are often impressive radiations (see Ponder, this volume; Ponder and Clark 1990). The Pleuroceridae and Unionidae are specialists in the shoal waters of the rivers of the United States where nearly all the rich freshwater fauna of central and southeastern North America evolved in or adjacent to a riffle or shoal habitat (Stansberry 1971). The Hawaiian achatinellines live in trees where they feed on fungal filaments on leaves. *Partula* of French Polynesia are similarly specialized, and include one species which is carnivorous (Cowie, 1992), and others which are humidity sensitive (Bloxam, *et al.* 1983). The Rhytididae of New Zealand have radiated into a variety of habitats from lowland forests to alpine grasslands, and are found deep in acidic leaf mould where they feed on earthworms and millipedes (Meads, *et al.* 1984).

5) The species for which there are data on reproduction show many similarities (Table 1.3). Threat-prone molluscs are relatively late in maturing: one and a half years in the pleurocerids, four to six years in the achatinellines, and 15 years in the rhytidid *Powelliphanta*. Many of the species are relatively long-lived: some pleurocerids live at least three years; achatinellines live 6 to 11 years, and *Powelliphanta* in New Zealand is thought to live at least 40 years. A record of 67 years for a unionid (Stober 1972) may be overly optimistic, and its life span is more probably 10-15 years (Dudgeon and Morton, 1981). Despite their long lives, fecundity is low: the achatinellines produce one to four offspring per year and no more than 60 eggs per year are known in the Helminthoglyptidae.

Table 1.2 Characteristics of molluscan families and subfamilies with major numbers of threatened and recently extinct species.

FAMILY/SUBFAMILY	SIZE	% RESTRICTED DISTRIBUTION	Hydrobiidae
Hydrobiidae	Small: <10mm	93%	Habitat
Pleuroceridae	Large: 30-50mm	83%	Habitat
Achatinellinae	Large: >20mm	100%	Habitat/Food
Bulimulidae	Large: >50-70mm	100%	Habitat
Helminthoglyptidae	Large: 15-30mm	100%	Habitat
Rhytididae	Large: >90mm	100%	Habitat/Food
Uionidae	Large: >70mm	70%	Habitat/Larvae/Fish Host

In the Unionidae and Hyriidae the life cycle is complicated by the insertion of the glochidium stage in the life history, and the water-borne larva must attach to a fish host.

Molluscs that are successful

Not all molluscs are on threatened and endangered lists. Many species are well known for large population densities and broad geographical ranges. Among these "successful" molluscs are the giant African snail, *Achatina fulica* and the carnivorous snail *Euglandina rosea* both of which are now widespread on Pacific islands, and the freshwater bivalve, *Corbicula fluminea*, which made its way through rivers and streams from California to the Rio Grande drainage of Texas between 1956 and the early 1960's and then to the eastern seaboard by 1972 (McMahon 1983).

The dispersal of these molluscs is clearly associated with human activity. They also have in common early maturation, high fecundity, considerable interpopulation variability, and they are easily dispersed and highly adaptable. They are representatives of

TAXON	AGE 1ST REPRODUCTION (YEARS)	LONGEVITY (YEARS)	FECUNDITY	REFERENCES
Table 1.3 Reproduction characteristics of some threatened and "successful" molluscs.				
THREATENED MOLLUSCS				
GASTROPODA				
Achatinellinae				
Achatinella mustellina	7	11	1	Hadfield and Mountain 1980
Partulina redfieldii	4	11	1-4	Hadfield 1986
Partulina proxima	5-7	18-19	6.2	Hadfield and Miller 1989
Partulidae				
Partula spp.	.8-1.5	16-17	16-19	Murray and Clarke 1966
Bulimulidae				
Liguus fasciatus	4	6	~19	Voss 1976
Rhytididae				
Powelliphanta/Paryphanta	15	40	3-20	Meads, et al. 1984; O'Connor 1946
Helminthoglyptidae				
Helminthoglyptids	3-5	5-10	60	Walton 1963;Roth, pers. comm.
BIVALVIA				
Margaritiferidae				
Margaritifera margaritifera	12-15	70-100	3-4 million (glochidial larvae, fish hosts)	Young and Williams 1984a, 1984b
"SUCCESSFUL" MOLLUSCS				
GASTROPODA				
Achatinidae				
Achatina fulica	0.5	5-6	1200	Mead 1961
Oleacinidae				
Euglandina rosea	<1	1-2	100-200	Chiu and Chou 1962
BIVALVIA				
Corbiculidae				
Corbicula Fluminea	<1	1-2	8,000 (lab) 68,678 (field) (veligers)	McMahon 1983

4

families which are evolutionarily conservative, usually with only one to three genera in the families.

The reproductive and dispersal potential of all three molluscs are legendary. *Achatina fulica* was transported from its native Africa to Asia for food in the 1920's, and since then has been hand carried, transported in mud on jeep tires during World War II, and carried in flower pots, across the Pacific and even to Florida (Mead 1961). The giant African snail is reported to mature in less than a year (Pawson and Chase, 1984) and may produce 300 eggs per clutch with clutches deposited four times a year. Mead (1961) calculated the potential offspring from a snail of this sort could number about seven billion in three years. *Euglandina rosea* also matures in less than a year (Chiu and Chou 1962), and is highly fecund and capable of building up large populations within a short period of time. Population studies in Hawaii indicate that following the release of about 600 snails in 1955, the population tripled within two years, and numbered some 12,000 snails within three years (Davis and Butler 1964). Initially released in the lowlands where *Achatina fulica* infestations were significant, *Euglandina* was recorded in the Koolau mountains of Oahu in 1967 and in the Waianae range in 1969 (van der Schalie 1969). On Moorea, in French Polynesia, *E. rosea* was similarly introduced to control the giant African snail in 1977, and spread within a year from its point of introduction into the adjoining forests. By 1980 its range covered approximately 4 km^2, nearly a third of the island (Clarke *et al.* 1984), and by 1987 it was found at or near the top of every mountain crest on the island (Murray *et al.* 1988).

The small bivalve, *Corbicula fluminea*, an Asian immigrant to North America, is similarly invasive. Eurytopic and seemingly unaffected by changes in temperature, pH and siltation, *Corbicula* matures in less than a year and produces enormous numbers of offspring: one individual can release perhaps as many as 68,670 juveniles per year (McMahon 1983). A European counterpart, *Dreissena polymorpha*, which spread from the Black and Caspian Seas to London docks in 1824 (Morton 1969), has since become a pest in the reservoirs and water systems of India, Hong Kong, southern China, and the United States.

The spectrum of life history

The life histories and habits of all organisms lie on a spectrum of time and strategy. What emerges in this analysis is a profile in which threat-prone molluscs are at one end of the spectrum and the successes on the other. Those molluscs which are actively evolving, specialized, late maturing, and which have low fecundity are at one end; they are found on the east coast of the United States, in southern Europe, on oceanic islands and in isolated lakes. The opportunists and the generalists which mature early and have a high fecundity are at the other end of the spectrum. In addition to the successes that do not appear on the list, there are a variety of other molluscs with life histories and habits which do not qualify them for the extinction-prone list. The basommatophorans such as *Lymnaea* fall on the spectrum near the "successes": they survive drought and flood, grow quickly, mature early, and can produce large numbers of offspring. Most marine molluscs are not on the list by virtue of their habits and physiology: they are easily dispersed, have wide ranges and are highly fecund. Those which

are on the list, for example, the giant clam *Tridacna*, have a restricted distribution, extremely large size and long period of growth (Yamaguchi 1977).

The model proposed above is consistent with the model for land snail diversity proposed by Solem (1984). Indeed, if Solem's model were expanded to include freshwater molluscs the two models would be entirely congruent.

Which molluscs will survive?

There remain two questions. What is the impact of the present burst of extinction on mollusc families? Which molluscs will survive?

There are about 90 families of non-marine molluscs. More than 80% percent of the families are represented on the list. Within those families, the species on the list represent 57% of the 200 species of North American Hydrobiidae, 52% of the 150 species of Pleuroceridae; more than 85% of the 190 species of Unionidae; 59% of the 41 species of Hawaiian achatinelline snails; more than 30% of the 48 species of the Rhytididae of New Zealand; and more than 50% of the 57 species of Galapagos Islands' Bulimulidae. More of the molluscs not now on the list will undoubtedly be added to it. Among these molluscs are the Bulimulidae of South America, the Camaenidae of the Philippines, the South Australian cowries with restricted ranges and direct development and the highly endemic element of marine molluscs in the Red Sea.

The survivors will form the nucleus of a vastly reduced pool of species. In the case of the Mollusca, those species which survive are the opportunistic species which can rapidly exploit vacant niches by making widespread use of food resources, which are relatively short-lived with high rates of population increase, which are adaptable to a wide range of environments, and which prosper in disrupted habitats, especially those habitats which have been impacted by humans.

A useful distinction has been made between short term or ecological success and long term or evolutionary success (Hickman 1982). This distinction can serve both for interpretation of the geological record of the past and predictions for the future. The geological record of the Pleurotomariidae (Figure 1.1) may serve as a model. As a family the Pleurotomariidae was diverse in Jurassic time, but suffered bottlenecks of extinction in the Triassic and Paleogene. Some members of the family survive today but they are few in number and far less diverse in habit and form than they were in the Jurassic (Hickman 1984). If the ecological successes among the molluscs of today are the only survivors of the present extinction will they become evolutionary successes, or will the world of molluscs be reduced to a few common species?

Acknowledgements

I am grateful to the many malacologists who have provided me with lists and insights into this problem of rare and endangered species. I am especially grateful to Brian Smith, formerly of Melbourne, Australia, and Mike Kerney, British Museum (Natural History), for the many hours they spent in both discussion and the provision of lists.

Literature cited

BASCH, P.F. 1963. A review of the recent freshwater limpet snails of North America (Mollusca: Pulmonata). *Bulletin of the Museum of Comparative Zoology*, Harvard University, 129: 399-461.

BLOXAM, Q.E., S.J. TONGE, R. HORTON. 1983. A preliminary account of the history and management of populations of endangered Moorean tree snail *Partula* spp. at Jersey Wildlife Preservation Trust. *Dodo, Journal Jersey Wildlife Preservation Trust* 20: 73-79.

BOGAN, A.E. AND PARMALEE, P.W. 1983. *Tennessee's Rare Wildlife*, Volume II: *The Mollusks*. Tennessee Wildlife Resources Agency, Nashville, Tennessee, 123 pp.

CHIU, S-C. AND CHOU, K-C. 1962. Observations on the biology of the carnivorous snail *Euglandina rosea* Ferussac. *Bulletin of the Institute of Zoology, Academia Sinica*, 1: 17-24.

CLARKE, A.H. 1976. Endangered freshwater mollusks of north-western North America. *Bulletin of the American Malacoogical Union*. 1976: 18-19.

CLARKE, B., J. MURRAY, AND M.S. JOHNSON. 1984. The extinction of endemic species by a program of biological control. *Pacific Science*, 38: 97-104.

COPPOIS, G. AND S. WELLS. 1987. Threatened Galapagos snails. *Oryx*, 21: 236-241.

COWIE, R.H. 1992. Evolution and extinction of Partulidae, endemic Pacific island land snails. *Phil. Trans. R. Soc.* Lond. B 335: 167-191.

DAVIS, C.J. AND G.D. BUTLER. JR. 1964. Introduced enemies of the giant African snail, *Achatina fulica* Bowdich, in Hawaii (Pulmonata: Achatinidae). *Proceedings of the Hawaiian Entomological Society*, 18: 377-389.

DUDGEON, D. AND B. MORTON. 1983. The population dynamics and sexual strategy of *Anodonta woodiana* (Bivalvia: Unionacea) in Plover Cove Reservoir, Hong Kong. *Journ. Zool. London* 201: 161-183

HADFIELD, M.G. 1986. Extinction in Hawaiian achatinelline snails. *Malacologia* 27: 67-81.

HADFIELD, M.G. AND B.S. MOUNTAIN. 1981 [for 1980]. A field study of a vanishing species, *Achatinella mustelina* (Gastropoda, Pulmonata), in the Waianae mountains of Oahu. *Pacific. Science* 34: 345-358.

HADFIELD, M.G. AND S.E. MILLER. 1989. Demographic studies of *Partulina proxima*. *Pacific Science* 3: 1-16.

HICKMAN, C. 1982. The single helix: successful gastropods or successful paleontologists? *Third North American Paleontological Convention Proceedings*, 1: 237-242.

HICKMAN, C. 1984. *Pleurotomaria*: pedigreed perseverance. In: Eldredge, N. and S.M. Stanley (Eds.), *Living fossils*. Springer-Verlag, New York. 291 pp.

HUBRICHT, L. 1981. The endangered land snails of the eastern United States. *Bulletin of the American Malacological Union*, 1981: 53-54.

MCMAHON, R.F. 1983. Ecology of an invasive pest bivalve. *Corbicula*. In: W.D. Russell-Hunter (Ed.), *The Mollusca*, Vol. 6. pp. 505-561. New York: Academic Press.

MEAD, A.R. 1961. *The Giant African snail. A Problem in economic malacology*. Univ. of Chicago Press. 257 pp.

MEADS, M.J., WALKER, K.J., AND G.P. ELLIOTT. 1984. Status, Conservation, and management of the land snails of the genus *Powelliphanta* (Mollusca: Pulmonata). *New Zealand Journal of Zoology*, 11: 277-306.

MORTON, B. 1969. Studies on the biology of *Dreissena polymorpha* Pall. I. General anatomy and morphology. *Proceedings of the Malacological Society of London*, 38: 301-321.

MURRAY, J. AND B. CLARKE. 1966. The inheritance of polymorphic shell characters in *Partula* (Gastropoda). *Genetics* 54: 1261-1277.

MURRAY, J., E. MURRAY, M.S. JOHNSON, AND B. CLARKE. 1988. The extinction of *Partula* on Moorea. *Pacific Science* 42: 150-153.

PAWSON, P.A. AND R. CHASE. 1984. The life-cycle and reproductive activity of *Achatina fulica* (Bowdich) in laboratory culture. *Journal of Molluscan Studies* 50: 85-91.

PONDER, W.F. AND G.A. CLARK. 1990. A radiation of hydrobiid snails in threatened artesian springs in western Queensland. *Records Australian Museum* 42: 301-363.

VAN DER SCHALIE, H. 1969. Man meddles with nature - Hawaiian style. *The Biologist* 51: 136-146.

SOLEM, A.G. 1984. A world model of land snail diversity and abundance. In: A. Solem and A.C. Van Bruggen, (Eds.), *World-Wide Snails*. E.J. Brill/ Dr. W. Backhuys, Leiden. 289 pp.

SOLEM, A.G., E-L. GIRARDI, S. SLACK-SMITH, AND G.W. KENDRICK. 1982. *Austrassiminea letha*, gen. nov., sp. nov., a rare and endangered prosobranch snail from south-western Australia (Mollusca: Prosobranchia; Assimineidae). *Journal of the Royal Society of Western Australia*, 65: 119-129.

STANSBERRY, D.H. 1971. Rare and endangered freshwater mollusks in eastern United States. In: S.E. Jorgenson and R.W. Sharp, *Proceedings of a Symposium Rare and Endangered Mollusks (Naiads) of the U.S.* U.S. Dept. of the Interior Fish and Wild Life Service Bureau of Sport Fisheries and Wildlife Region 3.

STOBER, Q.J. 1972. Distribution and age of *Margaritifera margaritifera* in a Madison River (Montana, U.S.A.) mussel bed. *Malacologia* 11:343-350.

TAYLOR, D.W. 1980. Endangered and threatened freshwater mollusks of Armagosa drainage, California-Nevada. In: Williams, J.E., G.C. Kobelich and C.T. Benz (Eds.), *Management Aspects of Relict Populations Inhabiting the Armagosa Drainage*. University of California Press, Berkeley.

VOSS. G. 1976. Observations on the ecology of the Florida tree snail *Liguus fasciatus* (Muller). *Nautilus* 90: 65-69.

WALTON, 1963. Length of life of west American land snails. *Nautilus* 76: 127-131.

YAMAGUCHI, M. 1977. Conservation and cultivation of giant clams in the tropical Pacific. *Biological Conservation* 11: 13-20.

Figure 1. Generic diversity of the Pleurotomariidae over geological time. (Adapted from Hickman 1984).

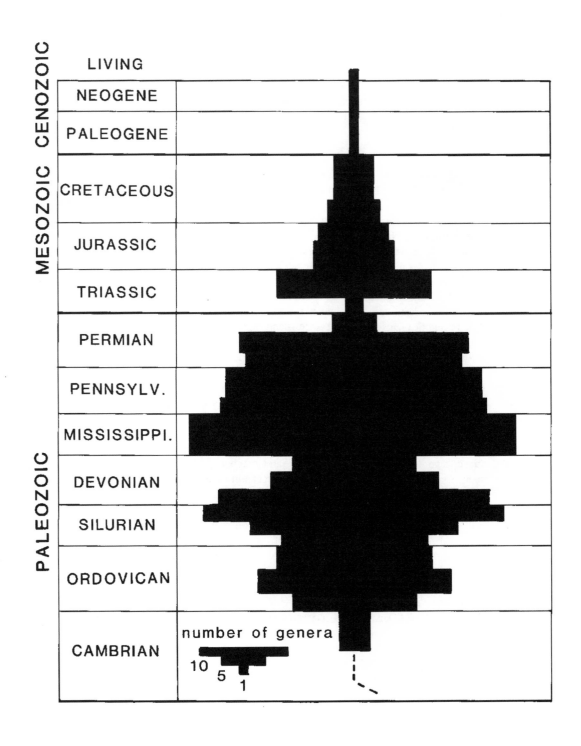

Chapter 2: The vulnerability of "island" species

Threatened galapagos bulimulid land snails: an update

Guy Coppois

Contribution No. 412 of the Charles Darwin Foundation for the Galapagos Islands.
Laboratoire Biologie Générale. CP. 168.
Université Libre de Bruxelles, 28 avenue Paul Héger,
B-1050 Bruxelles, Belgium.

Abstract

The Galapagos malacofauna is largely dominated by the Bulimulidae (90% of the species present). Many species of these endemic gastropods have, or had, their natural habitat in areas where local residents are developing their settlements. These areas are considered "colonised zones", excluded from the National Park, and legislation relating to environmental protection does not apply in these zones.

Human activities have contributed to the reduction in distribution of the bulimulids and are responsible for the extinction of many species. The original vegetation has been destroyed or altered in some areas through the introduction of exotic plants, and forests have suffered from heavy grazing by introduced goats, pigs and cattle. Other human activities, such as road building, fire-wood collection and setting intentional or accidental fires, may also result in localised but drastic changes in the biotope which lead to the elimination of entire populations of bulimulids. Introduced predators such as the little fire ant (*Wasmannia auropunctata*), and the black rat (*Rattus*) have great impact on the native biota. Potential competitors, for example, *Subulina octona* and *Deroceras* sp., have also been introduced. The influence of climatic changes is discussed with special reference to the consequences of the Niño event of 1982-1983.

Introduction

The Galapagos fauna has provided abundant material for the study of speciation and adaptive radiation. The groups most studied are the vertebrates, such as the tortoises (*Geochelone elephantopus*) and the well known finches (Geospizinae) used by Charles Darwin (1859) to support his theory of evolution. Among the invertebrates, land snails in the Bulimulidae also underwent a spectacular speciation process within the archipelago. With about 65 described species and several subspecies or forms, totalling 93 taxa, the Galapagos Bulimulidae far outnumber Darwin's finches.

The morphological diversity shown in the Galapagos bulimulids is surprising: the general shape of the shell, the shape of the aperture and of the umbilicus, the sculpture of the umbilicus, colour and size vary from one species to another. Smith (1966) noticed that "no where else has so large a number of species been found within an equally limited area; and nowhere else do they exhibit so great a variation in so many different particulars". The

Galapagos bulimulids are adapted to a wide range of climatic conditions and habitats: some species live in near-desert conditions, others are found only in humid forests with a more temperate climate.

All bulimulid species found in the Galapagos are endemic. They are represented on almost all sizable islands of the Archipelago, but are not found on Wolf or Darwin (which are isolated far north of the central group of islands), or on Marchena, Genovesa (Tower), Seymour Norte or Baltra. Species generally differ from one island to another and few species are found on more than two or three islands. Usually there is higher diversity on the elevated islands where a marked vegetal zonation parallels the climatic gradient from the arid coastal zones to humid highlands and where habitats are more diversified. For instance, Santa Cruz (altitude 864m) has the greatest diversity with 23 species (Coppois and Glowacki 1982; Coppois 1984), and is the island with the most varied vegetation. One exception is Pinta (altitude 777m) which has only one species.

Many species were described at the end of the 19th century from Floreana, San Cristobal and Santiago, but most of these are now extinct. Specimens in various museums around the world testify to their former existence, but they cannot be found in the field today. Furthermore, many of the remaining species are now endangered (Coppois and Wells 1986). In this review, two main categories of threats are considered: that resulting from human colonisation of the Galapagos, and that due to natural climatic changes.

Colonisation of the Galapagos Islands

Human colonisation of the Galapagos began early in the 19th century with a small settlement on Floreana (Hickman 1985). The first arrival, in 1807, was an Irishman, Patrick Watkins, who stayed involuntarily for two years only, growing vegetables to survive. He was followed by Ecuadorian settlers led by General Villamil who established an important penal colony on Floreana after the islands were annexed in 1832. The Ecuadorians introduced many domestic animals and brought land into cultivation. In 1835, the year Charles Darwin visited the Islands, the human population of the Archipelago numbered only 200 at most. After the failure of their "orchilla" industry (collecting dyer's moss, *Rocella tinctoria*), the settlers moved to San Cristobal around 1847. Santa Cruz was neglected for a long time, and colonized only after 1920. This is certainly the reason why so many bulimulid species are still found on Santa Cruz: unlike the three other inhabited islands, the effect of colonisation has not yet become so destructive.

The situation has changed over the last two decades: from 3500 people in 1973, the human population of the Galapagos is now more than 12,000. On Santa Cruz alone, the local population (Ecuadorian colonists and a few foreign families) rose from 850 in 1973 to more than 4500 in 1986. More than 20,000 tourists visited the Galapagos in 1986, although their direct impact on bulimulid habitat is negligible.

Habitat Destruction

It is important to realize that the National Park does not include all the Galapagos. People are allowed to settle in what are termed the "colonized zones". These zones include villages along the coasts where most people live, as well as wide areas in the highlands where farms have been established. Huge areas of native forest were cleared for agriculture and transformed into grassland for cattle and horses. Unfortunately, these zones with a humid and temperate climate and *Scalesia* forests were also the most suitable habitat for many land snail species. Entire populations were exterminated. For example, *Bulimulus (Naesiotus) blombergi* was, when it was described, a common tree snail on Santa Cruz at an altitude of 250-400m. The remaining living populations inhabited relic forests along the road between the villages of Bellavista and Santa Rosa, at "Occidente". Although the forests survived, the microclimate was modified by clearing of the surrounding areas for sugar cane plantations, and *B. blombergi* disappeared in 1975. Similar examples can be found on all of the inhabited islands.

On Floreana, the habitat has been greatly changed as the native forests were destroyed and replaced by crops, orange trees, and guava trees (*Psidium guajava*, Myrtaceae). The exotic guava is spreading rapidly on all islands where it has been introduced, replacing the local vegetation. Such changes in habitat are fatal to the malacofauna and other native invertebrates. Only two bulimulid species (*B. nux nuciformis* and *B. ustulatus*) are still found in remnants of the native forest near the base of Cerro Pajas, the top of Floreana. Not more than 15 years ago, another fast growing tree, *Cinchona succirubra* (Rubiaceae), was introduced on Santa Cruz,and is modifying the highland region (Eliasson 1982).

Uncontrolled fires sometimes spread out of the colonisation zones and cause drastic habitat destruction. The last one of a long list was disastrous enough to attract the attention of the mass media around the world. It lasted for at least four months (from late February to June 1985 (Anon. 1985a, 1985b)), and destroyed many populations of three bulimulid species on Sierra Negra Volcano (behind Villamil) from an altitude of 200m to the rim. Some populations of these species still survive in other places on the southern slopes of Sierra Negra but their chance of survival is reduced as most of them are located in the colonised zone. This catastrophic fire originated from a fire to burn rotten coffee trees.

Since transport has always been a problem on the inhabited islands, roads have now been built. Although destruction was localised, entire hills have been destroyed, both within and without the National Park, in order to obtain gravel. In one place at least,

on Cerro Maternidad (Santa Cruz), gravel pits destroyed a sizable part of the very limited habitat of *B. cavagnaroi* and altered the microclimate on the slope of the hill where the remaining population lived.

Introduced animals

Habitat destruction is sometimes not intentional but is a consequence of other activities, such as the release of goats or other domestic animals on deserted islands. The first known case of the introduction of exotic animals into the Galapagos was reported by Captain David Porter (1822) from the U.S. frigate *Essex*: in 1813 four goats were lost on Santiago, where they had been dropped for grazing. More recently, in 1954 on Pinta, local fishermen released goats to provide fresh meat when they returned for the next fishing trip. Feral goats reproduce rapidly and they soon became one of the major threats to Galapagos wildlife. They have had an extremely destructive impact on the vegetation of at least nine islands, and have caused severe erosion which has resulted in the loss of land snail habitat. *B. darwini* is one of the goats' victims and must now be considered extinct. The last live specimens were seen in 1975 (pers. observ.).

Bulimulids have a few natural predators such as the mockingbird (*Nesomimus parvulus*), the woodpecker finch (*Camarhynchus pallidus*) and the Galapagos centipede (*Scolpendra galapagensis*). Predation by mockingbirds on *B. reibishi* and *B. wolfi* has been seen in the "transition zone" of Santa Cruz. The body of the snail was seized in the beak and the shell knocked against a stone until it broke. The woodpecker finch used the same method to pick up specimens of *B. deridderi* in the valley of Cerro Coralon (Santa Cruz highlands, altitude 650m); as no stones were available, the shell was shaken against the twigs of bushes, mainly *Sida rhombifolia* on which *B. deridderi* was common. Such observations have not previously been reported and are worth mentioning. As the land snails are rarer in these areas now, their disappearance will affect the finches' diet. Predation by the centipedes has never been observed directly, but, in the centipedes' hiding places under lava blocks, broken shells are common, and careful observation of the hiding places has shown that there are no other possible predators. Observed prey of centipedes are *B. tanneri* and *B. wolfi* in the arid and transition zones on Santa Cruz. Other possible natural predators are endemic rice rats, but these are now extinct on Santiago, Floreana and Santa Cruz. Only two species of rice rat are still living, one on Fernandina (*Nesoryzomys narboroughi*) and one on Santa Fe (*Oryzomys bauri*). Characteristically broken shells were collected on Santa Fe and support the idea that endemic rats effectively prey on land snails, but no other information is available. All these natural predators had a very limited impact on snail populations, unlike the introduced predators such as fire ants (*Wasmannia auropunctata*), black rats (*Rattus rattus*) and mice (*Mus musculus*), although little is known of the impact of the last mentioned in the Galapagos as no studies have been carried out.

The little fire ant, *Wasmannia auropunctata*, was introduced to Santa Cruz less than half a century ago, between 1924-1934 (Kastkalen 1982; Clark *et al.* 1982; Lubin 1984, 1985). It is now common on all inhabited islands and also on some of the uninhabited islands, often around the landing places. Although only 2mm long, the fire ants outcompete other ant species and prey on other invertebrates. In areas of high densities of *Wasmannia*, bulimulid populations are low or even absent. Direct attack of *Wasmannia* has been observed on land snails on rare occasions, and these ants can inflict a painful sting even on humans. A possibly greater threat than the direct attack on adult snails is predation by the ants on juveniles and eggs. Bulimulids often lay their eggs in empty shells which are also used by the ants as nests. So far, no successful methods for eliminating fire ants have been found.

The other main introduced predator, the black rat (Clark, D.A. 1980, Clark, D.B. 1980), is widespread and was already established on some of the islands by the time of Darwin's visit (Patton 1984). In the El Junco area on San Cristobal, it is difficult to find any intact snails: on most shells of *B. nux incrassatus*, the apex is chewed. The snail may survive if just the tip of the shell has been removed, but empty broken shells are found along the "rat paths" in the vicinity of rat burrows. Similar observations have been made on other islands, such as Santiago (*B. darwini*), Sierra Negra volcano (*B. albemarlensis, B. tortuganus*) and Santa Cruz (*B. ochsneri, B. cavagnaroi, B. wolfi, B. deridderi* and many other species) where broken shells are common in some places.

I should also mention that two molluscs were introduced in some places (mainly the inhabited colonised zones): *Subulina octona* and a slug, *Deroceras* sp. However, there is no evidence of competition between these molluscs and the bulimulids. In one place, along the occasional stream from El Junco lake to Fresh Water Bay on San Cristobal, *S. octona* is the only live snail to be found; all bulimulids, including *B. achatellinus* (Smith, 1971), had disappeared by the beginning of the century, probably because of habitat destruction.

Natural climatic changes

The El Niño event of 1982-1983 (Robinson and del Pino 1985) had a catastrophic impact on many bulimulid populations. El Nino is the name of an abrupt change in the weather that usually begins around December and causes a rapid rise in sea water temperature and heavy rainfall. Since 1940, there have been 10 El Nino events, but none of them had as serious an impact on Galapagos wildlife as the El Nino of 1982-1983. Using coral aging techniques, Peter Glynn (pers. comm.) showed that the previous El Nino event of comparable importance in the Galapagos could only have happened 160 years ago; similar measurements in Panama suggest 190 years.

In early 1983, sea water temperature rose from 4 to 8°C above the average temperature. These high temperatures persisted long enough to destroy or alter the populations of many marine organisms on which other animals depended, such as the marine iguanas, birds and sea lions (Merlen 1985). Rainfall was ten times higher from December to July than the average for the previous 17 years: 3223mm of rain was recorded at the Darwin Station (arid coastal zone, altitude 2m, south Santa Cruz) between December 1, 1982 and July 31, 1983; the average precipitation recorded for the same eight month period from 1965 to 1982 (inclusive) was 345mm. No precise data are available to show how bulimulid land snails responded to these unusual conditions. In fact, it seems that many bulimulid species benefited from the abundance of water,

particularly in the arid zones (Andre De Roy, pers. comm.). However, in the *Scalesia* forests, the trees began to rot and subsequently fell, causing major modification of the land snails' habitat.

Scalesia pedunculata trees are 10 to 15m high and form a closed canopy which provides continuous shade for the undergrowth where the bulimulids live, in a protected and temperate microclimate. After the El Nino of 1982-1983, few trees remained, and the herb and shrub layer was exposed directly to the sun. The habitat would have become rapidly drier once the heavy rainfall ceased. Unfortunately, the years 1984 and (mainly) 1985 were unusually hot and dry, and many bulimulid species living in these forests died from excessive drought. At the Darwin Station, a total of 2768.9 mm precipitation was recorded in 1983, 146.9mm in 1984, but only 62.8mm in 1985. The annual average from 1965 to 1982 was 386.5mm. However, the *Scalesia* forest is already recovering and young trees, 1.50m high, are now abundant (August 1986) but need ten more years to reach the size of those that fell.

It is still too early to know how many bulimulid species survived the El Nino event and the subsequent dry years. I had the opportunity to visit only a few sites in July and August 1986, and in many places on Santa Cruz, only empty shells were found. Some species with restricted distributions are obviously extinct because of these drastic climatic changes. However, this does not mean that all species disappeared and it can be assumed that at least for some, relic populations will survive, unless other adverse factors intervene. On Sierra Negra volcano where fire had already reduced their numbers, *B. albemarlensis* and *B. tortuguanus* were still common in some areas. These species were even found on introduced vegetation (*Kalanchoe pinnata* and *Pothomorpha peltata*), an observation which is quite uncommon.

Discussion and conclusions

About one half, and possibly even two-thirds, of the Galapagos bulimulid species are now extinct, including *Bulimulus nux* Sowerby, 1832, the first species to be described. Bulimulids were major victims of human colonisation of the islands, and suffered from habitat destruction and introduced predators. Some were victims of the drought after the dramatic 1982-1983 El Nino event. After previous similar El Nino events, bulimulids survived and entered a spectacular speciation. In fact, the survival of isolated populations after such an event could be a factor in bulimulid speciation. But, for many populations, the chances of surviving such an unusual event were certainly reduced by the destruction and changes brought about by human colonisation, resulting in the extinction of many species which might have survived if the 'human factor' had not been present. Numerous bulimulid species occurred on Santa Cruz until recently, often in high densities. Most of these disappeared in a relatively short period after the colonisation of the island. Similar processes took place on other inhabited islands at the beginning of this century. In colonised zones, the habitat was modified and there were microclimatic changes. Modification of the habitat in these places could also have altered the climate in surrounding areas, outside the colonised zone, although this is difficult to prove.

It has been suggested that the climate has become drier over the last 50 years (Kastdalen 1982), which could explain the extinction of certain species, such as *B. planospira* from Champion, where no human interference has been noticed. In fact, objective meteorological data only exist for the last 25 years; and they do not indicate any special trends. Colinvaux (1972) and Colinvaux and Schofield (1975) have shown from palynological studies that the Galapagos climate was drier between 34,000 and 10,000 years ago, and that the present humid climate has been stable over 10,000 years. However, at the scale of a land snail's lifetime, one or two years of severe drought would be sufficient to destroy the entire population. Moreover, it is almost impossible to separate the influence of human activities from possible long term natural climatic changes. In a previous paper, Coppois (1984) reported that bulimulid populations disappeared for no obvious reason from the *Scalesia* forests of Santa Cruz in 1974, before the El Nino event. Is this extinction the result of a natural although undetected change in the climate, or the effect of some unknown factor, or is it the consequence of human activity? The question is still to be answered.

W.H. Dall (1896) wrote almost a century ago, "May it not be hoped, therefore, that someone will undertake to make a thorough and complete survey of the malacology of these islands *the Galapagos* before it is too late. The study of development of specific forms can never be made complete in the Hawaiian Islands, because the sheep and goat have preceded the investigator. There is still a chance to study the problem in the Galapagos Islands, and it should not be lost." Unfortunately, it is possible that we are once again too late to study the adaptive radiation shown by an insular group of land snails, and that Galapagos bulimulids will slowly go extinct if no conservative action is taken immediately.

Acknowledgements

I wish to thank Prof. Jean Bouillon, the Fondation Leopold III and the Ministere de la Communaute francaise de Belgique for providing the funding for the mission; Prof. Karl Hainaut (Laboratoire de Biologie generale, ISEPK, U.L.B.) for providing equipment; the Galapagos National Park Service for providing the authorisation for this work and for their cooperation; Marco Robalino of the Charles Darwin Research Station for gathering the meteorological data; and finally Sue M. Wells who made a critical review of the text and suggested many improvements.

Literature cited

ANON. 1985a. Ordeal by fire and water. *Noticias de Galapagos* 41: 1-2.

ANON. 1985b. The great fire on Isabela. *Noticias de Galapagos* 42: 4-5.

CLARK, D.A. 1980. Age and sex dependent foraging strategies of a small mammalian omnivore *Rattus rattus*. *Journal of Animal Ecology* 49: 549-564.

CLARK, D.A. 1982. Foraging behaviour of a vertebrate omnivore *Rattus rattus* meal structure sampling and diet breadth.*Ecology* 63: 763-772.

CLARK, D.B. 1982. Population ecology of *Rattus rattus* across a desert montane forest gradient in the Galapagos Islands, Ecuador. *Ecology* 61: 1422-1433.

CLARK, D.B., GUAYASAMIN, C., PAZMINO, OL, DONOSO, C., DE-VILLACIS, Y., 1982. The tramp ant *Wasmannia auropunctata* autecology and effects on ant diversity and distribution on Santa Cruz Island, Galapagos, Ecuador. *Biotropica* 14 196-207.

COLINVAUX, P.A. 1972. Climate and the Galapagos Islands. *Nature* 240: 17-20.

COLINVAUX, P.A. and SCHOLFIELD, E.K. 1976. Historical ecology in the Galapagos Islands. I. A Holocene pollen record from El Junco lake, Isla San Cristobal. *Journal of Ecology* 64: 989-1012.

COPPOIS, G. 1984. Distribution of bulimulid land snails on the northern slope of Santa Cruz Island, Galapagos. *Biological Journal of the Linnean Society* 21: 217-227.

COPPOIS, G. and GLOWACKI, C. 1982. Bulimulid land snails from the Galapagos: 1. Factor analysis of Santa Cruz Island species. *Malacologia* 23: 209-219.

COPPOIS, G. and WELLS, S. 1987. Threatened Galapagos snails. *Oryx* 21: 236-241.

DARWIN, C. 1859. *The origin Species by Means of natural Selection, the Preservation of favoured Races in the Struggle for Life.* John Murray, London. 458 pp.

ELIASSON, U. 1982. Changes and constancy in the vegetation of the Galapagos Islands. *Noticias de Galapagos* 36: 7-12.

HICKMAN, J. 1985. *The Enchanted Islands. The Galapagos Dis-covered.* Anthony Nelson, Oswestry, England. 169 pp.

KASTDALEN, A. 1982. Changes in the biology of Santa Cruz Island between 1935 and 1965. *Noticias de Galapagos* 35: 7-12.

LUBIN, Y.D. 1984. Changes in the native fauna of the Galapagos Islands following invasion by the little red fire ant ,*Wasmannia auropunctata*. *Biological Journal of the Linnean Society* 21: 229-242.

MERLEN, G. 1985. The 1982-83 El Nino: some of its consequences for Galapagos wildlife. *Noticias de Galapagos* 41: 8-15.

PATTON, M.J. 1984. Genetical process in the Galapagos. *Bio-logical Journal of the Linnean Society* 21: 97-111.

PORTER, D. 1822. *Journal of a cruise made to the Pacific Ocean by Captain David Porter in the United States Frigate Essex in the years 1812, 1813, 1814.* Philadelphia. New York.

ROBINSON, G. and DEL PINO, E. 1985. *El Nino in the Galapagos Islands, the 1982-83 event.* Publ. Charles Darwin Foundation for the Galapagos, Quito. 534 pp.

SMITH, A.G. 1966. Land snails of the Galapagos. In: Bowman, R.I. (Ed.). *The Galapagos.* Proceedings of the Symposia of the Galapagos International Scientific Project. University of California Press, Berkeley. pp. 240-251.

SMITH, A.G. 1971. New record for a rare Galapagos land snail. *Nautilus* 85: 5-8.

Demographic studies on Hawaii's endangered tree snails

Michael G. Hadfield

University of Hawaii, Kewalo Marine Laboratory and Department of Zoology, 41 Ahui Street, Honolulu, Hawaii 96813, U.S.A.

Published as: Hadfield, M.G. and S. E. Miller. 1989. Demographic studies of Partulina proxima. Pacific Science 43 (1): 1-16.

Abstract

Members of the pulmonate subfamily Achatinellinae are endemic to the Hawaiian Islands. Species of these large (15-25mm), colourful tree snails have been going extinct over the last 80-100 years, and remaining populations are found only in high-altitude stands of native forest. In spite of the massive collections of shells that have been accumulated by the world's museums, only meagre, anecdotal information has been collected on achatinelline biology and life history. *Partulina proxima* is one of the four achatinelline species currently under study, using mark-recapture techniques to assess major life history parameters. The study area is on the island of Molokai at an elevation of 1200m. Three single-bush populations have been visited bi-monthly for two years, and all snails found on each visit have been marked, measured and released. Average numbers of snails in the three bushes were 10, 14, and 30, and there was no evidence of significant immigration. Thus population fluctuations appeared to result from birth and death alone. Numbers of reproductively mature adults were only 2, 2, and 6 (about 15% of the snails present) in the three bushes, and each of these adults produced 4-6 offspring per year. Early mortality (and/or out migration) was extremely high, but adult longevity is probably great. The life history traits observed for *P. proxima* (large birth size; slow growth; late maturity; low fecundity; and long life) are similar to those of closely related species in this sub-family studied by the author, but differ in specific details. A life history pattern of this type can only exist in the virtual absence of predation on adult snails. Causes of extinction will be discussed.

Mound spring snails of the Australian Great Artesian Basin

W.F. Ponder

Invertebrate Division, Australian Museum, Sydney, New South Wales, Australia.

Abstract

Many of the springs associated with the Great Artesian Basin of Australia contain rare flora and endemic fishes and invertebrates, including at least 24 species of hydrobiid snails in five genera, three of them endemic. Numerous springs have become extinct in the last hundred years because of water extraction from the Great Artesian Basin, and most of the remaining springs are threatened.

Introduction

The central problem in most conservation issues is the protection of habitats. Once these are adequately protected, the survival of the species contained in those habitats is much more likely. Other issues, such as the introduction of exotic competitors, predators or diseases, are secondary, although often very serious, problems.

Situations most difficult to resolve are those in which man's needs for a particular resource conflict with the conservation of that resource. Proper management measures involve controlled access, often resulting in a reduction in utilization which may affect an individual's income or livelihood. The access to water in arid lands is one of the fundamental rights that anyone utilizing such lands might expect but, in arid Australia, the use of artesian water is central to the continued existence of at least 38 species of aquatic invertebrates which live in unusual and biologically unique springs.

Artesian springs

Springs fed from artesian waters are known in several parts of the world and, particularly in arid areas, often contain relict and endemic biota (Cole 1968). The Great Artesian Basin (GAB), one of the largest artesian systems in the world, occupies about 22% of the Australian continent, or about 1.76 million square kilometres, extending through western Queensland to the south-eastern corner of the Northern Territory, north-eastern South Australia and north-western New South Wales (Habermehl 1980). Numerous artesian springs lie on the fringes of this basin (Figure 1), and, because they are a source of permanent water, are of considerable significance in this generally arid area.

Active and extinct spring-formed mounds are distinctive features of the arid landscape in northern South Australia and parts of western Queensland and it is for this reason that the springs are usually called "mound" springs. They are sometimes conspicuously vegetated but often appear as almost bare, white hills.

Calcareous deposits (travertines) are often important in mound formation. Wind-blown sand and accumulated plant debris, as well as mud, sand and gravel carried up with the water, also assist in forming mounds. Some groups of springs mounds are composed predominantly of sand or clay; others are mostly calcareous. Some larger, hill-like formations represent an accumulation of mounds that have welded together. Many artesian springs, however, particularly the more active ones, have not developed a mound and lie at ground level.

There are in excess of 600 springs and spring groups associated with the GAB. They range from damp areas to actively flowing, some with large pools and outflows several kilometres long. The total discharge from all of the GAB artesian springs is estimated to be about 1500 litres per second (Habermehl 1980). Available information is reviewed by Ponder (1986), Zeidler and Ponder (1989) and Boyd (1990).

Climate

The climatic regime in which the springs in South Australia and western Queensland lie, has temperature fluctuations from below zero to well in excess of 40° C. This can have a major impact on the spring biota because, in many spring outflows, the water is only a few millimetres deep and closely follows air temperature (Ponder 1986). Rainfall over most of the GAB is erratic with yearly averages in the 125-250mm range in South Australia and the most western part of Queensland but in the 250-500mm range in the rest of Queensland. Severe flooding occasionally occurs. In some parts of Queensland floods are an annual event but, in the area around Lake Eyre, they occur only about once every 8-10 years. All water courses in the region are ephemeral drainage channels. The larger ones may contain waterholes, many of which are maintained by groundwater seepage. Some springs also occur in water courses and are thus flooded periodically.

A typical spring comprises a vent, an outflow often forming a channel, and a tail which may form an extensive marsh in large springs. A pool is sometimes formed at or near the vent.

Springs may occur in groups associated with the same local fault system. Larger aggregations of springs or spring groups are termed Spring Complexes. Geographically related spring complexes form larger groupings or Supergroups, of which eleven can be recognised around the GAB (Habermehl 1982; Ponder 1986). These are listed and identified on the map in Figure 1. For information on the geology of these springs see Habermehl (1982).

Hydrology

Habermehl (1980) has summarised the chemical composition of artesian water throughout the GAB and Williams (1967) has reviewed the available information on the chemistry of the spring water flowing from the basin.

Total dissolved solids in the springs generally range around 2000 - 4000 mg/l, those in the Lake Eyre Supergroup from about

2000 - 10,000 mg/l and Dalhousie Springs 650-2000 mg/l. The pH varies from about 7 to nearly 10.

Temperatures taken at the vents range from near air temperature to about 45°C, and the water in the more active springs is typically warm to hot. Paralana Spring, on the eastern side of the Flinders Ranges, which is probably fed at least in part from the GAB, is 62°C and is also radioactive. The temperature in most thermal springs remains remarkably constant. The large warm pools of Dalhousie springs remain very constant but in most springs, particularly the smaller ones, the water rapidly approaches air temperature as it moves away from the vent.

The rate of water flow varies from small seepages to flows of 14.3 megalitres per day from one of the Dalhousie springs. The flow from Dalhousie Springs is the greatest of all the spring groups, being about 670 l/sec (Williams 1979; Williams and Holmes 1978; Habermehl 1982).

The spring biota

The flora

Most springs (in all supergroups) contain a luxuriant growth of sedges (usually species of *Cyperus*) which helps to stabilize the sediments and provide shelter for the aquatic fauna. Green and blue-green algae are usually conspicuous. *Phragmites* and, more rarely, *Typha*, form dense stands around the head of some springs. Some of the larger, cooler pools contain aquatic macrophytes.

Only one plant, the button grass *Eriocaulon carsonii* is considered to be endemic to artesian springs. It is found in a few springs near Hermit Hill, in two groups near the northern end of the Flinders Ranges and in Elizabeth Springs in western Queensland (Ponder 1985). Very recently it has also been found living in a few small springs in northern New South Wales. A few other rare plants are also found associated with the springs (Fatchen 1984; Symon 1984, 1985).

The fauna

The fauna of the GAB springs includes a number of endemic invertebrates and fishes. Studies on the fishes in the South Australian springs have been in progress since the 1960's (Glover 1973, 1979, 1982; Glover and Inglis 1971; Ivantsoff and Glover 1974; Glover and Sim 1978a, 1978b) but the rich fauna of invertebrates in these same springs, with one exception, were first collected by W. Zeidler in 1974. A comprehensive survey was carried out in 1978 by a team from the Nature Conservation Society of South Australia and included studies on the limnology of the springs (Mitchell 1985). A considerable amount of additional work on the endemic invertebrates has been done subsequently by W. Zeidler and the writer but the results are largely unpublished to date.

Fishes

Little information is known about fishes of the Queensland springs but nine species are said to inhabit the South Australian mound springs (Glover and Sim 1978b; Glover 1979; Crowley and Ivantsoff 1990), although recent electrophoretic evidence suggests that this number may be larger. Most of the fishes found in the South Australian springs also occur in other water bodies, only two

species apparently restricted to springs. The introduced Mosquito Fish (*Gambusia*) is common in some of the Queensland springs and, because it is a predator, may pose a threat to the survival of endemic animals.

Molluscs

Small prosobranch snails of the family Hydrobiidae are known to speciate in arid zone springs in the Americas (e.g. Taylor 1966; Hershler 1985) but few other examples have been reported. The hydrobiids found in springs in South Australia and Queensland are often very abundant. There are two major radiations of these snails in South Australia, one in the Lake Eyre Supergroup, the other as yet unnamed, in the Dalhousie Supergroup. In a study of the Lake Eyre radiation (Ponder, Hershler and Jenkins 1989) taxa were conservatively separated morphologically. This study recognises two endemic genera (*Trochidrobia* and *Fonscochlea*) and ten species with four or five species coexisting in most springs. One species (*Fonscochlea zeidleri*) is amphibious, and two groups of congeners, one about half the size of the other, are aquatic. The aquatic species have speciated geographically but *F. zeidleri*, which is much more resistant to desiccation, has not. One or two species of *Trochidrobia* are found in most of the springs and are aquatic and photopositive, differing in behaviour from species of *Fonscochlea* which tend to retreat from light.

The snails in Dalhousie Springs appear to be a single radiation of a genus related to the most speciose of the genera of the Lake Eyre Supergroup. There is good geological evidence (Kreig 1989) to show that Dalhousie Springs developed in the Pleistocene. The speciation of the hydrobiids (Ponder and Colgan, from work in progress) does not appear to have stabilized. There are two sympatric species in the large pools of a few springs, but in most other habitats only one or the other of these species is found. Unlike the snails in the Lake Eyre springs the taxa are not clear-cut and considerable variation occurs within some populations. Different morphotypes occur in different parts of the spring, sometimes separated by long areas of outflow in which only non-endemic snails (*Lymnaea* and *Thiara*) occur. Observations suggest that there is differentiation in response to a number of physical differences in the springs - e.g. spring size, type of water body, speed of current and in particular, water temperature. There is also, apparently, a response to predation by catfish. Snails appear to be larger and thicker-shelled where they coexist with catfish than when they live in similar habitats that lack these fish. Another species belonging to *Fluvidona*, a genus found widely in S.E. Australia, is found in some outflows and seeps at Dalhousie Springs.

The hydrobiid snail radiation in the Lake Eyre Supergroup shows the greatest diversity, and the sympatric taxa currently recognized are readily differentiated. The ranges of some of the taxa are considerable, several found in widely separated spring groups. Morphologically such populations are essentially indistinguishable, although small differences exist in many cases the total number of endemic hydrobiid taxa that are currently recognised in the Lake Eyre Group is 10 (Ponder *et al.* 1989), but recent electrophoretic studies indicate that subdivision of some taxa is necessary.

In any one spring complex in the Lake Eyre Supergroup, the same fauna is found in virtually every type of active spring, whereas at Dalhousie Springs physically different springs, or parts of springs, contain morphologically distinct snails. These observations suggest that different selection pressures are important in driving the speciation in these two supergroups.

Additional species of hydrobiid snails have also been found in the Springvale Supergroup and the Eulo Supergroup in Queensland and the Lake Callabonna springs of the Lake Frome Supergroup (South Australia). Only a single species (genus *Jardinella*) occurs in all of the Queensland localities but in Edgbaston Springs in the Barcaldine Supergroup, there are six sympatric species of *Jardinella* and a bithyniid, as well as an additional allopatric species of *Jardinella* (Ponder and Clark 1990).

Other invertebrates

The crustacean spring fauna includes several interesting endemics. A phreatoicid isopod, *Phreatomerus latipes*, is widespread and abundant in the springs of the Lake Eyre Supergroup and belongs to a monotypic genus and subfamily (Nichols 1943). Species of *Austrochiltonia*, a gammarid amphipod, live in the Lake Eyre, Dalhousie and Barcaldine Supergroups.

An ostracod, *Ngarawa dirga*, is very abundant in many of the Lake Eyre springs and is endemic to this Supergroup. Like the isopod, it has been placed in a monotypic subfamily (DeDeckker 1979). Other undescribed endemic ostracods occur in GAB springs. An unpigmented, blind amphipod lives in some of the seeping mounds at Dalhousie Springs (Zeidler, 1991). A tiny flatworm (Macrostomida) found in the Lake Eyre Supergroup is only one of two records of this order from Australia (Sluys 1986) and a new (undescribed) genus of oligochaete has also been found. No doubt, with careful collecting, additional minute animals will be discovered that will prove to be spring endemics.

Other possible endemic invertebrates in the springs include atyid prawns (Caridina sp.) which have been recorded from Coward and Elizabeth Springs in the Lake Eyre Supergroup (Mitchell 1985) and another atyid, Caridina thermophila, which occurs in springs in the Barcaldine Supergroup. Although this latter species was described from a bore drain it was located near these springs and probably evolved in them. A freshwater crayfish (Charex sp.) may also be endemic to Dalhousie Springs (Sokol, 1987).

Origin and evolution of the spring fauna

The presence of endemic animals, including endemic genera and subfamilies, in some artesian springs suggests that these animals have been isolated in this environment for a considerable period of time. It is probable that at least some of the spring endemics may represent relicts of a more ubiquitous fauna from a generally wetter climatic period in the late Tertiary or early Pleistocene, or they may be a much older fauna that has been associated with artesian springs through much of the Tertiary. The little fossil evidence does not particularly favour either view (Ponder 1986). The two endemic hydrobiid genera in the Lake Eyre Supergroup are found in Pleistocene mounds in that area, indicating that the fauna was diverse then. No older fossil mounds are known.

The springs can be likened to aquatic islands in an arid sea, with each Spring Group a small island group and a Spring Complex an archipelago. Under these circumstances one might expect to see differentiation in populations several kilometres apart as the level of gene flow must be very small. Somewhat surprisingly, observations on the fauna in the springs of the Lake Eyre Supergroup have shown that, at least at the morphological level, marked differentiation does not appear to occur within Spring Groups and Spring Complexes. The hydrobiid snails show the greatest speciation and interpopulation differentiation/variation but even these can show some large ranges, in some cases the same taxon occurring in widely separated spring groups (Ponder *et al.*,1989). Preliminary results of electrophoretic studies on the hydrobiids, crustaceans and fishes indicate, however, that the diversity is greater than indicated by morphological studies.

Hydrobiid snails and crustaceans are absent or reduced in diversity in isolated springs (Ponder *et al.*, 1989; Zeidler 1984;). These observations have important management implications indicating that it is important to maintain a number of springs in a group rather than attempt to salvage only one.

The majority of springs in the northern and eastern areas of the basin do not appear to support endemic faunas (with one notable exception). The eastern springs (see fig 2.1) are in wetter areas with large rivers and contain essentially the same fauna found in other water bodies in the area. The artesian springs in western Queensland are, in many cases, in areas subjected to regular catastrophic flooding. Some of the springs in the Lake Eyre Supergroup that lack fauna are near Lake Eyre south and are occasionally flooded.

Whereas flooding may be an important dispersal agent, especially for fishes, the evidence suggests that flooding can cause extinction or severe depletion of the spring fauna. This, however, is a natural phenomenon whereas termination of spring flow through the interference of humans immediately exterminates the fauna.

Conservation and management

Because the mound springs were, until recently, the only sources of water in some of the arid parts of Australia, they were extremely important to wildlife. Numerous artifacts associated with almost all springs indicate their importance to aborigines and the early explorers used them as stepping stones on their route to the interior (Harris 1981).

Many of the early pastoralists fenced the springs to protect them from stock damage but, with the introduction of artesian wells and bores late last century, the dependence on the springs ceased and the fences were allowed to fall into disrepair. Trampling and fouling of the springs by stock has caused considerable degradation of many of them, affecting both the flora (Symon 1985) and the fauna (Ponder 1985, 1986).

Most of the area in which the springs are found is suitable only for sheep and cattle grazing and this industry, like the towns in the area, is dependent on artesian water. About 211 megalitres of water per day is removed from the basin in South Australia alone, compared with 83 megalitres for all of the springs in that state (Boucat and Beal 1977). The heavy usage of artesian water in the last century has been the cause of the extinction of many springs and with them, their aquatic biota. All but one very small group of the once numerous springs in north western New South Wales are now dry, as are many in Queensland, particularly in the western, northern and southern parts of the basin. In some areas the few remaining springs are so reduced in flow that they are highly vulnerable to stock damage and extinctions appear to be inevitable in these instances.

Some pastoralists modify the springs by damming or digging them out, usually resulting in the extinction of the endemic invertebrate fauna (Ponder and Hershler 1984).

Habermehl (1980) has suggested that the GAB has achieved a new steady state condition in which total recharge and discharge are approaching equilibrium again provided no new, major developments occur. Some of the enormous waste that is occurring from free-flowing stock bores is being reduced by the bore capping and control programs being undertaken by the Queensland and South Australian governments but one major development, the bore field supplying water to the Olympic Dam uranium mine (Kinhill Stearns Roger 1982; Kinhill Stearns 1983, 1984), is located near an important group of South Australian springs.

Although overlooked until recently, the conservation of mound springs is now considered to be a matter of importance (Casperson 1979; Harris 1981, 1992; Ponder 1985, 1986; Ferguson 1985; Murphy 1985). It must, however, be appreciated that many of the springs still in existence have been drastically altered since late last century and need to be properly rehabilitated.

The recent incorporation of Dalhousie Springs in a National Park is a long overdue recognition of the importance of that spring group and reflects a growing concern in that State for these unique habitats. Similar protection of other spring groups is essential but must be coupled with proper management and conservation of artesian water if their continued existence and the survival of their endemic biota are to be assured.

Acknowledgements

This work has been done in cooperation with W. Zeidler of the South Australian Museum, and it was he who introduced me to the springs. R. Hershler, D. Winn, J. Gillispie, A. Miller, G. Clark, B. Jenkins and D. Colgan have all assisted me on the project. A grant provided by the South Australian Govt., and Roxby Management Services enabled work to be done on the Lake Eyre Supergroup. The Australian Research Grants Scheme and the Australian Museum have also provided funds for the project.

Literature cited

BOUCAT, W.R.P. and BEAL, J.C. 1977. Great Artesian Basin in South Australia, importance of rehabilitation of the uncontrolled flowing wells. Department of Mines of South Australia, Report Bk 77/109.

BOYD, W.E., 1990. Mound springs. In: *Natural History of the North East deserts*. M.J.Tyler, C.R. Twidale, M. Davies and Wells C.B. (Eds.) Royal Society of South Australia, Adleaide. 107-118.

CASPERSON, K.C., 1979. Mound springs of South Australia. Part 1 - Physical features, history, biota and conservation requirements. Department of Environmental Planning of South Australia (unpublished report).

COLE, G.A., 1968. Desert limnology. In: G.W. Brown, Jr. (Ed.) *Desert Biology* 1: 423-486. Academic Press, New York.

CROWLEY, L.E.L.M. and IVANTSOFF, W., 1990. A second hardyhead, *Craterocephalus gloveri* (Pisces: Atherinidae) from Dalhousie Springs, Central Australia. Ichthyol. Explor. Freshwaters 1(2): 113-122.

DEDECKKER, P., 1979. Ostracods from the mound springs area between Strangways and Curdimurka, South Australia. *Transactions of the Royal Society of South Australia* 103: 155-168.

FATCHEN, T.J., 1984. Vegetation. *In: Supplementary environmental studies - mound springs*. Kinhill Stearns, Adelaide. pp. 4-1- 4-23.

FERGUSON, D., 1985. The mound springs: lens on a looming tragedy for Australia's desert lands. *Habitat* 13: 32-33.

GLOVER, C.J.M., 1973. Adaptations of a central Australian gobiid fish. *Bulletin of the Australian Society of Limnology* 5: 8-10.

GLOVER, C.J.M., 1979. Studies on central Australian gobiid fish. *Bulletin of the Australian Society for Limnology* 5: 8-10.

GLOVER, C.J.M., 1982. Adaptations of fishes in arid Australia. Paper 26 *In:* Barker, W.R. and Greenslade, J.M. (Eds.) *Evolution of the flora and fauna of Arid Australia*, pp. 241- 246. Peacock Publications, Frewville, South Australia.

GLOVER, C.J.M. and INGLIS, W.G., 1971. Freshwater fish of South Australia. *South Australian Yearbook*: 27-34.

GLOVER, C.J.M. and SIM, T.C., 1978a. Studies on central Australian fishes: a progress report. *South Australian Naturalist* 52: 35-44.

GLOVER, C.J.M. and SIM, T.C. 1978b. A survey of central Australian ichthyology. *Australian Zoologist* 19: 245-256.

HABERMEHL, M.A., 1980. The great artesian basin, Australia. *B.M.R. Journal of Geology and Geomorphology* 5: 9-38.

HABERMEHL, M.A. 1982. Springs in the Great Artesian Basin, Australia - their origin and nature. B.M.R. Report 235 (unpublished).

HARRIS, C.R., 1981. Oases in the desert: the mound springs of northern South Australia. *Proceedings of the Royal Geographical Society of Australasia, South Australian Division* 81: 26-39.

HARRIS, C.R., 1992. Mound springs: South Australian conservation initiatives. *Rangelands Journal* 14: 157-173.

HERSHLER, R. 1985. The systematics and evolution of the hydrobiid snails (Gastropoda: Rissoacea) of the Cuatro Cienegas Basin, Coahuila, Mexico. *Malacologia* 26: 31-123.

IVANTSOFF, W. and GLOVER, C.J.M., 1974. *Craterocephalus dalhousiensis* n.sp., a sexually dimorphic fresh water teleost (Atherinidae) from South Australia. *Australian Zoologist* 18: 88-98.

KINHILL-STEARNS ROGER, 1982. Olympic Dam project: draft environmental impact statement, prepared by Kinhill Stearns for Roxby Management Services Pty Ltd. 103 pp.

KINHILL STEARNS, 1983. Olympic Dam project. Supplement to the Draft Environmental Impact statement. Prepared for Roxby Management Services by Kinhill Stearns Pty Ltd.

KINHILL STEARNS, 1984. Olympic Dam Project. Supplementary Environmental Studies - Mound Springs. Prepared for Roxby Management Services by Kinhill Stearns Pty Ltd.

KRIEG, G.W. 1989. Geology. In Zeidler, W. and Ponder, W.F. (Eds.) Natural History of Dalhousie Springs, South Australia Museum, Adelaide. XIV + 138pp.

MITCHELL, B.D., 1985. Limnology of mound springs and temporary pools south and west of Lake Eyre. In: Greenslade, J., Joseph, L. and Reeves, A. Eds.) *South Australia's mound springs*. Nature Conservation Society, South Australia. pp. 51-63.

MURPHY, D., 1985. Mound springs: threatened cutback ecosystem. *Australian Conservation Foundation Newsletter* 17 (8): 8.

NICHOLS, G.E., 1943. The Phreatoicoides. Part 1. The Amphisopidae. *Papers Proceedings of the Royal Society of Tasmania* (1942): 1-145.

PONDER, W.F., 1985. South Australian mound springs. Relict faunas in the desert. *Australian Natural History* 21 (8): 352-355.

PONDER, W.F. 1986. Mound springs of the Great Artesian Basin. In: DeDecker, P. and Williams, W.D. (Eds.) *Limnology in Australia.* pp. 403-420. CSIRO, Melbourne, and W. Junk, Dordrecht.

PONDER, W.F. and CLARK, G.A., 1990. A radiation of hydrobiid snails in threatened artesian springs in western Queensland. Records of the Australian Museum 42: 301-363.

PONDER, W.F. and HERSHLER, R., 1985. Hydrobiid studies. In: Supplementary environmental studies - mound springs. Kinhill Stearns, Adelaide. pp. 5-1 - 5-16.

PONDER, W.F., HERSHLER, R. and JENKINS, B. 1989. An endemic radiation of Hydrobiidae from artesian springs in northern South Australia; their taxonomy, physiology, distribution and anatomy. *Malacologia* 31: 1-140.

SLUYS, R. 1986. First representative of the Order Macrostomida from Australia (Platyhelminthes, Macrostomidae). *Records of the South Australian Museum* 19: 400-404.

SOKOL, A. 1987. Yabbies at Dalhousie Springs, northern South Australia: morphological evidence for long term isolation. *Transactions Royal Society of South Australia* 111: 207-209.

SYMON, D.E., 1984. A checklist of plants of Dalhousie Springs and their immediate environs. *Journal of the Adelaide Botanic Gardens* 7 (1): 127-134.

SYMON, D.E., 1985. Botanical notes on mound springs and bores. In: J. Greenslade, L. Joseph and Reeves, A. (Eds.). South Australia's mound springs. pp. 78-83. *Nature Conservation Society of South Australia, Adelaide.*

TAYLOR, D.W. 1966. A remarkable snail fauna from Coahuila, Mexico. *The Veliger* 9: 152-228.

WILLIAMS, A.F., 1979. Sampling and measurement of mound springs, Great Artesian Basin, South Australia. Progress Report no. 3 Warrina, Oodnadatta, Billakalina, and Curdimurks sheets. Geological Survey of South Australia Report Bk 79/66 (unpublished).

WILLIAMS, A.F. AND HOLMES, J.W., 1978. A novel method of estimating the discharge of water from mound springs of the Great Artesian Basin, South Australia. *Journal of Hydrology 38: 263-272.*

WILLIAMS, W.D., 1967. The chemical characteristics of lentic surface waters in Australia - a review. *In*: Weatherby, A.H. (Ed.) *Australian inland waters and their fauna.* Australian National University Press, Canberra. pp. 18-77.

ZEIDLER, W., 1984. *In:* Other fauna studies. Supplementary environmental studies - mound springs. Kinhill Stearns, Adelaide. pp. 6-1 - 6-6.

ZEIDLER, W., 1991. A new genus and species of phreatic amphipod (Crustacea: Amphipoda) belonging in the "Chiltonia" generic group, from Dalhousie Springs, South Australia. *Transactions of the Royal Society of South Australia.* 115: 117-187.

ZEIDLER, W. and PONDER, W.F., 1989. Natural History of Dalhousie Springs. South Australia Museum, Adelaide. XIV + 138pp.

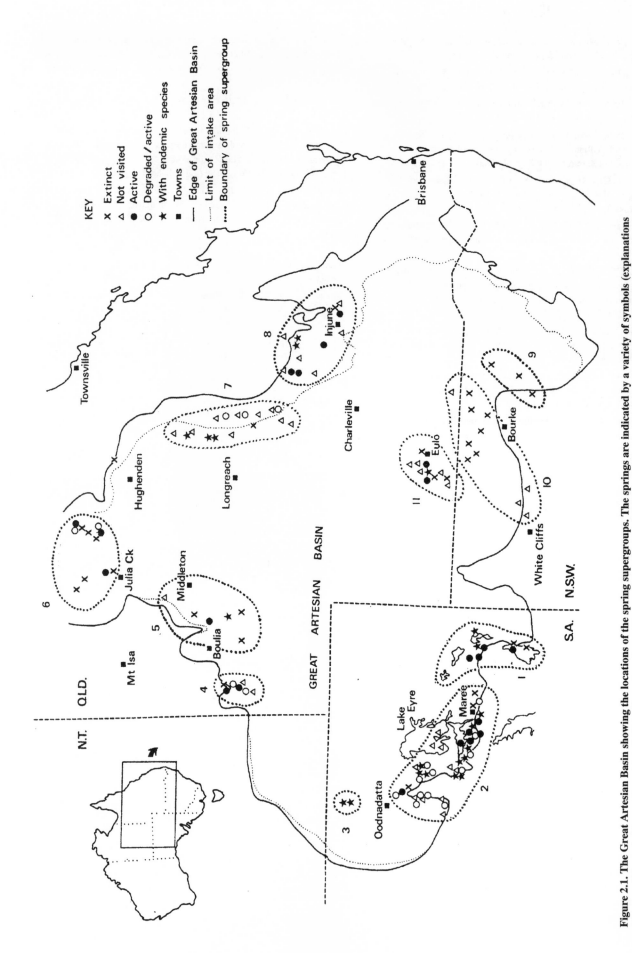

Figure 2.1. The Great Artesian Basin showing the locations of the spring supergroups. The springs are indicated by a variety of symbols (explanations given on diagram). The outline of the GAB is shown by a heavy line and the approximate limits of the recharge areas indicated by dotted lines. Redraw from Ponder (1986). The spring Supergroups are numbered from 1 to 11 and are named as follows:

1. Lake Frome Supergroup; *2.* Lake Eyre Supergroup; *3.* Dalhousie Supergroup; *4.* Mulligan River Supergroup; *5.* Springvale Supergroup; *6.* Flinders Supergroup; *7.* Barcaldine Supergroup; *8.* Springsure Supergroup; *9.* Bogan River Supergroup; *10.* Bourke Supergroup; *11.* Eulo Supergroup.

Endangered species of land molluscs in Sweden and Madeira

Henrik W. Waldén

Natural History Museum, S-402 35 Gothenburgh, Sweden.

Abstract

The threat situation for land molluscs in Sweden and Madeira is reviewed. Sweden and Madeira offer highly contrasting examples of topography, climate, human impact and the composition of their respective molluscan faunas. In both cases the molluscan faunas are fairly well known, and long historical records permit an estimate of declining trends and disappearance of species.

Of the 113 species recorded from Sweden, one species may have become extinct in recent years. A further 24 species are subject to threat (e.g. from forestry practices), including species which are highly endangered and species which are still relatively widespread but which may be declining and require special attention. None is endemic to Sweden.

In Madeira the number of indigenous species and subspecies is now estimated to be 190, of which 164 are endemic. Of these, 17 species have not been seen during the last 100 years. A further 55 species are subject to threat of varying degree. Together these species correspond to 33% of the indigenous molluscan fauna, and 36% of the endemic element. Most of the vanished or threatened species are confined to the remnants of the original damp, leafy woodland, and are unable to endure the effects of human impact. The remnants of extremely shell-rich fossil deposits, mainly of Pleistocene age, in the Madeiran islands must also be preserved.

Introduction

In 1968 a symposium on rare and endangered molluscs of North America was held at Corpus Christi, Texas. As far as the author knows, this was the first meeting of its kind. Very pessimistic views of the future of molluscs were expressed by the convenor (Clarke 1970) and most of the participants. Since then, the topic has been studied systematically, and a listing of endangered and threatened molluscs in the United States has been compiled (U.S. Fish and Wildlife Service 1984, 1986). What is the situation in other parts of the world? Examples will be given here from two quite different regions of the Old World.

Sweden and Madeira provide strongly contrasting examples of the problems of preservation of land molluscan faunas. Both in Sweden and Madeira the land molluscs are fairly well known, and a rather long historical record permits an estimate of trends in decreasing numbers and disappearance of species.

Sweden is a wide, sparsely settled country with a climate and vegetation of the northern type. It is, however, impacted by technically advanced industries. The moderately rich mollusc fauna is composed of, in most cases, widely distributed species, none of which is endemic. Madeira, on the other hand, is a small archipelago of oceanic islands, with very pronounced topography, a subtropical climate, and a dense human population exerting a strong pressure on fairly limited natural resources. The mollusc fauna is extremely rich, largely endemic, and of great interest from the scientific point of view. The basic problem in both cases, however, is the same: maintenance and protection of habitats.

Endangered species in Sweden

Sweden encompasses an area of about 450,000 km^2 of which about 55% is woodland. In addition, there is a considerable amount of wetland, alpine area and other wilderness. The climate varies from subarctic to central European cool-temperate. The country is sparsely populated, with an average of 18.5 inhabitants per km^2, but over much of central and northern Sweden there are fewer than three people per km^2.

The land molluscan fauna

A total of 113 species of land molluscs have been recorded from Sweden (Walden 1984a). Some of these apparently occurred only accidentally and then disappeared, or exist only in extremely sheltered conditions, e.g. in greenhouses.

None of the estimated 93 "natural" species is endemic to Sweden, although a few have their main distributions restricted to this country and adjacent Norway. For the majority of species, their presence in Sweden represents only a minor part of an extensive distribution in Europe, or the Holarctic as a whole. The question in Sweden, therefore is not that of preserving species from total extinction, but of maintaining species as part of the fauna at the national level, and so far as is possible, to maintain them in reasonably extensive and vigorous populations. For some species, now nearly extinct outside Scandinavia, the situation for protecting populations is particularly favourable in Sweden. This implies a national responsibility to protect these species.

Endangered species

Beginning in 1975 an extensive survey was carried out to identify the endangered species of all groups of terrestrial invertebrates in Sweden. The survey includes information on type and intensity of threat, and the measures required for preservation of species. For molluscs, the survey was essentially based on the extensive and detailed material resulting from the faunistic survey of the Natural History Museum of Gothenburg (see Walden 1965, 1986), in the course of which nearly 20,000 mollusc localities were investigated.

A total of 768 species of invertebrates, of which 25 are terrestrial molluscs, have been placed on a national "Red Data List" (Andersson *et al.* 1987). Most of these molluscs are woodland species, and are treated more thoroughly in a recent publication (Ehnstrom and Walden 1986).

One species, *Vallonia enniensis*, seems to have died out in recent years at its only known site. Four species, known from single or very few sites, are regarded as directly endangered, five as vulnerable, 10 as rare, and a further five are listed as sensitive and of special concern in the context of forestry practice. In addition, there are at least 10 species which will probably never become endangered at the national level, but which are showing decreasing abundance over much of the country, and may become rare if present land use practices persist. They are not listed here, but include, e.g. *Acanthinula aculeata* (Muller) and *Clausilia cruciata* Studer.

Ecological considerations

Most of the species fall into three habitat categories: old woodland species, stenotopic calcareous fen species, and species of dry, steppe-like habitats.

Old woodland species depend on stability and little disturbance. Like certain beetles, they are particularly useful indicators of old woodland. About half of the species are of this type, although some also occur in other habitats. Characteristic species are *Spermodea lamellata*, *Ena montana*, some of the clausiliids, and, in several provinces, *Acanthinula aculeata* (which is not included on the national list).

Twelve species can be included among the stenotopic calcareous fen species, although, again, some can also occur in other habitats as swampy woodlands. The need for habitat protection is particularly urgent for this group. The rate of destruction of calcareous fens is very rapid. In the province of Ostergotland, about 50% of the fens were drained between 1970 and 1980. In the province of Scania 97% of the wetland, of which a significant part was distinctly eutrophic or calcareous, was drained over a hundred year period. Most species in this group are in the Succineidae and Vertiginidae.

Dry, steppe-like habitats are, to a considerable extent, remnants of a former more open and grazed landscape, and are today dependant on active management for their continued existence. Species characteristic of dry, steppe-like habitats are all more or less pronounced calciphiles. A few are sometimes also found in dry, open woodland on calcareous soil. Characteristic are the *Truncatellina* and the Helicellinae species.

Main threats

In Sweden the greatest threat to land molluscs undoubtedly is from forestry, a consequence of the importance of woods in the country's economy. Not only is the woodland fauna threatened, but so also is the fauna of pastures and glades, as well as the fens, which are drained, and then planted with trees. These habitats are also seriously threatened in farming districts where they have nearly disappeared along with the small deciduous spinneys and swamp woods in hollows, which formerly supported a varied flora and fauna. This landscape is now dominated by monocultures. Other impacts include construction work for roads, buildings, tourist facilities, etc. and the effects of pollution and acid rain. Intensified tourism and recreation cause considerable disturbance to the environment from which even protected areas are not exempt.

Conservation measures

Much of the pressure to which the fauna and flora is now subjected can only be mitigated within the framework of a general coordinated environmental policy. Management of nature reserves must be better adjusted to the requirements of endangered species, as well as to mollusc life in general. It is also important to influence forestry practice so that greater consideration is given to molluscan habitats: marginal vegetation must be spared along shores, in ravines, on slopes and on rough ground in general, so that molluscs can find refugia and survive. Considerable emphasis is laid on such practical recommendations by Ehnstrom and Walden (1986).

Compared with habitat protection, legislation to prohibit collecting is unnecessary in the Swedish context, with the exception of a few, very special cases. No cases of disastrous over-collecting have been reported for molluscs so far (whereas this seems to be a real threat for certain Coleoptera), but it is recommended that the precise sites for certain rare species should not be published.

Endangered species in Madeira

The Madeira archipelago covers a very small area compared to that of Sweden, only ca. 800 km^2. The islands are extremely rugged, with mountain heights up to 1861m. Only small remnants of the original extensive woodland exist today, mainly on the northern slope of the main island of Madeira. The climate is sub-tropical, but varies greatly between islands and at different altitudes. Parts of the main island are very wet. The human population is dense, with an average of 340 inhabitants per km^2, and land use is intense, particularly with terraced agriculture.

The land molluscan fauna

The mollusc fauna is extremely diverse. 194 recent indigenous species and subspecies have been reported and there are also at least 43 introduced species. Of the indigenous molluscs, 171 or 88% are endemic[1]. The richness of the land molluscan fauna of Madeira is particularly remarkable when compared with the fauna of central and northern Europe where some 280 native and naturalized species are known from an area of about 2.5 million km^2 (Kerney *et al.* 1979). Very few are endemic to the area.

The most striking feature of the Madeiran fauna is its pronounced relict character. Most of the endemic taxa belong to genera or subgenera which are now either extinct in Europe or have evolved from ancestors in Europe. The colonization of Madeira seems to have taken place largely in the mid-Tertiary and was probably facilitated by the presence of now sunken islands between Madeira and the Iberian Peninsula (Pastouret *et al* 1980). Thus Madeira can be considered a living museum for a Tertiary molluscan fauna now extinct elsewhere.

The land molluscs of Madeira were first described in a series of classic works by Lowe (1831, 1852, 1854, 1860) and Wollaston (1878), with contributions from Albers (1854) and Paiva (1867). When these authors were describing the fauna, considerably more woodland existed than is present today, particularly on the southern slope of Madeira proper. The only remaining evidence for several species described in the 19th century is in the collections and published works of the authors.

---

[1] *Census 1986 (Unpublished). The figures deviate from those given in previous papers (Walden, 1983, 1984), owing to recent discoveries and taxonomic revision, and also becuse the present census is restricted to living taxa, whereas the previous figures included extinct forms.*

Extinct and endangered species

The current status of the Madeiran molluscan fauna should be assessed in relation to the early studies. Of the endemic taxa, 17 species have not been seen for 100 years despite the collecting efforts of many workers throughout this period, but especially in recent years. These molluscs may now be extinct, or near extinction, although surprising re-discoveries are still possible, such as the recent finding (Hemmen and Groh 1984) of *Idiomela subplicata*.

A further 22 species are very rare; several are restricted to single populations or small areas, and are clearly endangered or vulnerable. There are also 25 rare, though at present not threatened, species. Except for two of the last mentioned, all these threatened species are endemic to the Madeiran archipelago. In all 64 species are concerned.

The figures correspond to 33% of the indigenous taxa and 36% of the endemic taxa. Several species and subspecies, restricted to small, inhabited islands where no threat is discernible, have not been included in the list. Local subspecies of relatively widespread species are also omitted if the species as a whole is not endangered, even if some of the subspecies are highly endangered. There are also some other species for which there have been no records for a long time, but it is uncertain to what extent this is due to insufficient searching. If these actually or potentially threatened species are included, then about 40% of the indigenous species of molluscs can be considered threatened.

Ecological aspects of endangered species

Eleven of the presumed extinct species were confined to damp laurel woodland, and 12 species in the other categories are also found in this or other wooded habitats. Twenty-one species of all categories live in dry, open habitats, a few on Madeira proper, the remaining on the smaller, generally dry islands. In addition there are 20 species which have more specialized modes of life, such as on flushed, mossy precipices or in rocky terrain, although these habitats can occur as mosaic elements in wooded or open terrain.

Main threats

The most serious threat to the land molluscs of Madeira is the destruction of damp laurel woodland. Except for a few species, which can survive in other habitats, the endemic mollusc fauna is virtually totally eliminated when an area of laurel woodland is cleared. Most of this woodland was destroyed in the centuries immediately following human settlement, and it is probable that a number of species had already disappeared when scientific study began in the 19th century. The secondary woodland, largely of pines and *Eucalyptus*, is colonized mainly by introduced species, with a few relatively catholic native species (in particular some large vitrinids).

Other serious threats to the Madeiran molluscan fauna include overgrazing by cattle and construction work for purposes of industry, military activity, and tourism. The establishment of nature reserves for recreational purposes can sometimes conflict with preservation interests.

In contrast to the fauna of laurel woodland, many Madeiran species live on lower levels in dry or mesic habitats, and they appear to have a remarkable ability to survive the impact of man and his animals. Some species seem almost to flourish under these conditions and have even been favoured by the clearing of the former dry, open bushwood. Several species use man-made habitats, such as gardens, terraces and stone walls.

Conservation measures

The conservation of the endemic, relict land molluscan fauna of Madeira must be regarded as a high priority for international conservation action. The question is, however, how such action can be implemented, given the heavy population pressure and the need for improving the standard of living. A project for comprehensive protection and management has been established in the National Park of Madeira (cf. Bramwell *et al.* 1982), and will eventually obtain financial support from international sources. The following measures are necessary with regard to the molluscan fauna:

1) Reserve management must ensure suitable conditions for species sensitive to environmental change. In particular, the impact of tourism - the demands of which the reserves are also intended to satisfy - must be monitored, and encroachment into vulnerable habitats and vegetation must be prevented.

2) The localities of the narrowest endemics should be identified and strictly protected. Threats can be very direct, as is already apparent from construction work, quarrying, plantations, etc. Fortunately, the reserves which have been proposed mainly for botanical reasons coincide fairly closely with the areas where endangered land mollusc species live.

Subfossil deposits

There are extensive Pleistocene and Holocene deposits with land mollusc shells in Porto Santo and easternmost Madeira (Ponta Sao Lourenco). These deposits are of interest not only because they extend the background of the local fauna, but also for evolutionary and ecological reasons. Today the larger part of the deposits has been removed and used for various construction purposes, and preservation of the remaining deposits is now an urgent need.

Addendum

The preceeding article is accordant with the presentation at the IX International Malacological Congress, 1986. Data given and opinions expressed are unchanged. However, during the past nine years extensive further evidence has accumulated, which to a considerable degree is the result of intentional search for threatened species, carried out from 1987 and onwards.

Instead of modifying the original text the current situation is presented in this addendum. - Publications, which were not available when the original manuscript was compiled, are indicated by asterisks in the literature list.

Sweden

A program for systematic inventory of the till then insufficiently known northern regions was launched in 1987. From 1987 through 1994 a further 989 localities were investigated here. Local surveys have also been carried out in certain tracts in southern Sweden. These surveys have considerably extended the knowledge on distribution and ecology of several of the endangered species. A consequence to this is that some species have been moved to lower threat categories. An updated Red Data List for Invertebrates was published in 1993 (Ehnstrom *et al.*), which included 1876 species (Categories 0-4), compared with 768 species in the first edition (Andersson *et al.* 1987). The increase mainly refers to groups whose threat situation had not yet been adequately surveyed at the time of the first edition.

The present threat situation for Swedish terrestrial molluscs is summarised in Table 2.1.

Regarding the number of sites four species have a major part of their extant distribution in Sweden, *viz. Vertigo angustior, genesii* and *geyeri,* and *Catinella arenaria.* These are also placed on the International Red Data List of IUCN (1990) and specifically addressed in the report of Wells & Chatfield (1992). For these species Sweden has an international preservation responsibility.

Madeira

Madeira has attracted increasing interest by malacologists in recent years. Further evidence has been published e.g. by Cook *et al.* (1990), Hemmen & Groh (1985), and Holyoak & Seddon (1986), Hutterer & Groh (1993). A preliminary list of endangered species was published in the report by Wells & Chatfield (*ibid*). However, several taxonomical complexes are still badly understood and revision work is ongoing, and some figures in the present census are uncertain.

In a new census (1994) the number of indigenous recent species and subspecies is estimated to be 203, of which 167 are endemic. The number of introduced species is estimated to be at least 36, of which several have become naturalized and are now widespread.

According to the present census 11 species are now presumed to have become extinct during the last more than 100 years, 48 species (including two which are possibly subspecies) fall in the categories 1-3. A further 15 rare species have not been seen for a long time, but evidence is too uncertain to allow any judgement (category K). Some may even be extinct. Finally there are at least 7 species, still relatively widespread but which must be regarded as potentially threatened (category 4). In the report of Wells & Chatfield (*ibid.*) concern is expressed for the long-term survival of a further 12 species, but these are all well established; some are even among the most common species in the archipelago.

Summing up, six species which a few years ago were supposed to be extinct, have been refound alive, but otherwise the survival situation for the threatened endemic species must now be regarded as more critical than in 1986.

Table 2.1 Degree of threat to terrestrial molluscs in Sweden.				
Probable Category 0 (=Ex) species	Habitat	**Category 3 (=R) species**		Habitat
Vallonia enniensis (Gredler)	F	*Catinella arenaria* (Bouch.-Chant.)		F
		Vertigo extima (Westerlund)		F,S
Category 1 (=E) species		*Vertigo geyeri* Lindholm		F
Vertigo moulinsiana (Dupuy)	F	*Vertigo genesii* (Gredler)		F
		Spermodea lamellata (Jeffreys)		W
Category 2 (=V) species		*Clausilia dubia* Draparnaud		W,S
Acicula polita (Hartmann)	W,F	*Trochoidea geyeri* (Soós)		D
Cochlicopa nitens (Gallenstein)	F	*Perforatella bidentata* (Gmelim)		F,W
Ena montana (Draparnaud)	W	= 8 species		
Laciniaria plicata (Draparnaud)	S			
Bulgarica cana (Held)	W	**Category 4 (=S) species**		
Oxychilus glaber (Rossmässler)	S	*Succinea oblonga* (Draparnaud)		F,S
= 6 species		*Columella columella* (v. Martens)		F,S
		Truncatellina cylindrica (Férussac)		D
		Truncatellina costulata (Nilsson)		D
		Vertigo angustior Jeffreys		F.W.S
		Lauria cylindracea (Da Costa)		W,S
		Macrogastra ventricosa (Draparnaud)		W
		Balea biplicata (Montagu)		W,S
		= 8 species		

Legend for Tables 1 and 2: W = woodland, F = fen, D = dry habitat, S = special habitat
The Categories of Threat correspond to the pre 1994 IUCN Red List Categories.

Table 2.2 Degree of threat to terrestrial molluscs in Madeira.			
Possible category 0 (=Ex) species	**Habitat**	**Category 2 (=V) species**	**Habitat**
Leiostyla simulator (Pilsbry)	W	*Craspedopoma lyonnetianum* (Lowe)	W
Leiostyla abbreviata (Lowe)[1]	W	*Leiostyla filicum* Holyoak & Seddon	W
Leiostyla cassida (Lowe)	W	*Amphorella melampoides* (Lowe)	D
Leiostyla lamellosa (Lowe)	W	*Amphorella cimensis* Waldén	D
Leiostyla gibba (Lowe)	W	*Cylichnidea ovuliformis* (Lowe)	W
Discus guerinianus (Lowe)	W	*Celilioides nyctelia* (Bourguignat)	S
Geomitra coronata (Deshayes)	S	*Geomitra moniziana* (Paiva)	S
Geomitra delphinuloides (Lowe)	S	*Caseolus commixtus* (Lowe)	D
Caseolus galeata (Lowe)[2]	W	*Caseolus subcalliferus* (Reeve)	S
Discula lyelliana (Lowe)	D	*Caseolus calculus* (Lowe)	D
Pseudocamphylaea lowei (Férussac)	S	*Caseolus leptostictus* (Lowe)	D
= 11 species		*Disculella spirulina* Cockerell	D
		Actinella actinophora (Lowe)	W
Category 1 (=E) species		*Actinella obserata* (Lowe)	W
Leiostyla concinna (Lowe)	W	*Actinella armitageana* (Lowe)	S
Leiostyla heterodon (Pilsbry)	W	*Actinella giramica* (Lowe)	W
Leiostyla laevigata (Lowe)	W	*Actinella anaglyptica* (Reeve)	D
Leiostyla corneocostata (Wollaston)	D	*Discula leacockiana* (Wollaston)	S
Leiostyla degenerata (Wollaston)	W	*Discula oxytropis* (Lowe)	D
Lauria fanalensis (Lowe)	W	*Discula turricula* (Lowe)	D
Geomitra tiarella (Webb & Berth.)	D	*Leptaxis portosancti* (Lowe)	W
Geomitra spec. nov[3]	D	*Leptaxis furva* (Lowe)	W
Actinella effugiens (Waldén)	D	*Idiomela subplicata* (Sowersby)	S
Discula tabellata (Lowe)	D	= 23 species	
Discula testudinalis (Lowe)	D		
Leptaxis nivosa wollastoni (Lowe)	S	**Category 3 (=R) species**	
= 12 species		Leiostyla vincta (Lowe)	S
		Leiostyla laurinea (Lowe)	W
Species of uncertain status (=K)		*Leiostyla ferraria* (Lowe)	S
(very rare, some possibly extinct, but adequate observations lacking)		*Boettgeria obesiuscula* (Lowe)	S
		Balea perversa (Linnaeus)	S
Leiostyla relevata (Wollaston)	D	*Spirorbula squalida* (Lowe)	S
Leiostyla loweana transiens (Wollaston)[4]	W	*Caseolus calva* (Lowe)[5]	S
Ceciliodes eulima (Lowe)	S	*Actinella laciniosa* (Lowe)	D
Amphorella iridescens (Lowe)	D	*Actinella carinofausta* Waldén	S
Amphorella producta (Lowe)	D	*Discula cheiranthicola* (Lowe)	S
Geomitra grabhami (Wollaston)	S	*Discula bulweri* (Wood)	S
Actinella robusta (Wollaston)	W	*Discula tectiformis* (Sowerby)	D
Discula tetrica (Lowe)	D	*Lampadia webbiana* (Lowe)	S
In addition 7 species living in the marine epilittoral		= 13 species	
= 8+7 species			
		Category 4 (=S) species	
		Craspedopoma trochoideum (Lowe)	W
Footnotes to table 2.2:		*Leiostyla monticola* (Lowe)	S
[1] Recent record doubtful.		*Boettgeria crispa* (Lowe)	W
[2] Syn. *Lemniscia galeata* (Lowe).		*Janulus stephanophora* (Deshayes)	S
[3] Figured by Hemmen and Groh (1985, Fig.6) as *G. moniziana* (Paiva).		*Spirorbula latens* (Lowe)	W
[4] Possibly a distinct species.		*Discula michaudi* (Deshayes)[6]	W
[5] Syn. *Lemniscia calva* (Lowe).		*Discula albersi* (Lowe)	S
[6] Syn. *Lemniscia michaudi* (Deshayes).		= 7 species	

Acknowledgements

The author is sincerely indebted to several persons for support and advice in preparing this article. To Professor E. Alison Kay, Honolulu and Ms. S.M. Wells, Cambridge, for critical comments and scrutinizing the English text. To Drs. M. Biscoito and G. Maul, Funchal, for support for field work in Madeira. Several malacological colleagues have also supplied new information concerning the state of the Madeiran molluscan fauna, particularly Professor R.A.D. Cameron, Birmingham; Dr. B. Colville, Leeds; Dr. L. Cook, Manchester; Dr. K. Groh, Darmstadt; Dr. H. Pieper, Kiel; and Mr Th. E. J. Ripken, Delft. Field surveys on endangered species in Sweden have been supported by, e.g., the National Board of Forestry and the National Environment Protection Board, and on Madeira by the Fauna and Flora Preservation Society, London, and the Royal Society of Sciences and Arts, Gothenburgh.

Literature cited

Note : indicates that the paper was not available at the date of the original manuscript (1986), and not mentioned in the original version.

ALBERS, J.C. 1854. *Malacographia maderensis sive enumeratio molluscorum quae in insulis Maderae et Portus Sancti aut viva extant aut fossilia reperientur.* Berlin, 94 pp.

ANDERSSON, H., COULIANOS, C.C., EHNSTROM, B., HAMMARSTEDT, O., IMBY, L., JANZON, L.A., LINDELOW, A. AND WALDEN, H.W. 1987. Hotade evertebrater i Sverige. (With English abstract). *Entomologisk Tidskrift* 108: 65-75.

BRAMWELL, D. MONTELONGO, V., NAVARRO, B. AND ORTEGA, J. 1982. Informe sobre la conservacion de los bosques y la flora de la isla de Madeira. Mimographed report. I.U.C.N., 13 pp.

CLARKE, A.H. 1970. Foreword. Symposium on the rare and endangered mollusks of North America. *Malacologia* 10 (1): 3.

* COOK, L.M., CAMERON, R.A.D. AND LACE, L.A. 1990. Land snails of eastern Madeira: speciation, persistence and colonization. *Proc. R. Soc. Lond.* B239: 35-79.

* EHNSTROM, B., GARDENFORS, U. AND LINDELOW, A. 1993. Rodlistade evertebrater i Sverige 1993. Databanken for hotade arter Press. 69 pp.

EHNSTROM, B. AND WALDEN, H.W. 1986. *Faunavard i skogsbruket. Del 2 - den lagre faunan.* (With English summary: The protection and management of endangered and declining invertebrate species in Swedish woodlands). Skogsstyrelsen Publishers, Jonkoping. 351 pp.

HEMMEN, J. AND GROH, K. 1984. Die Gattung *Idiomela* stat. nov. auf Porto Santo (Mollusca: Pulmonata: Helicidae). *Courier Forschungs Institut Senckenberg,* 71: 17-26.

* HEMMEN, J. AND GROH, K. 1985. Eine neue Art der Gattung *Geomitra* SWAINSON auf Porto Santo. *Arch. Moll.* 116, 2/3: 73-80.

* HOLYOAK, D. H. AND SEDDON, M. 1986. An undescribed *Leiostyla* (Gastropoda, Pupillidae) from Madeira. *J. of Conch.* 32: 191-193.

* HUTTERER, R. AND GROH, K. 1993. A review of Macaronesian *Truncatellina* (Gastropoda: Vertiginidae) with description of four new species. *Bocagiana.* No. 151, 19 pp.

KERNEY, M.P., CAMERON, R.A.D. AND RILEY, G. 1979. *A field guide to the land snails of Britain and North-west Europe.* Collins Ltd., 288 pp.

LOWE, R.T. 1831. Primitiae faunae et florae Maderae et Portus Sancti. *Transactions of the Cambridge Philosophical Society* 4: 5-66.

LOWE, R.T. 1852. Brief diagnostic notices on new Maderan Land Shells. *Ann. Mag. Nat. Hist.* Ser. 2, 10: 112-120 and 275-279.

LOWE, R.T. 1854. Catalogus Molluscorum Pneumatorum Insularum Maderenseium. *Proceedings of the Zoological Society of London* 28: 161-218.

LOWE, R.T. 1860. The Cyclostomas of Madeira belonging to the genus *Craspedopoma* of Pfeiffer: with description of four new Madeiran and one new Canarian species. *Annals and Magazine of Natural History* Ser. 3, 6: 114-118.

PAIVA, CASTELLO DE, 1867. *Monographia molluscorum terrestrium, fluviatilium, lacustrium insularum maderensium.* Lisboa, 168pp.

PASTOURET, L., AUZENDE, J.-M., LE LANN, A. AND OLIVET, J.-L. 1980. Temoins des variations sur le Banc de Gorringe (Atlantique du Nord-Est). *Palaeogeography, Palaeoclimatology, and Palaeoecology* 32: 99-118.

U.S. FISH AND WILDLIFE SERVICE. 1984. Endangered and threatened wildlife and plants; review of invertebrate wildlife for listing as endangered or threatened species. *Federal Register* 49 (100): 21664-21675.

U.S. FISH AND WILDLIFE SERVICE. 1986. *Endangered and Threatened Wildlife and Plants.* Washington, D.C., 30 pp.

WALDEN, H.W. 1965. Terrestrial faunistic studies in Sweden. *Proceedings of the First European Malacological Congress*: 95-109.

WALDEN, H.W. 1983. Systematic and biogeographical studies of the terrestrial Gastropoda of Madeira. With an annotated checklist. *Annales Zoologici Fennici* 20: 255-275.

WALDEN, H.W. 1984a. Sveriges landmolluker - en artlista med kommentarer. (With English summary: an annotated check-list of the Swedish land Mollusca with remarks on their investigation and comparisons with the other Nordic countries). *Fauna och Flora* 79: 29-43.

WALDEN, H.W. 1984b. On the origin, affinities, and evolution of the land Mollusca of the mid-Atlantic islands, with special reference to Madeira. *Boletim Museum Municipal du Funchal* 36 (158): 51-82.

WALDEN, H.W. 1986. The 1921-1981 survey on the distribution and ecology of land Mollusca in southern and central Sweden. *Proceedings of the Eighth International Malacological Congress*: 329-336.

* WELLS, S.M. AND CHATFIELD, J.E. 1992. Threatened non-marine mollusc species of Europe. *Nature and environment, No. 64. Council of Europe Press.* 163 pp.

WOLLASTON, T.V. 1878. *Testacea Atlantica or the Land and Fresh-water shells of the Azores, Madeiras, Salvages, Cape Verdes and Saint Helena.* L. Reeve and Co., London, 588 pp.

Chapter 3: Endangered Mollusca and methods of conservation

The extinction of endemic snails (genus *Partula*) in French Polynesia: is captive breeding the only solution?

S.M. Wells

56 Oxford Road, Cambridge CB4 3PW, United Kingdom

[**Update**: Since this paper was written, the seven species of *Partula* endemic to Moorea have become extinct in the wild although several species still exist in captivity. Further information is available in (*a*) Murray, J., Murray, E., Johnson, M.S. and Clarke, B.C. 1988. The extinction of *Partula* on Moorea. *Pacific Science* 42: 150-154 and (b)Pearce-Kelly, P. and Clarke, D. (Eds). 1992. *Partula* '92. Proc. Annual Meeting of the *Partula* Propagation Group, August 1992. Zoological Society of London.]

Abstract

Seven species of *Partula* are endemic to the island of Moorea in the Society Islands, French Polynesia. They have been the subject of intensive genetics research since the 1960s, providing an example of microgeographical differentiation that is quoted in many text books on evolution and population dynamics. As a result of fairly continuous fieldwork, they provide a unique case history of species apparently doomed to extinction in the wild as a result of a programme of biological control. In 1977, the carnivorous snail *Euglandina rosea* was introduced to Moorea in an attempt to control the agricultural pest, the giant African snail, *Achatina fulica*. *E. rosea* is estimated to be spreading through the island at 1.2km a year, eliminating the native *Partula* in its path. One species and one subspecies are considered to have become extinct in the wild since 1981. The ranges of the remainder are rapidly diminishing; one species is probably restricted to a single valley. There appears to be little hope of preserving the species *in situ* at present and efforts are therefore being focused on breeding colonies in captivity. This case history provides an example of the ease with which terrestrial molluscs may go extinct.

Introduction: the Moorean Partula

The land snails of the genus *Partula* are widespread on high volcanic islands in the Pacific, reaching their greatest diversity in the Society Islands of French Polynesia, where 65 species are found. Although little is known about the ecology and general biology of most Pacific land-snails, *Partula* has been studied in detail. It was the subject of three classic monographs by Crampton (1916, 1925, 1932), describing the species from the islands of Tahiti, Guam and Moorea, respectively. The species from Moorea,

in the Society Islands, have been further investigated by Clarke and Murray (1969), Johnson *et al.* (1977), Murray and Clarke (1980), and Murray *et al.* (1982). There are two species complexes on the island, one with two species (*P. taeniata* and *P. exigua*) and one with four (*P. suturalis, P. aurantia, P. tohiveana* and *P.mooreana*). Within the complexes there are frequent cases of local hybridisation and introgression between species. The two complexes are linked through *P. mirabilis*, which hybridises with *P. taeniata* on the southern slopes of Mt. Rotiu, and with *P. aurantia* and *P. tohiveana* in the laboratory. At any particular place on the island, however, as many as four taxa may coexist without interbreeding, remaining clearly distinct in their genetics, morphology and behaviour.

Partula's unique combination of ovoviviparity, low mobility, short generation time, and extensive polymorphism, combined with the comparative ease of its culture in the laboratory make it ideal material for the study of ecological and evolutionary genetics.

Moorea, lying about 20km northwest of Tahiti, is the caldera of an extinct volcano. It has high mountainous ridges (with a maximum altitude of 1207m) dividing the island into a series of steep-sided valleys, the upper parts of which usually support forest that is habitable for *Partula*. The lower ridges are often covered by dense ferns that form barriers to the dispersal of the snails. The Moorean *Partula* are arboreal, found on shrubs and on the trunks of *Hibiscus tiliaceus*, the commonest forest tree. They feed predominantly on epiphytic fungi and algae. Distinct ecological differences have been found between sympatric species. For example, *P. taeniata* predominates on shrubs between two and five metres in height, *P. suturalis* favours the trunks of *Hibiscus*, whereas *P. tohiveana* is most often found on the leaves of the climbing pandanus, *Freycinetia demissa*.

The impact of the introduced predator *Euglandina rosea*

Regular visits to Moorea by Clarke, Murray and Johnson have provided a unique history of the extinction of species by an introduced predator (Clarke *et al.* 1984; Tillier and Clarke 1983). In 1977 the carnivorous snail *Euglandina rosea* was introduced at Paopao, Moorea, with the approval of the Service de l'Economie Rurale and the Division de Recherche Agronomique, in an attempt to control the spread of the agricultural pest *Achatina fulica*, the giant African snail. A second introduction was made later in the northwest of the island. Estimated to be spreading at the rate of 1.2km a year, *E. rosea* now occupies most of the island. Although the giant African snail has declined since 1978, the decline may have had little to do with *E. rosea*, since there was a similar decline on the island of Huahine, where *E. rosea* has not been introduced.

Despite its uncertain effect on *Achatina, E. rosea* has had a devastating impact on *Partula*. With one possible exception, the endemic species are entirely absent within the range of the predator. All seven *Partula* species have been eliminated from the greater part of the island. *P. aurantia* has not been found since 1981 and is probably extinct. *P. mirabilis, P. tohiveana* and *P. olympia* (now considered a geographical race of *P. tohiveana*) are probably also extinct (Clarke *et al.* 1984). It is just possible that *P. mirabilis* may still occur in one isolated valley, but, if so, it is unlikely to survive the year.

P. exigua, which was restricted to the northeast of the island, appears to be exceptional in that a few individuals were found in 1982, within the range of *E. rosea*, although all other *Partula* had been eliminated. It is uncertain whether *P. exigua* still persists. It seems likely that all the remaining species will be extinct within about two years.

Introductions of *E. rosea* to other islands should be prevented. *Partula* in Tahiti, Guam and Saipan are already under threat. *E. rosea* was introduced to Tahiti in 1974, is currently spreading, and appears to have eliminated all the *Partula* in its path. *E. rosea* and two other carnivorous snails, *Gonaxis quadrilateralis* and *G. kibweziensis*, have been introduced to Guam and Saipan and it is thought that there is little hope for the malacological fauna on those islands. In Hawaii, where *E. rosea* has also been introduced, the plight of the subfamily Achatinellinae is already well known, and it is thought to be unlikely that the group will survive much longer in the wild (Hadfield 1986).

Captive breeding

Partula

The only hope of survival for the Moorean *Partula* seems to be captive breeding. Seven species are being bred at universities in Nottingham (United Kingdom), Charlottesville (U.S.A.), and Perth (Western Australia).

Stocks are generally stable but occasionally succumb to what is presumed to be an unidentified disease. Following experiments at Nottingham, the snails there are fed a diet consisting of a finely ground mixture of the following: 3 tsp native chalk, 3 tsp grass, 1.5 tsp trout pellets, 3 tsp oats, 20mg Vitamin E and 0.25 tsp dog food 'Stress'. The addition of Vitamin E seemed to produce an improvement in reproductive success, especially among *P. tohiveana* but the same treatment produced no noticeable improvement in the University of Western Australia stocks. These are breeding reasonably well, with the exception of *P. aurantia*, but survival to adulthood is not very good.

At the University of Virginia in Charlottesville, *P. suturalis* and *P. taeniata* are doing particularly well. Like the Perth snails, they are kept in plastic boxes (12 x 12 x 2.5cm) with moistened toilet paper on the floor, and are fed twice weekly with a few flakes of rolled oats and a dusting of powdered natural chalk. Lettuce is fed occasionally. The boxes are cleaned at each feed. The addition of Vitamin E to the diets of the Charlottesville snails seems to have had little impact. All species of *Partula* need a fairly rapid cycle of wet and dry conditions, rather than a constantly humid regime which is harmful. Temperatures above 26°C also seem to be harmful. It is curious that snails from a tropical rainforest should be susceptible to high humidity and high temperatures.

In 1981, a captive breeding colony of five taxa was established at the Jersey Wildfowl Preservation Trust (JWPT) with the financial support of the Fauna and Flora Preservation Society (Bloxam *et al.* 1984; Bloxam and Tonge 1986). After initial problems, these are doing fairly well and in 1986 there were nearly 400 individuals. Breeding of *P. mirabilis* has been particularly successful but *P. tohiveana* proved difficult and one remaining individual was returned to Nottingham recently. Numbers fluctuate, apparently regardless of husbandry. The current diet of the snails at Jersey is porridge oats, cuttle bone and baby food (8:8:1). At Edinburgh Zoo, a colony derived from individuals supplied by the JWPT had similar problems and the snails had died by 1987. Early efforts at London Zoo were abandoned, but another attempt is being made.

Problems in the captive breeding of invertebrates

Over the centuries, invertebrates have been bred in captivity for food, other economic reasons (e.g. silkworms *Bombyx mori* for silk), for research and for educational purposes, but there are few instances where the main purpose has been to preserve the species (Cooper 1986). The captive breeding of endangered vertebrates, however, is a fully accepted technique of conservation, high among the goals of an increasing number of zoos (Seal 1986). Soule *et al.* (1986) suggest that about 2000 species of large terrestrial animals may have to be kept in captivity for 500 to 1000 years in order to prevent their extinction. Species such as Pere David's Deer *Elaphurus davidianus* and Przewalski's Horse *Equus przewalskii* have already become extinct in the wild, and survive only because of captive breeding programmes. Attempts at reintroduction are now under way for several species of mammals, including the Arabian oryx *Oryx leucoryx*, which was re-introduced to Oman and which is now successfully breeding in the wild (Stanley Price 1986), and many birds, including the well-known case of the Hawaiian goose or nene, *Branta sandvicensis* (Fyfe 1977).

The bias towards vertebrates in efforts to conserve species may lead us to overlook the ease with which invertebrates can be bred. They can often be reared in small spaces, and they may not require costly equipment or housing. They tend to have short generation times, so that breeding success can easily be monitored. They can provide valuable models for the study of problems relevant to other endangered species, such as the problems of inbreeding depression, epizootic disease, and strategies of release.

An explosive growth of butterfly houses in the United Kingdom illustrates how successful programmes can be for breeding and rearing invertebrates. Although butterfly houses are often primarily commercial, their educational role in conservation is important. They have the potential to play an active role, by directing efforts towards rare species, or by initiating field projects (Collins 1986).

The medicinal leech *Hirudo medicinalis* is being bred in captivity because it is heavily in demand for various medical applications, and for research. There is hope that eventually world demand can be met from captive-bred specimens and that the pressure on the dwindling wild population will be reduced (Wells and Coombes 1987).

At present the only real interest in the captive breeding or 'farming' of snails is in Europe, where progress is being made in cultivating *Helix aspersa* to meet an increasing demand for luxury food and, in certain areas, for traditional local food. The breeding of the Roman snail, *H. pomatia*, has met with less success.

Unfortunately there is no commercial incentive to breed the endangered species with which this paper is concerned. Snails such as *Partula* lack the glamour that is generally required in zoo animals. Generally the attention and finance devoted to animals is proportional to their position on the evolutionary scale. Twenty five million dollars have been spent on the captive breeding of the California condor, but there have been difficulties in raising even one hundredth of one percent of that figure for the captive breeding of *Partula*.

Nevertheless, there is scope for a captive breeding programme. 'Snailaria' could be established by more zoos and wildlife collections, either in existing facilities for endangered species (for example, in the New York Zoological Society's St. Catherines Island centre), or in the increasingly popular 'ecosystem exhibits' (for example those illustrating tropical forests). Some zoos already have 'insect houses', and some allocate space in their aquaria to terrestrial as well as to aquatic forms. Berlin Zoo has a specially designed 'Insectarium' (Klos and Lange, 1986).

Some of the Pacific snails are very colourful, and they would make an attractive and educational exhibit. The story of *Partula* is, after all, a unique lesson in island biology and in the fragility of island ecosystems. Commercial butterfly houses, which are anxious to be involved in conservation, often have general invertebrate exhibits. Some already display the giant African snail. They may have the potential to be involved in a captive breeding programme for snails.

There is already a growing awareness that captive breeding can play a valuable role in insect conservation. Morton (1983) proposed the establishment of a "Captive Breeding Institute" for insects. A code of practice for the re-establishment of insect populations (or their reintroduction) has been produced (Joint Committee for Conservation of British Insects 1986) and many of the ideas embodied in this could be extended to other invertebrates. In any case, closer collaboration between field workers, private collectors, laboratories and zoos is clearly needed (Cooper 1986). This is particularly true of *Partula*, where breeding has been successful in research laboratories, but the techniques of culture have only recently been passed on to a few zoos. The IUCN Captive Breeding Specialist Group provides an international forum for the development of collaborative plans for captive breeding programmes (Seal 1986) and is currently considering developing a plan for *Partula*.

Reintroduction to the wild

The ultimate aim of most captive programmes is the reintroduction of endangered species into the wild. Invertebrates are perhaps better known in the context of unwelcome introductions, whether they be accidental, such as that of the giant African snail, or intentional, such as that of *Euglandina rosea*, which was introduced as an agent of biological control. However, there are already a few cases where threatened invertebrates have been successfully re-established, or translocated to a safer habitat. They may provide useful models for future projects. At Woodwalton Fen in Britain, for example, a free-living population of the Dutch race of the Large Copper Butterfly, *Lycaena dispar batavus*, is supplemented annually by specimens reared in captivity (Duffey 1968). The Large Blue Butterfly, *Maculinea arion*, which went extinct in Britain in 1979, was reintroduced experimentally in 1984 using Swedish individuals. So far, the trials have been successful (Regan 1986).

Several species of the threatened New Zealand endemic land snail *Placostylus* have been successfully translocated to islands that are free of predation, and other such translocations have been recommended (Ogle 1979). Molluscs may prove easier to re-establish than many vertebrates. Their low mobilities should facilitate monitoring of introduced populations, although this advantage may sometimes be outweighed by their cryptic habits. Several introductions may be necessary before a population becomes established.

If breeding colonies of *Partula* can be maintained successfully, and if *E. rosea* dies out on Moorea (as could happen through food shortage and cannibalism, although this is perhaps more possible rather than probable), a reintroduction programme could be initiated for *Partula*. For such a programme to be successful, Moorea must continue to provide a suitable habitat. Unfortunately, although it has long been considered one of the most beautiful of the Pacific islands, and although the scientific interest in its fauna and flora is well documented, there have been no local attempts to deal with conservation issues, and no integrated approach to terrestrial research. Natural forests at low altitude have largely disappeared and the remaining vegetation is under pressure from expanding agriculture and a variety of introduced species (Holyoak 1974). Tourism is now a mainstay of the economy. Although still largely restricted to the coast, it may well expand inland, capitalising on the dramatic beauty of the interior.

Much of the remaining endemic fauna and flora is now restricted to the steepest and most inaccessible patches of forest, and is relatively safe. Nevertheless such areas are shrinking. If a reintroduction programme were to be initiated, a firm guarantee of the long term survival of the forest would be required. Holyoak (1974) has called for the protection of the entire mountainous interior, and for its management to cater for the demands of the developing tourist industry. Moorea would be suitable for the creation of a multiple-use reserve, such as a Biosphere Reserve, a form of protected area developed by Unesco's Man and the Biosphere Program. Biosphere Reserves are designed with zoning systems which include core areas that protect natural ecosystems and genetic diversity, areas reserved for traditional uses, experimental areas and rehabilitation areas. The reserves aim to involve local communities in programmes of research and education within their confines. The reintroduction of *Partula* into a reserve created along these lines would provide the necessary framework for the continued protection of the species.

As Conway (1986) points out, preserving segments of habitat without their key species, be they condors, gorillas or snails, is like saving a husk without a kernel: 'Captive propagation of endangered species is to do with kernels'. If the captive breeding and reintroduction of *Partula* is not pursued, there are few other options. Future research may provide techniques for preserving zygotes and embryonic cells, and for regenerating viable individuals, but this will take many years (Soulé *et al.* 1986). There is also a strong case for preserving the DNA of endangered species, a procedure that is relatively simple and cheap, and that retains a large amount of important scientific information, but does not save the animals themselves. At present it must be recognised that *Partula* and its Pacific relatives will be better 'bred than dead'.

Acknowledgements

I am very grateful to Professor B.C. Clarke for reading and criticising the manuscript, and for providing details about the breeding programme in Nottingham. I am also very grateful to Professor J.J. Murray Jnr., Dr. M.S. Johnson and Mr. Q. Bloxam for giving details about the programmes in Charlottesville, Perth and Jersey respectively.

Literature cited

BLOXAM, Q.M.C., TONGE, S. AND HORTON, R. 1984. A preliminary account of the history and management of populations of endangered Moorean tree snails *Partula* spp. at the Jersey Wildlife Preservation Trust. *Dodo, Journal Jersey Wildlife Preservation Trust*, 20: 73-79.

BLOXAM, Q.M.C. AND TONGE, S. 1986. Breeding programmes for reptiles and snails at Jersey Zoo: an appraisal. *International Zoo Yearbook*, 24/25: 49-56.

CLARKE, B.C. AND MURRAY, J. 1969. Ecological genetics and speciation in land snails of the genus *Partula*. *Biological Journal of the Linnean Society*, 1: 31-42.

CLARKE, B.C., MURRAY, J. AND JOHNSON, M. 1984. The extinction of endemic species by a program of biological control. *Pacific Science*, 38 (2): 97-104.

COLLINS, N.M. 1986. Conservation and exploitation of terrestrial invertebrates. In: *Exotic Animals in the Eighties*. Proceedings of the 25th Anniversary Symp. British Veterinary Zoological Society. April 1986: 111-115.

CONWAY, W.G. 1986. The practical difficulties and financial implications of endangered species breeding programmes. *International Zoo Yearbook*, 24/25: 210-219.

COOPER, J.E. 1986. Captive breeding of invertebrates. *International Zoo Yearbook*, 24/25: 74-76.

CRAMPTON, H.E. 1916. Studies on the variation, distribution and evolution of the genus *Partula*. The species inhabiting Tahiti. *Carnegie Institution of Washington Publication*, 228: 1-311.

CRAMPTON, H.E. 1925. Studies on the variation, distribution and evolution of the genus *Partula*. The species of the Mariana Islands, Guam and Saipan. *Carnegie Institution of Washington Publication*, 228A: 1-116.

CRAMPTON, H.E. 1932. Studies on the variation, distribution and evolution of the genus *Partula*. The species inhabiting Moorea. *Carnegie Institution of Washington Publication*, 410: 1-335.

DUFFEY, E. 1968. Ecological studies on the large copper butterfly *Lycaena dispar* Haw. *batavus* Obth. at Woodwalton Fen National Nature Reserve, Huntingdonshire. *Journal of Applied Ecology*, 5: 69-96.

FYFE, R.W. 1977. Reintroducing endangered birds into the wild: a review. In: Temple, S.A. (Ed.), *Endangered Birds: Management Techniques for Preserving Threatened Species*. Univ of Wisconsin Press, Croom Helm Ltd.

HADFIELD, M.G. 1986. Extinctions in Hawaiian Achatinelline Snails. *Malacologia*, 27(1): 67-81.

HOLYOAK, D.T. 1974. Les oiseaux des îles de la Societé. *L'Oiseau et la Revue Francaise d'Ornithologie*, 44: 1-27,153-184.

JOINT COMMITTEE FOR CONSERVATION OF BRITISH INSECTS. 1986. Insect re-establishment - a code of conservation practice. *Antenna*, 10 (1): 13-18.

JOHNSON, M.W., CLARKE, B. AND MURRAY, J. 1977. Genetic variation and reproductive isolation in *Partula*. *Evolution*, 31: 116-126.

KLOS, H.-G. AND LANGE, J. 1986. The modernisation of the aquarium at Berlin Zoo. *International Zoo Yearbook*, 24/25: 322-332.

MORTON, A.C. 1983. Butterfly conservation - the need for a captive breeding institute. *Biological Conservation*, 25:19-33.

MURRAY, J. AND CLARKE, B. 1980. The genus *Partula* on Moorea: speciation in progress. *Proceedings of the Royal Society B*, 211: 83-117.

MURRAY, J., JOHNSON, M.S. AND CLARKE, B. 1982. Microhabitat differences among genetically similar species of *Partula*. *Evolution*, 36: 316-325.

OGLE, C.C. 1979. Critical status of *Placostylus* and *Paryphanta* land snails in the far north. *Fauna Survey Unit Report 14*, New Zealand Wildlife Service.

REGAN, S. 1986. The large blue comes home. *Butterfly News*, 8: 8.

SEAL, U.S. 1986. Goals of captive propagation programmes for the conservation of endangered species. *International Zoo Yearbook*, 24/25: 174-179.

SOULÉ, M., GILPIN, M., CONWAY, W. AND FOOSE, T. 1986. The millenium ark; how long a journey, how many staterooms, how many passengers? *Zoo Biology*, 5 (2): 101-113.

STANLEY PRICE, M.R. 1986. The reintroduction of the Arabian oryx *Oryx leucoryx* into Oman. *International Zoo Yearbook*, 24/25: 179-188.

TILLIER, S. AND CLARKE, B.C. 1983. Lutte biologique et destruction du patrimoine genetique: le cas des mollusques gasteropodes pulmones dans les territoires Francais du Pacifique. *Genetique, Selection, Evolution*, 15 (4): 559-566.

WELLS, S.M., PYLE, R.M. AND COLLINS, N.M. 1983. *The IUCN Invertebrate Red Data Book*. IUCN, Gland and Cambridge.

WELLS, S.M. AND COOMBES, W. 1987. Status of and trade in the medicinal leech. *Traffic Bulletin*, 8 (4): 64-69.

Conservation of marine molluscs in the British Isles

Norman A. Holme

Formerly of The Laboratory, Citadel Hill, Plymouth PL1 2PB, England, now deceased.

Abstract

With a long and varied coastline, broad continental shelf, and long stretches of continental slopes, the seas around the British Isles are exceptionally rich in habitats for marine molluscs. Moreover, their situation at the interface between Boreal and Lusitanian faunas provides interesting examples of distributions limited by climate-related factors. Offshore, the sea bed is typically characterised by sediment communities with such infaunal bivalves as *Venus*, *Abra* and *Nucula*, while commercially exploitable stocks of scallops and queens (*Pecten*, *Chlamys*) occur on the surface. Because the waters around the British Isles have good water circulation due to strong tidal streams, pollution is not a significant problem offshore, but there is increasing evidence of damage to benthic populations through use of heavy fishing gear.

Inshore, there are local problems from water pollution from domestic and industrial sources, from oil spills and from anti-fouling paints. Land reclamation schemes and commercial dredging provide additional pressures, as does usage of the coastline for recreation, food and bait collection, field classes, etc. Areas particularly at risk appear to be sediment habitats in estuaries, and the sea inlets or rias such as occur in southwest England.

In the United Kingdom, some progress has been made towards designation of statutory Marine Nature Reserves to include both the intertidal zone and shallow water offshore. Some half a dozen voluntary marine conservation areas have also been established.

Introduction

The British Isles are favourably placed to support a wide variety of marine, brackish and estuarine communities, in which molluscs frequently play an important part. The total coastline of Great Britain and Ireland exceeds 20,000km; that of England and Wales together is estimated at 4415km (Steers 1976), while the much more dissected coastline of Scotland, with its many islands, is estimated at 10,200km (Countryside Commission for Scotland 1978).

Coastlines

The coasts are of varied character, depending on the local geology, past history of changing sea levels and glaciation, and degree of exposure to wave action. In Great Britain they range from the rocky coasts which predominate in the west to low-lying sandy coasts, often associated with dunes and salt marshes, on the east coast, or backed by machair pastures as in the Outer Hebrides. In Scotland there are many sea lochs, and in southwest England their counterparts are the drowned valleys or rias which contain a particularly rich fauna and flora under sheltered and fully marine conditions. In some sheltered inlets, particularly in parts of Scotland and at Lough Ine in Ireland, tidal rapids occur, supporting a diverse fauna and flora on current-swept substrata (Lewis 1964). Estuaries of many types occur, but lagoonal systems are restricted in extent, the best examples being the Fleet in southern England and the brackish sea lochs of the Uists and Benbecula in the Outer Hebrides.

On rocky shores the nature of the substratum is of importance: where this is slaty it is likely to provide crevices which harbour a varied interstitial fauna (Morton 1954), where of limestone, soft sandstone or clay a suitable habitat is provided for borers, notably pholad molluscs. Granite shores have few crevices, and rock pools may be scarce.

Biogeography

The British Isles lie at the boundary of the Boreal and Lusitanian provinces (as was recognised over a century ago by Edward Forbes (Forbes and Godwin-Austen 1859)), many Lusitanian species showing a limited penetration into the south and west of the region (Earll and Farnham 1983). For such reasons, numbers of species are very much higher in the west and southwest than on North Sea coasts. Offshore, the British Isles are surrounded by a broad continental shelf linking them on the one side to the continent of Europe, and on the other to the slope and deep-sea communities of the eastern Atlantic. The shallow-water zone below low tide mark, previously poorly known, has been revealed through the use of SCUBA equipment, adding much to our knowledge of the species and communities, both of rock and sediment (Earll and Erwin 1983).

Offshore shelf

Farther offshore, the shelf typically supports sediment communities characterised by such infaunal bivalves as *Venus*, *Abra*, and *Nucula*, with commercially exploitable stocks of scallops (*Pecten maximus* (L.)) and queens (*Chlamys opercularis* (L.)) occurring on the surface. To the north and west of Britain the continental shelf gives way to the slope extending to 2000m and beyond, inhabited by a different suite of species (le Danois 1948).

Numbers of molluscs

It is difficult to arrive at an exact figure for the numbers of species of molluscs in the waters adjacent to the British Isles, as this must depend on the limits chosen. As a guide, the following figures for British marine molluscs are based on Seaward (1982):

Gastropoda:

Aplacophora	8	Prosobranchia	245
Polyplacophora	14	Opisthobranchia	215
Lamellibranchia	223	Pulmonata	4
Cephalopoda	32	Scaphopoda	5
		Total species:	746

The effects of fishing and pollution

Fishing

Because the waters around the British Isles have a vigorous water circulation due to strong tidal streams, pollution is seldom a significant problem offshore, and on the continental shelf the effects of man's activities are chiefly limited to those of fishing gear, and engineering structures such as oil and gas rigs and associated pipelines.

Trawls employing heavy chain groundlines for catching soles, and scallop dredges, are likely to cause considerable damage to the bottom fauna. Scallop dredges have a low catching efficiency, of around 10%, but it seems that, in addition, a similar proportion of the scallops are damaged without being taken (Gruffydd 1972; Caddy 1973; Noel 1982). Trawls and dredges also tend to damage burrowing invertebrates (de Groot 1984), or bring them to the surface where they are rapidly consumed by predators (Caddy 1973; Meyer *et al.* 1981). In addition, such operations break up and destroy hydroids and Bryozoa (notably *Cellaria* spp.) rooted in the bottom. These normally form attachment surfaces for young stages of both queens and scallops (Pickett and Franklin 1975; Pickett 1977), stocks of which are likely to suffer should these attachment surfaces be reduced.

One mollusc which seems particularly susceptible to damage by towed fishing gear is the fan-mussel, *Pinna fragilis* Pennant, which lives vertically in the sediment with its top protruding above the surface. It was formerly common off parts of the Cornish coast, where specimens were brought up entangled in fishing lines or hooks (Couch 1841). However trawls and dredges are likely to have inflicted far more damage to the populations, and today this species is rare, possibly surviving only where the ground is 'rough' and unsuitable for trawling or dredging (cf. Hignette 1983, who describes threats to the Mediterranean fan-mussel from both divers and fishing gear).

In the English Channel fishermen have recently learned to 'jig' for squid (*Loligo forbesi* Steenstrup) when these come inshore to spawn in the late autumn. This exploitation, and intensive bottom trawling for this species which attracts a higher price than many prime fish, seems to have markedly reduced stocks of squid off Plymouth in recent years.

Pollution

In coastal regions there are a variety of threats to molluscs, as to other forms of marine life. These include pollution from industrial and domestic sources, by oil and measures employed to combat it, and from antifouling paints. For example, the deleterious effects of tributyltin, leached from antifouling paints, on the common shore gastropod *Nucella lapillus* (L.) have been identified in a recent paper by Bryan *et al.* (1986). Even concentrations of tin (as tributyltin species) as minute as 1 ng/l. have been found to affect this species, which results in the acquisition of imposex features (male characteristics) by females. These authors have shown that populations of this species have been affected to a varying degree around almost the entire coastline of southwest England, with a very high degree of imposex near harbours and marinas where pollution from tributyltin is likely to be greatest. In the Fal estuary and Helford River *Nucella* is now absent at a number of sites where it was formerly common. Tributyltin was already known to affect

spatfall and shell development in *Crassostrea virginica* (Gmelin) (=*gigas*) (Alzieu and Portmann 1984; see discussion by Stebbing 1985); to what extent are other forms of marine life threatened at such low concentrations of this pollutant?

Land reclamation schemes and commercial dredging for aggregates for building provide additional threats (de Groot 1979), as does dumping of sewage and other forms of solid waste. Fish farms are another source of pollution, and there is the possibility that exotic species of clam cultivated in shellfish farms could become naturalised, with effects on the native fauna. Many of these forms of pollution , combined with other pressures (e.g. usage of the coast for recreation SCUBA diving, food and bait collection, field classes) tend to be concentrated in localised areas often around seaside towns or in estuarine and other inlets. Such sites are consequently particularly at risk.

Population declines

The decline of the native oyster, *Ostrea edulis* L., in British waters over the past 150 years or so has been well documented, and in recent years the sporozoan *Bonamia ostreae* has seriously affected stocks in certain areas (Bucke *et al.* 1984). But to what extent has there been a general decline in our molluscan fauna? The situation is complicated by the large fluctuations which regularly occur in populations from year to year. This seems to be found particularly in certain opisthobranchs. Bivalve species also, notably *Donax*, are well known to have a successful spatfall only exceptionally, so that populations may be very high over a period of years while a single year's brood grows up, followed by a drastic fall to low levels until another spatfall occurs. Other changes appear to be more long-lasting. Thus the bivalve *Spisula subtruncata* (da Costa) virtually disappeared from the Clyde at the end of the last century, and has not subsequently recovered to a significant degree (Barnett and Watson, in press).

An example of extension of the range of a species occurred about 19 years ago when the clam *Mya arenaria* L. suddenly appeared in estuaries in southwest England, where it had not previously been found. Efforts to conserve particular species seem to be fraught with problems when one is faced with such fluctuations in 'natural' populations, but there seems to be a good case for affording protective status to coastal areas having particularly important habitats, or where there are serious threats to the area.

Conservation efforts

Statutory marine reserves

In Great Britain, initiative for the setting up of statutory marine nature reserves (MNRs) has been taken by the Nature Conservancy Council (for progress in the Republic of Ireland and in Northern Ireland see papers in Jeffrey 1984). The groundwork for conservation measures was carried out through two working parties (NCC/NERC 1979), and with the passing of the *Wildife and Countryside Act* 1981, it became possible for the first time to establish reserves which extended below tidemark (Gibson 1984). NCC plan to have seven Marine Nature Reserves (MNRs) designated in the next few years, and progress is well advanced for the first two, in Lundy and Skomer, which will be followed by Bardsey and the Menai Straits in Wales and Loch Sween and St. Abb's Head in Scotland (Figure 3.1).

Voluntary conservation areas

There can be no doubt that voluntary conservation areas are much more easily and quickly set up than those with statutory designation - only time will tell how effective voluntary measures can be. Statutory designation allows for the control or prohibition of such operations as trawling, dredging, and spear-fishing (although discharge of any substance from a ship is not unlawful), whereas in voluntary reserves only moral pressures can be brought to bear.

A number of voluntary marine conservation areas or reserves have already been established (Figure 3.2) (Holme 1983; Gubbay 1986). One example of a voluntary reserve is the Roseland Marine Conservation area, set up to conserve a variety of habitats in the outer part of the Fal estuary in Cornwall. The area is threatened by a proposed container terminal on the opposite side of the estuary at Falmouth (Deeble and Stone 1984). The Conservation Area includes intertidal flats with a rich and varied fauna living under sheltered and fully marine conditions, a *Zostera* bed, and the most extensive bed of living calcareous red seaweed ('maerl') in England. There are in addition rocky shores, with varying degrees of exposure to wave action, and the Duchy of Cornwall oyster beds in the Percuil River. To my mind this blend of rich and unique habitats, subject to a potential threat, makes a more powerful case for conservation measures than some of the isolated islands and associated areas, under no particular environmental pressures, which are being considered for designation as Statutory MNRs. The Roseland Marine Conservation Area is listed as a threatened community in the IUCN Invertebrate Red Data Book (Wells *et al.* 183).

The nearby Helford River is another drowned valley or ria, having both rocky shores and intertidal sand and mud flats, with an extensive *Zostera* bed at Helford Passage. The River has a particularly rich molluscan fauna, some 189 species of molluscs having been listed from the River up to the year 1910 (Holme and Turk 1986), with many more having been recorded subsequently.

There is, however, evidence of a decline in the marine life of the River in recent years, which has resulted in a proposal to make the River a conservation area. Because of uncertainties as to the cause of the deterioration, it was decided as a preliminary move to make a 12-month survey of the River, with particular emphasis on the environmental pressures to which it is exposed. This study has been financed by the World Wide Fund for Nature. Pressures on the River include the traditional 'trigging' or raking for shellfish on Good Friday, and the work of Bryan et al. (1986) has shown that tributyltin pollution has resulted in the disappearance of Nucella from the River. Whether either of these have been major factors contributing to the general decline remains to be discovered.

The areas listed for statutory designation and those already established as voluntary marine conservation areas form but a negligible amount of the coastline of Great Britain. Clearly there is a need for conservation measures to be applied to much more extensive areas of coastline than is covered by present plans.

Acknowledgment

I am indebted to Dr. Susan Gubbay, Marine Conservation Society for permission to reproduce Figures 3.1 and 3.2.

References

Note that in several instances a single reference has been cited to give a lead in to the extensive literature on a particular topic.

ALZIEU, C. & PORTMANN, J. E. 1984. The effects of tributyltin on the culture of *Crassostrea gigas* and other species. *Proceedings of the Fifteenth Annual Shellfish Conference*, 15-16 May 1984, 87-100. Shellfish Association, London.

BARNETT, P. R. O. AND WATSON, J. in press. Long-term changes in some benthic species in the Firth of Clyde, with particular reference to *Tellina tenuis* da Costa. *Proceedings of the Royal Society of Edinburgh, B.*

BRYAN, G. G., GIBBS, P. W., HUMMERSTONE, L.G. & BURT, G.R. 1986. The decline of the gastropod *Nucella lapillus* around south-west England: evidence for the effect of tributyltin from antifouling paints. *Journal of the Marine Biological Association of the United Kingdom*, 66, 611-640.

BUCKE, D., HEPPER, B., KEY, D. & BANNISTER, R. C. A., 1984. A report on *Bonamia ostreae* in *Ostrea edulis* in the U.K. *International Council for the Exploration of the Sea*, Paper C.M. 1984/K:9.

CADDY, J. F. 1973. Underwater observations on traces of dredges and trawls and some effects of dredging on a scallop ground. *Journal of the Fisheries Research Board of Canada*, 30. 173-180.

COUCH, J. 1841. *A Cornish Fauna, being a Compendium of the Natural History of the County. Part II. Containing the Testaceous Mollusks.* Royal Institution of Cornwall, Truro.

COUNTRYSIDE COMMISSION FOR SCOTLAND 1978. *Scotland's Scenic Heritage*. The Countryside Commission for Scotland.

DANOIS, E. LE 1948. *Les Profondeurs de la Mer. Trente Ans de Recherches sur la Faune sous-marine au large des Cotes de France.* Payot, Paris.

DEEBLE, M. & STONE, V.1984. A port that could threaten marine life in England's Fal estuary. *Oryx*, 19(2): 74-78.

EARLL, R. & ERWIN, D.G. (EDS). 1983. *Sublittoral ecology. The ecology of the shallow sublittoral benthos.* Clarendon Press, Oxford.

EARLL, R. & W. FARNHAM. 1983. Biogeography. pp. 165-208 in R. Earll and D.G.Erwin (eds) *Sublittoral Ecology. The ecology of the shallow sublittoral benthos.* Clarendon Press, Oxford.

FORBES, E. & GODWIN-AUSTEN, R. 1859. *The Natural History of European Seas.* Van Voorst, London.

GIBSON, J. 1984. Marine nature reserves. *Journal of Planning and Environment Law*, October 1984, 699-706.

de GROOT, S. J. 1979. The potential environmental impact of marine gravel extraction in the North Sea. *Ocean Management*, 5, 233-249.

de GROOT, S. J. 1984. The impact of bottom trawling of benthic fauna of the North Sea. *Ocean Management*, 9, 177-190.

GRUFFYDD, LL.D. 1972. Mortality of scallops on a Manx scallop bed due to fishing. *Journal of the Marine Biological Association of the United Kingdom*, 52, 449-455.

GUBBAY, S. 1986. *Conservation of Marine Sites. A Voluntary Approach.* Marine Conservation Society, Ross-on-Wye, 18 pp.

HIGNETTE, M. 1983. Croissance de *Pinna nobilis* Linne (Mollusque Eulamellibranchie) après implantation dans la reserve sous-marin de Monaco. Rapports et procés-verbaux des Réunions. *Commission Internationale pour l'Exploration scientifique de la Mer Mediterranee.* 28(3), 237-238.

HOLME, N.A. 1983. Marine nature reserves. *Journal of the Devon Trust for Nature Conservation*, 4, 56-61.

HOLME, N.A. AND TURK, S.M. 1986. Studies on the marine life of the Helford River: fauna records up to 1910. *Cornish Biological Records*, 9, 26 pp.

JEFFREY, D.W. (ED). 1984. *Nature Conservation in Ireland. Progress and Problems. Proceedings of a seminar 24-25 February 1983.* Royal Irish Academy, Dublin.

LEWIS, J.R. 1964. *The Ecology of Rocky Shores.* English Universities Press, London.

MEYER, T.L., COOPER, R.A. AND PECCI, K.J. 1981. The performance and environmental effects of a hydraulic clam dredge. *Marine Fisheries Review*, 43(9), 14-22.

MORTON, J.E. 1954. The crevice faunas of the upper intertidal zone at Wembury. *Journal of the Marine Biological Association of the United Kingdom*, 33, 187-224.

NOEL, S. 1982. The scallops that get away... or do they? *Fishing News International*, 21(8), 42-43.

NCC/NERC 1979. *Nature Conservation and the Marine Environment.* Nature Conservancy Council/ Natural Environment Research Council, 65 pp.

NERC 1973. Marine Wildlife Conservation. *Natural Environment Research Council Publications Series B*, 39 pp.

PICKETT, G.D. 1977. Artificial collection of pectinid spat: preliminary experiments in Start Bay, S.W. England, 1975-1977 *International Council for the Exploration of the Sea*, Paper C.M. 1977/E:49, 10 pp.

PICKETT, G.D. AND FRANKLIN, A. 1975. Techniques for surveying queen scallop populations: experiments off south-west England in May-June 1974. *MAFF Technical Report*, 14, 19 pp.

SEAWARD, D.R. (ED), 1982. *Sea Area Atlas of the Marine Molluscs of Britain and Ireland.* Nature Conservancy Council, London.

STEBBING, A.R.D., 1985. Organotins and water quality - some lessons to be learned. *Marine Pollution Bulletin*, 16, 383-390.

STEERS, J.A. 1976. *The Coastline of England and Wales/* (2nd edn). Cambridge University Press, London.

WELLS, S.M., PYLE, R.M. AND COLLINS, M. 1984. *The IUCN Invertebrate Red Data Book.* International Union for the Conservation of Nature and Natural Resources, Gland, Switzerland

Figure 3.1 Proposed statutory Marine Nature Reserves in Great Britain (from Gubbay, 1986).

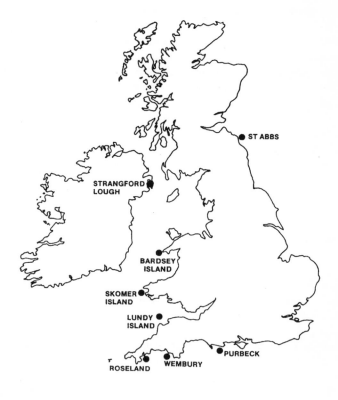

Figure 3.2 Location of voluntary Marine Reserves in Great Britain and Northern Ireland (from Gubbay, 1986).

Exploitation and conservation of marine molluscs in India

N.V. Subba Rao

Zoological Survey of India, M-Block, New Alipore, Calcutta 700053, India

[**UPDATE**: An updated and detailed version of the Status Report on Mollusca by the author appears in *Conservation of Biological Diversity in India* compiled and edited by the Indian Institute of Public Administration, New Delhi (In press).]

Abstract

In recent years shell fisheries have come to occupy a significant place in the Indian economy. Some of the species are collected for their utility as food while many are used in the preparation of ornaments and curios. The present level of exploitation of the marine shell resources does not indicate any rational approach to prevent the depletion of the natural stock. Some of the well known gastropods like *Trochus niloticus*, *Turbo marmoratus* and *Turbinella pyrum* are not as common today as these used to be a decade ago. *Ancilla ampla* which was once very common on the sandy beach at Digha, on the east coast of India, has now become scarce due to overcollecting for use in curios. The bivalve *Meretrix meretrix* is extensively used in the manufacture of poultry feed and lime and is collected by the tonne from the Subarnareka River in Orissa. These examples point out the need for a judicious exploitation of various species of molluscs. Conservation of some of the commercially important molluscs is suggested.

Conservation projects for the freshwater pearl mussel
Margaritifera margaritifera
in the Federal Republic of Germany

Jürgen H. Jungbluth

[1]*In der Aue 30 e, 69118 Schlierbach, F.R.G.* [2] *Mit Unterstutzung des Landes Hessen sowie anderer Bundeslander.*

Abstract

Since the beginning of the l9th century, a decrease in the occurrence of mother of pearl mussels has been observed in central Europe. Later in the century, when interest in mother of pearl subsided, so did the attention paid to the decreasing populations of the mussels. It was not until after World War II that interest focused on loss of mother of pearl mussel habitats in central Europe. The process was induced by Hertel's (1959) report in which he documented the diminution in the Saxon Vogtland which had been the centre of the pearl fishery in Germany. In subsequent years, publications repeatedly reported the disappearance of habitats of the mother of pearl mussels in the German Uplands and other habitats in Europe. By the end of the sixties, comprehensive studies were undertaken at several locations in Germany to investigate the occurrence, biology and population development of the mother of pearl mussel.

In spite of the fact that scientists have studied the pearl as a pearl mussel supplier for several centuries, the life cycle of this mussel is still largely unknown. In the literature, it has always been assumed that the life cycle is comparable to that of other naiads. Investigations recently undertaken in Hanover, Giessen/ Heidelberg and Bayreuth have largely elucidated the life cycle of the mussel, especially in connection with the species conservation project run in the Lüneburg Heath (cf. Jungbluth 1986). These studies provided for the first time hints of the actual extent of the decrease in mussel populations in central Europe. The publication of the first results raised interest in further extensive investigations and initiated other species conservation projects.

Finally, in 1985-1986, (Jungbluth *et al.* 1985a, 1986) a complete inventory and analysis of the situation of the mother of pearl mussel was undertaken nationwide . The results have not yet been published. At the same time, species conservation projects have been intensified and carried on. It is intended that an overall concept of species conservation be prepared. The project will cover all of the Federal Republic of Germany, and interlink ongoing individual projects.

Introduction

As elsewhere, successful species conservation projects for invertebrates have been rare in the Federal Republic of Germany for several reasons. For one thing, interest in studying the local invertebrate fauna on a general level has been decreasing since World War II, and especially since the end of the sixties. For another, systematics and taxonomy at German universities have been in a desperate condition. This state of affairs affects conservation of endangered species in several ways: the required basic biological knowledge, especially of population processes, is often lacking, and the data available on occurrence, density and distribution are, for the most part, many decades old. Frequently, the development of areas and consequent changes in the distribution of species cannot be completely reconstructed because recent records are mostly missing. Due to the continuous splitting-up of landscapes by human settlements and progressing land use, the missing data can no longer be secured. Another problem characterizing species conservation projects is, in general, insufficient financial support from the institutions promoting research in combination with a lack of understanding that species conservation is a long-term matter: in most cases it takes years or, depending on the species, even decades, before a conservation project will yield visible success. Added to this is the frequent need for preceding basic biological research to identify and define the way of life, behaviour, propagation and population development of the species of interest. Generally speaking, species conservation projects are extremely complex with diversified tasks which require not only a very large staff but also sufficient working possibilities (in the field and laboratory), if they are to be successful.

Mother of pearl mussel projects

Stimulated by repeated reports on continuous decreases in populations and losses of areas of mother of pearl mussels (*Margaritifera* (L.), Figure 3.1) in central Europe, W. D. Bischoff (Bischoff 1971; Bischoff and Utermark 1976) was the first to start measures for the conservation of mother of pearl mussel populations left in the Lüneburg Heath in the second half of the sixties. Subsequently, the author began another conservation project in the Vogelsberg/Hesse (Uplands region) (Jungbluth 1980), and since the beginning of the eighties, a third conservation project has been initiated in the Fichtel Mountains (Bauer 1979; Bauer and Eye 1986). All three projects concentrated on individual sites or regions, but from the very beginning, communication among the scientists was excellent, so that initial errors could be prevented. Two of the three projects are established projects today; the third was abandoned because the number of specimens was too small.

Securing chorological data

Each of the three conservation projects was preceded by more or less comprehensive regional inventories which provided insight into two essential facts:

1) The surveys revealed that the biological data contained in the literature were neither correct nor complete.

2) Despite the fact that amateurs and scientists had studied the occurrence of mother of pearl mussels in central Europe for several decades, not all sites of occurrence were known to them (Heuss 1962). Moreover, the distribution data are generally old, particularly for specimens in museum collections, but also in the literature.

Another drawback is the lack of computerized information services which could facilitate the reconstruction of distribution patterns. Because of these limitations, the species conservation projects never went beyond the local level. An overview of the distribution of the species is lacking to this day, and its realization may be very difficult in view of the jurisdictions of the federal and the regional governments.

Reports on the disappearance of populations and losses of habitat as well as species conservation efforts finally led to the first mother of pearl mussel inventory in Bavaria (Bauer 1979). After several attempts, it was finally possible, in 1985, to launch a nationwide analysis of the situation in the Federal Republic of Germany (Figure 3.2). The Project Group of Mollusc Mapping/ FRG (supervised by the present author) is responsible for the execution of the project, and it can refer to comprehensive data bases and literature data banks (Jungbluth *et al.* 1985a). This nationwide analysis of the condition of the mother of pearl mussels in our country will be completed by the end of 1987.

The objectives of the project include:

1. Mapping of the recent mother of pearl habitats and localities in the Federal Republic of Germany;
2. Investigation of the composition of the populations (age structure, number of individuals and density) ;
3. Analysis of the biotic and abiotic habitat conditions.

To accomplish these objectives, all data known from the literature on the occurrence of the mother of pearl mussels are being checked, as are locality data documented by specimens in private and museum collections. An estimate of the total number of examined pearl creeks amounts to more than 300 [in 1987].

The goal of the investigations is the development of an overall species conservation concept for the region covered by the Federal Republic of Germany.

Securing Biotopes

The results so far obtained from the project supply clear evidence of the necessity of comprehensive biotope conservation as an indispensable prerequisite to successful species conservation in invertebrates. This requirement has been taken into account in the current species conservation projects in that attempts have been made to secure appropriate sections of running water as nature conservation areas. Utilization of these areas is limited, alterations are not permitted, and access is prohibited to the extent necessary. Biotope improvement measures such as re-naturalization of the water sections and bank vegetation have also been instituted.

Securing populations capable of reproduction

Since the existing mussel populations are mostly over age and juvenile animals have not appeared for years or even decades, the most urgent task is to develop populations capable of reproduction. Generally, this means that the individuals still existing, yet dispersed over large sections of running water, have to be concentrated in selected creeks or trenches.

Securing propagation.

To secure propagation, a sufficient number of host fishes has to be made available for the larvae (glochidia) during the phase of their discharge from the gills of the mother. In central Europe, the only known host is the brown trout (*Salmo trutta fario* L.). Development from the larval stage to the independently viable juvenile mussel on the river trout has been observed repeatedly and documented (Jungbluth and Utermark 1981).

Since development of mussel larvae on the host fish is usually longterm, extending over the winter period (July/August to May/June), provisions must be made to make sure that the host trout will neither migrate nor be fished. These provisions will further ensure that the juvenile mussels will be concentrated and grow up in the selected water section (Wächtler 1986).

This work must be accompanied by studies in which particular attention is paid to the site where the juvenile mussels are developing during their first four years, in order to fill gaps still existing in knowledge of these aspects of life history. Today it must be assumed that the majority of juvenile mussels die during this phase in the hyporheic interstitial — most probably because of unsuitable abiotic living conditions.

Securing populations

The populations in the test facilities and areas require many years of observation and control if populations with a balanced age structure are to be restored. Suitable measures for this are half-artificial fish host infections under laboratory and field conditions (cf. Wellmann 1943). The test periods to be fixed for these species conservation projects are decades, not years.

Results

Since the end of the 1960's, several species conservation projects have been launched in the Federal Republic of Germany for preventing extinction of the mother of pearl mussel. The studies cited above helped to clarify most of the questions pertaining to the life cycle of these mussels. At the same time, critical phases of the life history of the mussels were identified. These provide timetables for the commencement of the conservation projects. Finally, the species protection projects prepared the ground for the realization of a nationwide situation analysis (1985/1987). Among other purposes, the results of this analysis will be used for developing an overall species conservation concept including and interlinking the individual projects hitherto underway. Nearly 20 years of continuous efforts of species conservation have also resulted in a comprehensive documentation of the literature on the mother of pearl mussel (Jungbluth *et al.* 1985b).

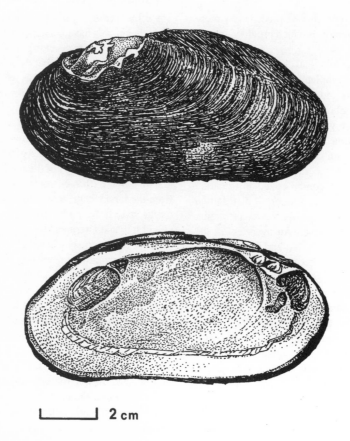

L_____J 2 cm

Figure 3.1 *Margaritifera margaritifera* (L.) Ellersbach - "Am Wald" E Rixfeld/ Vogelsberg/ Upper Hesse - Germany. In Coll. J.H.Jungbluth; Drawing: Helmut Stocker.

Literature Cited

BAUER, G. 1979. Untersuchungen zur Fortpflanzungsbiologie der Flusperlmuschel (*Margaritana margaritifera*) im Fichtelgebirge. *Archiv fur Hydrobiologie* 85, 152-165.

BAUER, G. AND EICKE, L. 1986. Pilotprojekt zur Rettung der Flussperlmuschel (*Margaritifera margaritifera* L.). *Natur und Landschaft* 61, 140-143.

BISCHOFF, W.-D. 1971. Die Flussperlmuschel in der Lüneburger Heide - ein Versuch ihrer Erhaltung. *Mitteilungen der deutschen malakozoologischen Gesellschaft* 2, 303-305.

BISCHOFF, W.-D. AND UTERMARK, W. 1976. Die Flussperlmuschel in der Lüneburger Heide, ein Versuch ihrer Erhaltung. 30 *Jahre Naturschutz und Landschaftspflege in Niedersachsen* 1976, 190-204.

HERTEL, R. 1959. Die Flussperlmuschel (*Margaritana margaritifera* L.) in Sachsen. *Abhandlungen und Berichte des Staatlichen Museums für Tierkunde Dresden* 24, 57-82.

HEUSS, K. 1962. Ein neues Flussperlmuschel-Vorkommen in der Röhn. *Mitteilungen der deutschen Malakozoologischen Gesellschaft* 1, 22.

JUNGBLUTH, J.H. 1980a. Biotopschutz-Projekte zur Bestandssicherung gefährdeter Arten am Beispiel der Flussperlmuschel [*Margaritifera margaritifera* (L.)]. *Verhandlungen der Gesellschaft fur* Ökologie 8 (Weihenstephan), 321-325.

JUNGBLUTH, J.H. 1980b. Probleme und Möglichkeiten des Arten-und Biotopschutzes bei Muscheln. *Natur und Landschaft* 55, 9-12.

JUNGBLUTH, J.H. and UTERMARK, W. 1981. Die Glochidiosis der Salmoniden in Mitteleuropa: Infektion der Bachforelle *Salmo trutta fario* L. durch die Glochidien der Flussperlmuschel *Margaritifera margaritifera* (L.). *Fisch und Umwelt* 10, 153-165.

JUNGBLUTH, J.H., BÜRK, R. NESEMANN H. and SCHEURIG, A. 1985a. Flussperlmuschel Erfassung in den Mittelgebirgen. Neckarsteinach und Mainz [unveröffentlichtes Gutachten über die rezenten Vorkommen in sechs Bundesländern].

JUNGGLUTH, J.H., COOMANS, H.E. AND GROHS, H. 1985b. Bibliographie der Flussperlmuschel *Margaritifera margaritifera* (Linnaeus 1758) [Mollusca: Pelecypoda]. *Verslagen en Technische Gegevens, Instituut voor Taxonomische Zoölogie* (Zoölogisch Museum) Universiteit van Amsterdam 41, XXXI, 220 s.

JUNGBLUTH, J.H., BÜRK, R. and GROH, K. 1986. Flussperlmuschel-Erfassung in Bayern. Neckarsteinach [unveröffentlichtes Gutachten über die rezenten Vorkommen in Bayern.

WÄCHTLER, K. 1986. Zur Biologie der Flussperlmuschel *Margaritifera margaritifera* (L.). *Entwicklung, Gefährdung, Aussichten. Naturwissenschaften* 73, 225-233.

WELLMANN, G. 1943. Fischinfektionen mit Glochidien der *Margaritana margaritifera*. Z. Fisch. 41, 385-390.

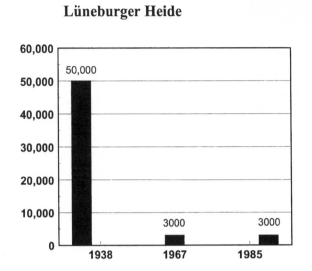

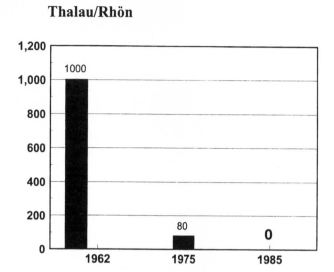

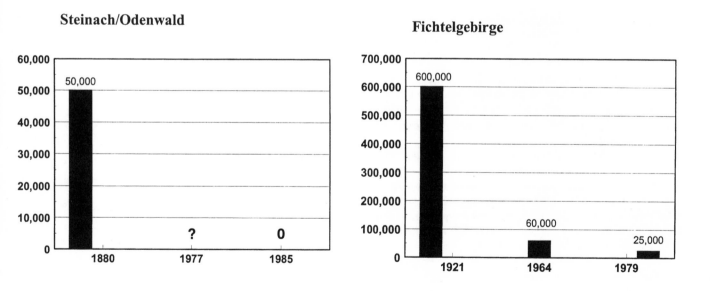

Figure 3.2 The decline of populations of the Mother of Pearls in Germany.

The freshwater pearl mussel, a protected but endangered species in Finland

Ilmari Valovirta

Zoological Museum, University of Helsinki, Finland.

Abstract

The freshwater pearl mussel (*Margaritifera margaritifera* (L.)) has been protected in Finland since 1955. In 1978, the World Wildlife Fund in Finland and the Zoological Museum of the University of Helsinki established a working group to study the distribution, ecology and protection of the species.

At the beginning of this century, there were about 200 rivers with this mussel in Finland. At this moment only 25% of these rivers have a population of the species. Decades ago, heavy collection, timber floating, and water pollution threatened the populations of *Margaritifera*.

The problem now is loss of proper environment for the species. This is caused by a variety of factors: deepening and straightening of water-courses for preventing flood damage during ice cover in the spring; building of power stations; daily regulation of water levels; pollution of water by agriculture, industry or settlement wastes; and pollution of river bottoms with organic matter during the drainage of peat-moors.

During the last eight years the "Margaritifera" group has checked about 60 rivers. The species is on the verge of extinction in southern and western Finland and in western Lapland. In this area it has been found in only ten rivers, and breeds in only three of these rivers.

In eastern Lapland, between 65°N and 67°N, the species is more common, and there are rivers with populations exceeding 100,000 mussels with densities exceeding 100 specimens/m^2. However, the populations are endangered here as well, mainly because of drainage of peat-moors.

Because of engineering works, about 4000 mussels have been transferred from one place to another in the same river, or from one river to another. After seven years the success rate is 80-90% in the same river and 50% at best in transfer to another river.

The "Margaritifera" group has carried out morphological and ecological baseline work as well. Growth of the shell is 25% slower in Lapland than in southern Finland. Morphological features are so typical in different rivers that it is possible tell the origin of a population, even to name the river of origin. Correlation analyses of water quality, humus content, vegetation, bottom quality, and the rate of water flow have been carried out in rivers from which the species has disappeared, in rivers where it no longer breeds, and in rivers where populations remain. Heavy metals have also been analyzed. Because of their long lifespan, the freshwater pearl mussel can be used as an indicator species of river quality over long periods of time.

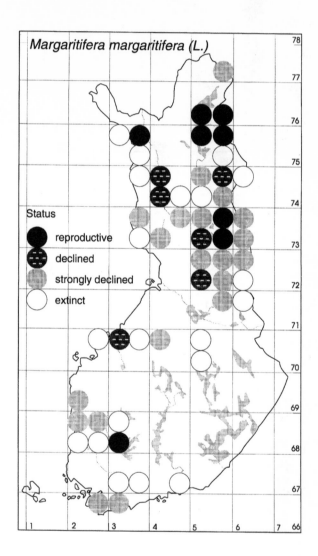

38

A proposal for placing three Slovak molluscs on the IUCN Red Data List

J. Stěffek

Update: Readers are referred to the following references for more recent information on Slovakian molluscs:

LOŽEK, V. 1989. Z červené knihy našich mekkýšů - relikt z konce doby ledové. Živa (Praha), 37 (6): 270.

LOŽEK, V. 1990. Z červené knihy našich měkkýšů - alpská vřetenatka na Vtáčniku. Živa (Praha), 37 (2): 78.

LOŽEK, V. 1991. Z červené knihy našich měkkýšů - k osudu skalnice Chilostoma rossmaessleri. Živa (Praha) 39 (2):79.

ŠTEFFEK, J. 1987. Some Slovakian molluscs entered in the International Red Book. Pamiatky a priroda (Bratislava) 18 (2): 68-69. (In Slovak).

ŠTEFFEK, J. 1987. Endangered, rare and important mollusc species in Slovakia. Ochrana prirody (Bratislava) 8: 43-52. (In Slovak).

ŠTEFFEK, J. 1992. In: Wells, S.M. and Chatfield, J.E. (Eds.). Threatened non-marine molluscs of Europe. Nature and environment 64. Council of Europe Press, Strasbourg. 164pp.)

Abstract

Whenever animal or plant species are exposed to danger, their rarity and significance can only be judged from knowledge of their ecology, distribution, and possible threats in the area of their distribution. The incessant growth of pollution and other negative impacts in the landscape implies that the word "protect" will have to be gradually superseded by the word "save".

This paper deals with an assessment of the current status of molluscs in Slovakia. V. Ložek, Vl. Hudec, J. Brabenec, S. Mácha, L. Lisický, V. Kroupová, and V. Pfleger have provided the information on exposure to danger, rarity and significance of each species.

The molluscs of Slovakia

Two hundred and forty six species of molluscs are known in the territory of Slovakia. Not considered are species that may have been imported with exotic plants or by aquarists and which live only in hothouses, aquaria, or thermal springs (for example, *Melanoides tuberculata, Helisoma trivolvis, Gulella io, Zonitoides arboreus, Pseudosuccinea columella*, etc.).

On the basis of the size of the area of distribution, number of localities of occurrence, and origin, the molluscs of Slovakia are classified into four groups:

1. Endemic species: those occurring only in a small part of Slovakia.

2. Species with wide distribution: those with distribution within the boundaries of Slovakia either at one or several localities.

3. Early Recent species: molluscs which have a patchy distribution.

4. Species with rapidly declining stocks, or in which the number of localities has recently declined either because of chemical pollution or habitat disruption or destruction.

Molluscs may also be categorized with respect to their degree of exposure to danger:

1. Critically threatened species: molluscs occurring at present in Slovakia at one or several localities, but which, if not protected, are in danger of extinction.

2. Threatened species: species found with declining frequency, in localities which are vanishing, or for which fewer than ten localities are known.

3. Rare species: species with their limits of distribution within Slovakia.

4. Significant species: species which, though not immediately threatened, nevertheless may be associated with endemics or which are important in terms of zoogeography.

Molluscs suggested for inclusion in the Red Book

Three mollusc species in Slovakia are proposed for inclusion in the IUCN Red List.

Spelaeodiscus tatricus Hazay, 1883, is endemic to the Belianské Tatry Mountains where it occupies a small area of the Tatra Basin in the area of the Suchá dolina Valley. It is neither abundant nor directly threatened. However, its entire distributional area coincides with that of the Tatra National Park, an attractive area for tourists, and thus it is a good candidate for inclusion with other rare species.

Cochlodina fimbriata remota Ložek, 1952, is endemic to the northern part of Vtáčnik Mountain. It occurs in a very small area in the neighbourhood of the Bystrý potok Brook. Its territory is in a flood valley between two rivulets in a sylvan environment within the Ponitrie Protected Landscape Area, a locality affected by the exhausts from nearby factories. The effect of these exhausts has not been monitored. Placing it on the register would protect it from clear felling which will change both climate and habitat conditions.

Alopia bielzi clathrata Rossmässler, 1857, is an endemic of the Slovak Karst. Its territory is that of the slopes of the Zádielska Dolina Valley and adjacent rocky biotopes. Its entire area of distribution is part of the Slovenský Kras Protected Landscape Area, which is further protected through its designation as a state nature preserve. The single potential threat to the area is the presence of a cement factory near the valley mouth. The effect of the exhaust from the cement factory has not been monitored.

Other endemic molluscs such as *Chondrina tatrica* Lozek, *Chilostoma cingulella* (Rossmässler, 1837), *C. rossmaessleri* (L. Pfeiffer, 1842), and *Sadleriana pannonica* (Frauenfield, 1865) are not proposed for protected status because of the many locations from which they are known and their relatively abundant populations.

Genetic aspects of mollusc conservation (*Nautilus*)

David S. Woodruff

Department of Biology, University of California, San Diego, La Jolla, California, 92093-0116, U.S.A.

Abstract

Fishermen presently harvest large numbers of *Nautilus pompilius* in the Philippines for the specimen shell trade. Overfishing has resulted in marked decreases in abundance of this species in some areas and population recovery is prevented by continued exploitation of these long-lived, K-selected cephalopods. Economic factors appear to prevent over-exploitation elsewhere as few fishermen are prepared to undercut the present price of approximately U.S.$1 per shell in the Philippines. Recent genetic studies by the author show that there are at least five or six other species of living *Nautilus*; these species and their ranges will be described. The conservation status of the rare *N. scrobiculatus* will be discussed.

Chapter 4: Sustainable utilization

The shell trade: a case for sustainable utilization

Elizabeth Wood[1] and Susan M. Wells[2]

[1]*Hollybush, Chequers Lane, Eversley, Basingstoke, Hants RG27 ONY, United Kingdom.*
[2]*56 Oxford Road. Cambridge CB4 3PW, United Kingdom.*

Abstract

The scale of international trade in ornamental shells has recently become a subject of considerable concern: more than 5000 species may be involved and international trade in unworked ornamental shells amounts to thousands of tonnes annually. The Philippines are a major exporter of shells; the United States and Japan are major importers. Major concerns are those of over-exploitation and the fear that ecological balance in some localities may be upset by depletion of species that play a key role in ecosystem function. The impact of commercial collecting on most of the species involved in trade is unknown. No marine shells are presently threatened with extinction because of over-collection, although some rare shells with restricted geographical distribution are subject to local depletion. A variety of management strategies are possible, including protection of vulnerable species, introduction of fishery quotas, and establishment of fishery and non-fishery zones. Unfortunately, little is known about the biology and distribution of many species.

Introduction

Marine molluscs are used by man for a variety of purposes and are also of considerable indirect benefit because of their role in food chains and their contribution to secondary production. Throughout the world there is an enormous food fishery, especially for gastropods, bivalves and cephalopods, amounting to millions of tonnes annually. In this study we concentrate on the use of molluscs for their shells.

This report is concerned primarily with molluscs which are valued for their aesthetic appeal. Most of these molluscs are tropical species. Despite their importance, particularly in developing countries, they have received little scientific attention compared with species valued as food. A number of terrestrial molluscs are involved in the ornamental shell trade, but these are outside the scope of this paper.

It is difficult to categorise shells satisfactorily according to their uses, as many are collected for several purposes. The main categories are shown in Table 4.1. With certain species, for

Table 4.1 Some uses of mollusc shell and examples of molluscs involved.

	EXAMPLE OF MOLLUSCS	OUTLETS/PRODUCTS
ORNAMENTAL SHELLS	Mostly large, colourful, relatively cheap, plentiful. Mostly gastropods*, some bivalves, including giant clams.	Whole shells used as 'souvenirs' and decorations. Trade; private collections.
'RARE' OR SPECIMEN SHELLS	Few in trade; expensive; mostly narrow endemics and/or deep water gastropods*.	Collectors' items. In trade; private collections.
SHELLCRAFT	a) *Strombus gigas, Cassis* spp., *Cypraea* spp. b) *Placuna* spp. (window-pane oysters) c) Small shells such as cowries, dove shells, cockles d) *Turbinella pyrum* (chanks)	Cameos, lampshades etc. as in c) Lampshades, windchimes, boxes. Handbags, jewellery, other decorative 'souvenirs'. Bangles, jewellery.
MOTHER OF PEARL OR COMMERCIAL SHELL	*Trochus niloticus* (commercial trochus), *Turbo marmoratus* (green-snail), *Pinctada maxima* (gold-lip pearl shell), *P. margaritifera* (black-lip pearl shell)	Buttons, inlay work, jewellery, shellcraft.
INDUSTRIAL SHELL	Giant clams (Tridacnidae)	Constituent of pottery glazes; manufacture of floor tiles.

*Families of molluscs particularly popular with shell collectors include cones (*Conus spp.*), cowries (*Cypraea spp.*), ceriths (*Cerithium spp.*), strombs (*Strombus spp.*), murexes (*Murex spp.*) and augers (*Terebra spp.*).

example, spider shells, *Lambis* spp., the queen conch, *Strombus gigas*, and giant clams, Tridacnidae, both shell and flesh can be used. Whether or not this happens depends on demand and relative values: in the Caribbean the meat of the queen conch is in great demand, and shells are often discarded; similarly, demand for the meat of giant clams in Southeast Asia is generally higher than for the shells, although the shells are also of great value, especially in the Philippines (Munro 1988, Munro and Heslinga 1983).

Shells of some species have several alternative uses. For example, the entire giant clam shell is used in the ornamental trade while broken pieces are used for jewellery. Ground up giant clam shell is used as a constituent of pottery glazes and in the manufacture of floor tiles. Some gastropods and bivalve shells are collected primarily for 'mother of pearl', and are traded as whole shells for ornamental purposes.

The number of species in trade is very large: 5000 species may be involved (Abbott 1980), about a quarter of the estimated world total of marine gastropod species. About 1000 species appear in Philippine trade alone (Anonuevo *et al.* 1982) with at least 139 'commercially viable species' used in the shellcraft industry. Of these species, 80 are common and widely used, 24 uncommon and sometimes used, and 35 rarely used.

Volume of trade

A clear picture of the volume of trade in shells is difficult to obtain for several reasons:
a) shells are often combined with other goods or marine products (especially corals) in official statistics;
b) trade statistics seldom differentiate between species, except for 'commercial' or mother of pearl species, and it is difficult to calculate the relative volume of each species in trade, or the numbers of individuals involved; and
c) international trade statistics do not include domestic trade (e.g. through gift shops in the country of origin) so that export figures cannot necessarily be equated with total exploitation.

Detailed records of catches are rarely kept for miscellaneous marine products such as shells, as the fisheries are often artisanal. FAO statistics considerably underestimate production. For example, annual production of *Trochus* shell is known to be about 6000 tonnes (Bouchet and Bour 1980), yet FAO statistics for 1985 give a figure of only 892 tonnes (Anon 1986). Nor do FAO statistics give a detailed species breakdown.

Shell exporters

Trade in ornamental shells is centred on the Philippines (Wells 1981, 1982) (Table 4.2), and has been important for many years. Fisheries statistics for the Philippines show exports of shells from

1955 to 1970 to be less than 1000 tonnes per year (643t [1955]; 670t [1960]; 451t [1965] and 990t [1970]). Trends after this are shown in Figure 1: exports of "other shells" rose to over 4000 tonnes in 1973, remained between 3000 and 4000 tonnes until 1980, but then declined to about 1000 tonnes in 1985.

Indonesia (Figure 4.2), Thailand, Singapore and Taiwan are also major suppliers, but a part of the Singapore and Taiwan totals may be re-exports. India is another important supplier, although the most recent figures (April 1984-March 1985) show a decline (Table 4.3). It is one of the few countries to record some species separately, in this case cowries. Exports of cowries have declined over the years from a peak of 45 tonnes in 1977. The Maldives also list cowries separately, and exports remain fairly high. In the 1960s 20-60 tonnes were exported annually, and in 1985, 17 tonnes were exported. At one time India exported substantial quantities of chanks, *Turbinella pyrum*, but exports declined from 55 tonnes in 1976 to 3 tonnes in 1981, just over one tonne in 1983, and none in 1984, when it had become illegal to export chanks in their natural state.

Import statistics for the United States suggest that Mexico and Haiti supply significant quantities of shells to the world market. Export statistics for the two countries are not available, but exports from these two countries to the United States have declined in recent years (Figure 4.3).

Table 4.2 Major producers and exporters of mollusc shells and estimated exports for 1985 (from export statistics unless otherwise stated).

COUNTRY	TONNES
Japan	2668[1]
Philippines	1067
United States	1016[2]
Singapore	846[3]
Taiwan*	361[3]
Indonesia**	228
Thailand	122
Mexico	[94][4]
Haiti	[69][4]
India	43

Notes
* estimate only, based on 1986 figure
** estimate only, based on 1984 figure
[1]probably includes shells of pearl oysters
[2]total exports 'marine shells crude' minus exports to Japan (see text)
[3]may include re-exports
[4]from United States import statistics.

Table 4.3 Exports in tonnes of unworked shells from India.
Totals are annual figures, April-March, e.g. 1985 figure is from April 1984 to March 1985.

	1976	1977	1978	1979	1980	1981	1982	1983	1984	1985
SHELLS	55	66	150	465	166	138	240	128	147	41
COWRIES	40	45	?	?	3	3	5	12	2	-

Figure 4.1 Exports of shells (unworked) and shell articles from the Philippines (1970 - 1986)

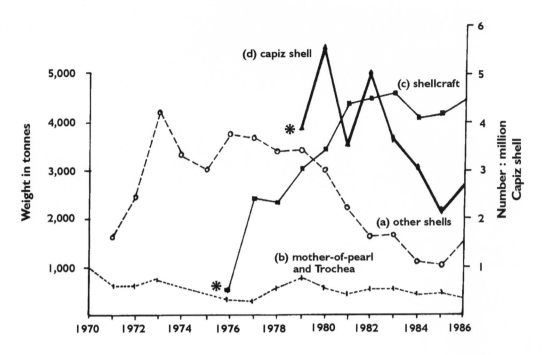

(a) 'other shells' (Wt: tonnes)
(b) 'Trochea shell': 'mother-of-pearl (shell) unworked' (Wt: tonnes)
(c) 'lamp shades, chimneys, globes and other light fittings, of shell' and 'other manufacture of animal shell' (Wt: tonnes)
(d) 'worked capiz shells' (window-pane oyster) (Number of articles: million)

* This commodity not included in Philippine Customs export statistics prior to date shown

Figure 4.2 Exports of marine shells from Indonesia (1970 - 1986). Source of data: Indonesia Customs Export Statistics.

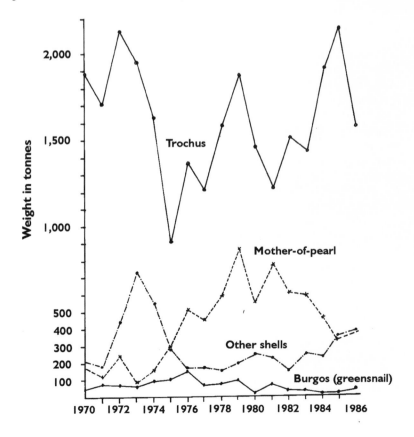

43

Figure 4.3 Imports of 'other shells' into the United States 1960 - 1986.

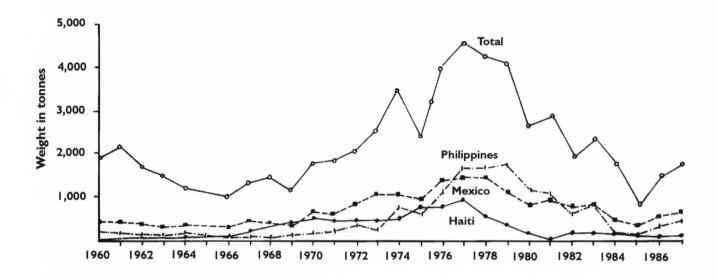

Shell importers

The main importer of ornamental shells is probably the United States (including Hawaii) followed by Japan, Taiwan, Canada and Europe (Table 4.4). The high figure recorded for Japan is a result of the inclusion of freshwater molluscs imported from the United States, as mentioned above. As indicated in Table 5, the United Kingdom is one of the largest European importers, followed by Italy and Spain. Imports in the United States reflect a trend similar to that of the Philippine exports: imports have risen from 1000-2000 tonnes a year in the 1960s to nearly 5000 tonnes in 1977 before dropping to around 1000 tonnes since 1983 (Figure 4.3). The United States has an estimated 1000 shell dealers; Florida alone has 5000-10,000 retail outlets such as gift shops, hotels and department stores (Abbott 1980).

Commercial shell

Fisheries for 'commercial' shell exist in many Southeast Asian and Pacific countries and in most cases are well documented. The main suppliers are listed in Table 6, and trends in Indonesian exports shown in Figure 4.2. World exports for 1985 were an estimated 4500 tonnes, compared with 5300 tonnes in 1978 (for the same countries). *Trochus niloticus* is the most important species and an annual demand of 6000 tonnes for this species alone was estimated by Bouchet and Bour (1980).

The main importers of commercial shell are listed in Table 7. Southeast Asia is the centre of the mother of pearl and button industry. Taiwan exports around 30 tonnes of worked mother of pearl and 200 tonnes of mother of pearl articles annually, and Japan has similarly large exports (Table 4.8). The Philippines are also important, exporting 13,149 articles of worked mother of pearl in 1985, probably from domestic supplies.In the Philippines, mother of pearl is also incorporated into shellcraft (see over the page).

Malaysia, Kenya, Sri Lanka and Australia are undoubtedly important suppliers of shells, but statistics for shells and their waste are combined with corals. Also, in the case of Malaysia, some of the figures are conflicting. For example, their export statistics for 1985 give a total of 344 tonnes of 'unworked coral, shell, powder and waste of shells' of which 56 tonnes went to Singapore. In the same year, Singapore trade statistics list imports of 7949 tonnes from Malaysia under the same category — a discrepancy of 7893 tonnes. The amount of 'ornamental' shell involved is difficult to ascertain. However, in 1982, when Singapore listed corals and shells separately, 23 tonnes of unworked shells were imported from Sabah, and 10,672 tonnes of powder and waste shells from Peninsular Malaysia. It is likely that the recent large imports to Singapore from Malaysia consist primarily of powder and shell waste destined for 'industrial' rather than 'ornamental' purposes.

Exports of corals, shells and their wastes from Kenya have increased fairly steadily from 85 tonnes in 1979 to 165 tonnes in 1984. Exports of chanks and their wastes from Sri Lanka are around 60 tonnes annually, while exports of other shells are in the region of 100 tonnes. According to the commodity description in trade statistics, both categories also include corals. Exports from Australia in the 1980s have been around 500 tonnes annually; in 1985 the figure was 460 tonnes.

Although the United States and Japan record large exports of marine shells in the categories 'marine shells' and 'shells of shellfishes' respectively, other evidence suggests that these quantities are not predominantly ornamental shells. A large proportion of the United States exports are dispatched to Japan, and are reported to consist primarily of freshwater pearl mussels (Abbott 1980). In 1985, 86% of the 'marine shells' (7370 tonnes) from the United States went to Japan, suggesting that possibly only about 1000 tonnes were ornamental shells. Japanese exports may also include pearl oysters: in 1985, 60% of exports went to the Republic of Korea, and 31% to Taiwan, both countries involved in pearl culture.

Table 4.4 Major importers and estimated imports of unworked shells for 1985, from import statistics unless otherwise noted.	
DESTINATION	TONNES
Japan	7935
United States	759
Taiwan*	792
Canada	[738][1]
Europe	[453][2]
Central/South Africa	[13][1]
South Korea	[76][3]
India and Pacific	[71][4]

Notes

* estimate only

[1] from United States' export statistics

[2] from United States', Japan's, Philippines', and Thailand's export statistics

[3] from United States' and Philippines' export statistics

[4] from Philippines' export statistics

Table 4.5 Imports of marine shells into Europe during 1985. Major importers and exporters only.				
IMPORTING COUNTRY	EXPORTING COUNTRIES Weight of marine shells in tonnes			TOTAL IMPORTS
	United States	Philippines	Japan	
United Kingdom	46	53	3	102
France	5	24	-	29
West Germany	16	-	-	16
Netherlands	-	20	-	20
Spain	-	45	-	45
Italy	-	50	-	54
Greece	-	23	-	23

Figure 4.4 Value of United States imports of 'articles of shells' 1961 - 1987.

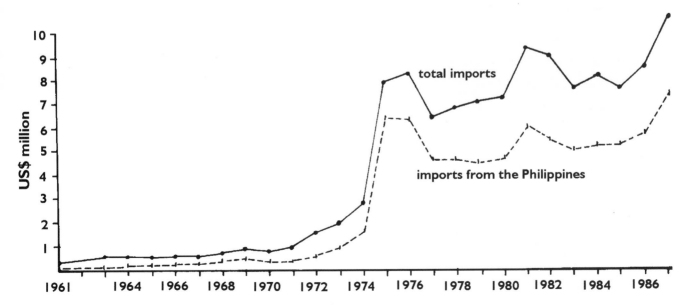

Table 4.6 Major exporters of unworked mother of pearl shells for 1978 and 1985. (Tonnes)		
COUNTRY	1978	1985
Indonesia	2249	2375[1]
Solomon Islands	297	[552][2]
Papua New Guinea	160	[514][2]
Philippines	594	251[3]
Fiji	104	235[4]
Marshall, Mariana, Caroline Islands	243	[139][5]
Cook Islands	12	[132][5]
New Caledonia	852	[115][2]
India	62	[89][6]
Australia	318	[79][2]
French Oceanic Territories	214	[63][5]
Vanuatu	191	35[7]
TOTAL	5296	4579

Notes

[1]Indonesia exports
[2]import statistics of Japan and Korea
[3]Philippine exports
[4]Fiji exports
[5]import statistics of Japan
[6]import statistics of Korea
[7]estimate based on 1984 figure

Table 4.7 Major importers of unworked mother of pearl shell 1985.	
COUNTRY	TONNES
Japan	3276[1]
South Korea*	2130[2]
Singapore*	777[3]
Europe*	175[3]
Taiwan*	97[4]
Hong Kong	64[5]

*estimate for 1985 using 1984 export figures for Indonesia
[1]import statistics
[2]export statistics from Indonesia and Philippines
[3]export statistics from Indonesia
[4]export statistics from Fiji, Indonesia and Philippines
[5]export statistics from Fiji and Indonesia

Table 4.8 Exports of worked shell products from Japan, 1983-1985			
SHELL TYPE	1983 *	1984 *	1985 *
Pearl buttons	83	113	134
Worked mother of pearl	43	89	40
* Tonnes			

Shellcraft

Southeast Asia is the centre of this industry, particularly the Philippines, where shellcraft is promoted by the government as a source of employment (Wells 1982). Japan, Taiwan and South Korea are also involved. In India over 2000 people rely directly on the shellcraft industry for their livelihood, and annual exports are in the region of 500 tons (Shenoy, 1984). Many species of gastropod are involved, including chanks (*Turbinella*), which are mostly collected in Tamil Nadu and sent to West Bengal where they are carved and manufactured into bangles and other jewellery (Heppell 1987). Similar items are made in Bangladesh, with chanks imported from Sri Lanka.

Shellcraft production has increased dramatically over the last two decades. In the 1960s annual imports of shellcraft into the United States were worth less than US$ 1 million, by 1981 US$ 9 million, and by 1986 over US$ 10 million. About 75% of these imports come from the Philippines (Figure 4.4). Exports of articles of worked shells from the Philippines have increased from less than 1000 tonnes in 1976 to more than 4000 tonnes in 1985. It appears that there has been a major shift in the Philippines from exporting raw ornamental shells, to the processing of them within the country and the exportation of shellcraft. The window-pane oyster, *Placuna*, is of particular value. The only major commercial fishery of the window-pane oyster (capiz) is in the Philippines where nearly 3.5 million worked capiz shells articles were exported in 1979 (import value over US$ 2 million) and just over 2 million in 1985 (import value over US$ 1 million).

Philippine shellcraft is exported to many countries around the world, with large quantities going in particular to the United States, Japan, France, United Kingdom, Germany, Italy and Australia (Tables 4.9 and 4.10).

Industrial shell

The shells of giant clams are used in the manufacture of pottery glazes and floor tiles, but details of the amounts involved are largely unknown, although in 1982 up to 660 tons of *Tridacna gigas* shells per month were being brought into Jakarta, Indonesia for that purpose (Usher 1984). Other shells and waste of shells are probally used in the construction industry but, again, little is known about this trade. The export of hundreds of tonnes of powder and waste of shells from Malaysia to Singapore has already been mentioned. India also exports large quantities of 'other shells including powder and waste' (1066 tonnes in 1985), mostly to Middle Eastern countries (Kuwait, Saudi Arabia and United Arab Emirates). Again, this may be for industrial uses. In 1985, Japan imported 1203 tonnes of 'shells and their powder and wastes, not elsewhere specified', mostly from the Philippines, Taiwan and the Marshall, Mariana and Caroline islands.

Conservation issues

Levels of exploitation

Information on population (stock) sizes and levels of exploitation is too poor to determine whether or not particular species are being seriously over-exploited. Data on the life history, abundance, productivity and rates of exploitation from specific localities are required for virtually every species involved in the shell trade.

Table 4.9 Major importers of shellcraft from the Philippines, 1985. Data from Philippines external trade statistics.			
	SHELLCRAFT - Gross weight in tonnes		
DESTINATION	Light fittings*	Other items	Total
United States	129	1044	1173
Japan	197	396	593
France	117	243	360
United Kingdom	182	170	352
Germany	210	130	340
Italy	259	81	340
Australia	66	134	200
Hawaii	14	165	179
Canada	30	53	83
Spain	11	69	80
Greece	7	64	71
Finland	4	29	33
Sweden	14	17	31
Netherlands	1	27	28
Portugal	1	24	25

*includeslampshades,chimneys,globesetc.

However anecdotal evidence suggests that conservation problems are on the increase and makes it possible to predict which areas and species are most vulnerable.

Areas vulnerable to stock depletion

Depletion of mollusc populations appears to be occurring on a local basis in some countries. Populations of molluscs in accessible areas and close to tourist centres are clearly more vulnerable to over-collection than those in remote areas. There are several reports of over-collecting in Kenya in areas where collectors concentrate their efforts in order to meet tourist demand (Evans et al. 1977; Kendall 1985) and commercial collectors are now going further afield for shells. There are also reports of over-collecting in Florida (Abbott 1980), Jeddah (UNEP/IUCN 1988), Singapore (Chou 1985), Guam (Hedlund 1977), the Solomon Islands (Craven 1986), the Philippines (Anonuevo et al. 1982), Reunion (Roberts 1977) and the Seychelles (Salm 1978). With the exception of the Philippines, these countries supply shells to the international market in relatively small amounts according to trade statistics and these reports of scarcity emphasize the danger of assuming that apparently minor exporters are free of conservation problems.

Vulnerability of marine molluscs

Most marine molluscs produce numerous planktonic larvae with great dispersal capacity and, potentially, these species should be able to withstand high levels of harvesting. In some instances, however, collecting pressure may be so heavy that even these species can be over-exploited. Species with less 'opportunistic' life histories are clearly more vulnerable.

Geographically widespread species heavily exploited throughout their range

Several edible and 'commercial' species fall into this category, and demonstrate how heavy demand and intensive fishing can have a considerable impact on populations as a whole, even though the species themselves are not at risk of extinction. A detailed resumé of the problems associated with these species is beyond the scope of this paper, but some examples are given below, together with references to more complete reports.

The queen conch, *Strombus gigas*, is heavily exploited in the Caribbean: an estimated six million animals are exported to the United States annually, and another six million are consumed locally. Populations are now seriously overfished and declining (Berg and Olsen 1988).

Commercial shells have been over-collected in many localities since the beginning of this century. Reports of declining populations and/or unavailability of large specimens come from French Polynesia (Salvat 1980), Papua New Guinea (Glucksman and Lindholm 1982), the Andaman and Nicobar Islands (Rao 1937), New Caledonia (Bouchet and Bour 1980), Indonesia (Usher 1984), Palau (Heslinga and Hillman 1981), Yap, Truk (McGowan 1958), Vanuatu (Devambez 1959) and Western Australia (Sarti 1983). In Madagascar, the black-lip pearl oyster, *Pinctada margaritifera*, has been so heavily exploited that it is now extinct in certain localities where previously it was numerous (Rabesandratana 1985).

Populations of the larger species of giant clams (Tridacnidae) have declined dramatically in many parts of the Indo-Pacific, as a result of over-collecting both for the shell and meat. The vulnerability of giant clams is due largely to their late reproductive maturity, comparatively short larval life span, poor recruitment to the adult population, and the ease with which they can be collected

Table 4.10 Major importers of worked capiz (*Placuna* spp.) shell articles from the Philippines, 1985. Data from Philippines external trade statistics. Only those countries importing more than 10,000 articles are included.

DESTINATION	NUMBER OF CAPIZ SHELL ARTICLES
West Germany	625,657
Switzerland	433,624
United Kingdom	256,191
Japan	130,479
United States	124,727
Paraguay	121,303
France	91,983
Hawaii	71,292
Hong Kong	64,275
Italy	63,512
Belgium	51,202
Guam	38,027
Sweden	22,130
Canada	20,595
Australia	11,115

from their shallow reef habitat. Stocks of *Tridacna gigas* and *T. derasa* in particular are in danger of extinction in many parts of their range (Munro 1988). Illegal collection by foreign (mainly Taiwanese) fishermen is a problem in many areas.

At present relatively few of the widely distributed 'ornamental' species are known to be similarly affected. The giant triton, *Charonia tritonis*, which occurs naturally at low densities (Wells et al. 1981), seems to have become rare through over-collection, for example in the Philippines (Wells 1981) and Guam (Hedlund 1977). The golden cowrie, *Cypraea aurantium*, now considered a fairly widespread species, but once highly prized because of its apparent rarity, is vulnerable to over-collection because of heavy demand yet relatively low populations. Large numbers of this cowrie entered the market from 1970 to 1975, collected mainly from eastern coastlines of the Philippines, but there has since been a 'radical nosedive' in yield (Anonuevo et al. 1982), suggesting that the gastropod has been over-exploited.

Species with restricted distribution

Many species of 'ornamental' and 'specimen' marine molluscs have a restricted geographical range and are therefore vulnerable to over-collection, particularly if they occur in shallow water. The likelihood of populations being adversely affected is also increased if the species concerned has a naturally low population density and/or low reproductive potential.

One of the few species which has been studied is the leafy-winged murex *Pterynotus phyllopterus*, an uncommon shell endemic to Guadeloupe and Martinique in the Lesser Antilles. It

is presently being over-collected (Lamy 1986), although it is not thought to be seriously threatened. There have been anecdotal reports of over-collection of several cowrie species such as the endemic *Cypraea mauiensis* in the Hawaiian Islands (Beals 1976); *C. cribellum*, *C. esontropia* and *C. broderipi* of Mauritius (Whatmore 1982); and *C. venusta*, *C. friendii* (= *C. thersites*) and others in south-western Australia (Anon 1985).

Volutes endemic to specific islands or island groups are also known to have become rare, for example, *Lyria deliciosa* and *Cymbiola rossiniana* from New Caledonia (Bouchet 1979). Other shells reported to have been over-collected include the imperial harp, *Harpa costata*, and the violet spider conch, *Lambis violacea*, both endemic to Mauritian waters (Whatmore 1982).

'Rare' species

There are a number of species that are in considerable demand because they are rarely found and collected. In some cases rarity may be a genuine reflection of population densities in the wild. In other cases, a species may be rare in trade simply because the bulk of the population is inaccessible, for example in deep water. Several deep-water species fetch high prices on the 'specimen shell' markets. New collecting techniques permit collection of comparatively large numbers, and incidental catches by fishermen on trawlers provide a further source.

Other ecological problems

Habitat damage

Various activities connected with shell collecting can alter or degrade habitats. Common types of disturbance include trampling and rock removal. Corals are also deliberately or inadvertently broken in order to remove shells.

Many shell collectors around Cebu in the Philippines, use a fine-mesh 'dredge' which they push across sand and rubble areas where molluscs live, but the practice has evidently declined to some extent, partly because the habitat was altered so drastically that 'even fishes were found to have been affected' (Anonuevo et al. 1982). The collectors have also been forced to collect from more remote areas because of declines in yield in the vicinity of Cebu.

Disruption of ecological balance

Little attention has been paid to the consequences of selective removal of shells on the ecosystem as a whole, but problems can arise. It has been suggested, for example, that over-collection of the giant triton, *Charonia tritonis*, which preys on large starfish, has contributed to population explosions of the crown of thorns starfish, *Acanthaster planci* (Endean and Cameron 1985). Plagues of the starfish have caused extensive damage to coral reefs in many parts of the Indo-Pacific. However the cause of these population explosions is still a matter of considerable controversy. A comparable sequence of events may be responsible for upsurges in numbers of sea-urchins, which graze the surface of corals and, in doing so, cause structural damage to reefs. Along parts of the Kenya coast, populations of the sea urchin *Echinometra mathaei* have increased, perhaps as the result of the selective removal of large numbers of predators such as the bullmouth helmet, *Cypraecassis rufa* (Kendall 1985; Muthiga and McClanahan 1988).

Conservation measures

There are several courses of action that can be taken to control trade in shells, and thus avoid over-exploitation and habitat damage. Conservation problems should not exist if the fisheries are properly managed on an ecologically sound, sustainable yield basis. Producer countries can implement management programmes and control exports, and importing countries can control imports. The problems would also be lessened if demand for ornamental shells declined. A greater 'public' awareness of the conservation issues could help in this respect.

Regulation of 'catches'

One way of controlling exploitation of marine shells is to place limits on the total number or weight that can be collected or exported. The disadvantage of this system is that, unless a quota is set for individual species, there is a temptation to collect the most valuable (and probably the rarest) shells. It is preferable to regulate collection of certain (or all) species by setting limits on number, weight and size of each species that can be taken at a time, and the localities from which they can be collected (see Protected Areas below). Commercial collectors should be licensed, and answerable to a fisheries or wildlife authority. Some examples of fishery management in existence are given in Table 4.11.

There are a number of practical difficulties in controlling exploitation of shells through management of the fishery. A primary difficulty concerns the enormous number of species involved. The lack of basic knowledge about life history, distribution and population dynamics of most of these species means that it is difficult at present to determine appropriate quotas or restrictions.

One of the species most thoroughly investigated is *Trochus niloticus*. Research on its biology and distribution in New Caledonia, the Cook Islands and Palau has enabled the calculation of sustainable yields for certain areas and development of appropriate management strategies. A variety of controls have been introduced in the past (see Table 4.11) and these new data should permit a more rational application of such techniques (Bour and Hoffschir 1985; Heslinga *et al.* 1984; Sims 1985). Potential management techniques include estimation of population density by using high resolution satellite imagery which pinpoints *Trochus* habitat, as is currently under investigation in New Caledonia (Bour *et al.* 1985).

Another difficulty results from the patchy distribution and abundance of some species, caused in part by habitat requirements. Sustainable yields may vary from one area to another, and a management policy devised for a certain species at a particular locality is not necessarily applicable to other areas. Detailed survey and monitoring work is needed in all major collecting areas to determine the type of management required, and to ascertain the success of such programmes.

Enforcement of regulations on quotas and other aspects of collecting is notoriously difficult in areas where large numbers of collectors are involved, especially when they work over a wide area and around remote islands as in the Philippines and in much of the Pacific. In these cases, control of the fishery by export regulations may be a more feasible approach. However, enforcement is a problem even in Australia where cowries are collected at night to avoid fisheries officers and export controls are circumvented by using the mail (Anon. 1985).

The considerable knowledge many collectors themselves have about the distribution and biology of exploited species could be put to use, and they could be encouraged to build on existing traditional techniques of management. Measures taken to ensure conservation of species or habitats are much more likely to succeed if people who are affected by management decisions are involved in their formulation.

Protection in country of origin

In some cases it may be necessary for countries to prohibit the collection of certain shells, such as endemic or rare species. Some examples of countries which have already introduced such legislation are listed in Table 4.11.

Protected areas

Another management technique is that of establishing protected areas where collection of shells is prohibited or restricted to certain zones. These areas can act as reservoirs from which adult molluscs and particularly larvae can spread to neighbouring areas. Most countries now have marine protected areas of some form in which collection of marine organisms is prohibited (among other regulations) (Wells 1988; UNEP/IUCN 1988). However, these sites have rarely been selected with management of mollusc populations in mind, and mollusc populations are generally not monitored. The success of this type of management strategy therefore has yet to be demonstrated. The system of *Trochus* sanctuaries in Palau has been studied and recommendations made for their improvement, including the redesignation of fewer, larger areas which are accessible for periodic surveillance (Heslinga et al. 1984). The four shell reserves established in the Seychelles (Table 4.11) are similarly poorly controlled and have not been monitored to determine whether they are beneficial to shell populations (Wells 1988; UNEP/IUCN 1988).

Improved collecting methods

Given the problems of implementing and enforcing appropriate management strategies, it is particularly important that collectors understand the importance of conserving stocks, and using collecting methods which do not damage the habitat. Guidelines or instructions could be produced for both commercial collectors and tourists. In Papua New Guinea collectors have been issued with a booklet on how to avoid wastage, habitat damage and over-exploitation (Anon. undated) but this programme has never been followed up. A similar booklet is now in preparation for Fiji, following a survey of the feasibility of setting up the shell trade (Parkinson 1982). Several malacological and conchological societies, such as the Hawaiian Malacological Society, issue 'Codes of Conduct' and instructions to collectors. The main principles, as outlined in Wells and Alcala (1987) are:

1) Eggs, juveniles and breeding groups should not be taken.
2) Shells with defects should not be taken (these are in any case generally unsaleable as 'specimen' shells).
3) The habitat should be disturbed as little as possible.
4) Living, attached corals should not be touched.
5) If stones, loose coral or boulders are moved, they should be returned to their original positions.

The United Kingdom-based Marine Conservation Society, in conjunction with the World Wide Fund For Nature (UK), is planning to publish leaflets and posters about the marine curio trade, and ways in which the ecological impact of collecting can be minimised. There is a need for such information to be made available much more widely than it is at present, for shell buyers are often unaware that conservation problems exist.

Controls on exports and imports

A number of producing countries are now introducing legislation to control exports of shells (Table 4.11). Exports may be controlled through a permit system, prohibition of the export of particular species, of unworked shells, etc. The Seychelles in particular has introduced such comprehensive legislation, and recently shells were included under the Wildlife Protection Act of 1984, thus prohibiting the export of native species. Legislation prohibiting the export of unworked shells is beneficial to the country concerned because it encourages the shellcraft industry which is labour intensive and increases the export value of the shells. Shellcraft industries are being promoted in countries such as India (Shenoy 1984) and the Philippines (Wells 1981), and evidence of their success is shown in the trends visible in trade statistics (see Figure 4.1).

Few countries have considered controlling imports of shells. In the United States, the Lacey Act is an effective piece of legislation because it prohibits import of illegally collected or exported wildlife, but at present molluscs are not included on its schedules. The Convention on International Trade in Endangered Species of Wild Fauna and Flora (CITES) provides a means of controlling international trade in species considered to be seriously threatened. At present, the only marine molluscs listed are the giant clams (family Tridacnidae). These are listed in Appendix II, which means that a valid export licence is required from the country of origin before the shells, meat or live animals can be traded between parties to the Convention. This provides a useful means of monitoring trade, particularly as custom and fishery statistics tend to be so poor for molluscs. However, the success of CITES depends on the extent to which party states can implement the necessary legislation. Furthermore, the Convention was drawn up specifically for species known to be threatened, and strict criteria must be fulfilled for the listing of species.

Mariculture

One way of relieving pressure on stocks of 'wild' shells is to use cultivated molluscs instead. Although mariculture programmes have been developed for many edible molluscs, they have only recently been attempted with species used in the shell trade: *Strombus gigas*, *Trochus niloticus*, *Pinctada margaritifera*, and giant clams.

Considerable success has been achieved with several of these species, larvae and juveniles being reared in hatcheries, and the adults kept in tanks for production of spawn and ultimately for harvesting. The possibility of culturing the leafy-winged murex, *Pterynotus phyllopterus*, has been investigated, but a full-scale project has not been put into operation (Lamy 1986).

It is also possible to use hatchery bred shells to re-seed depleted areas. This management technique is being developed in the Philippines for capiz (details in Wells 1988).

Mariculture clearly has potential and positive benefits, although a considerable amount of research is required before any scheme can be put into operation.

Acknowledgements

We are grateful for help from the staff of the Wildlife Trade Monitoring Unit, and other members of staff at the IUCN Conservation Monitoring Centre (now World Conservation Monitoring Centre) at Cambridge. We are also indebted to the World Wild Fund For Nature (UK) for financial assistance (to EW), and to the Marine Conservation Society for their general support.

Table 4.11 Examples of legislation controlling exploitation of marine molluscs. The Table is not exhaustive.	
INDIAN OCEAN/RED SEA/GULF	
Djibouti	Shell collecting prohibited under 1980 decree.
Egypt	Collection of shells prohibited in parts of the Sinai and Gulf of Agaba.
India	Chank Fisheries Act: export of unworked chanks prohibited. Pearl Fisheries Ordinance.
Israel	Permits required for collecting; collecting permitted only for scientific purposes (Fainzilber *in litt.* 1987).
Kenya	Permit required for commercial collecting; maximum 5kg ornamental shells collected per day. Visitors with licence may buy and export 5kg.
Madagascar	Collection of mother of pearl controlled since 1929.
Maldives	No official legislation but collection of marine organisms around resort islands prohibited by dive and tourist operators.
Mauritius	Fisheries Act 1980; permit required for import or export of shells. Collection of *Harpa costata* prohibited. In 1984, additional species given total protection: visitors can take up to six shells provided an export permit is obtained. A proposal also made to add a provision to the Act to prohibit commercial collecting.
Oman	Collection of living molluscs prohibited under regulations decreed by the Minister of Agriculture and Fisheries.

Table 4.11 (cont). Examples of legislation controlling exploitation of marine molluscs. The table is not exhaustive.	
Réunion	Collection of living molluscs prohibited under Arrêté 2862 of 21.7.76
Seychelles	Conservation of Marine Shells Act 1981 established 4 shell reserves (2 on Mahé, 1 on La Digue, 1 on Praslin), banned collection from reserves except dead shells on foreshore and collection anywhere of protected species (*Charonia tritonis* the only listed species at present). For other species there is a limit of 20kg per day. Sale and purchase of protected species prohibited; shells may only be exported for personal and non-commercial purposes. This Act repeals Protection of Shells Ordinance 1965, but is poorly enforced.
INDIAN OCEAN/RED SEA/GULF	
South Africa	Permits required for collecting; no collecting permitted in marine reserves (Fainzilber *in litt.* 1987)
Sudan	1975 Amendment of Marine Fisheries Regulations of 1937 prohibits collection of shells. Local order by Commissioner of Red Sea Province bans trade in shells.
CENTRAL INDO-PACIFIC REGION	
Australia	Wildlife (Regulation of Exports and Imports) Act (1982) prohibits unauthorised export of native species of molluscs; permit needed for private collecting, commercial sale and export. Closed season for *Cypraea thersites* (Coleman 1972); collection of *Charonia tritonis* banned.
Fiji	Collection of *Charonia tritonis* banned.
Guam	*Trochus* collection controlled. Collection of *Charonia tritonis* banned.
Hawaii	Collection banned in natural area reserves (Cape Kinau, Maui) and in protected zones on alternating two year basis (Diamond Head Beach Park, Oahu); collection of pearl oyster *Pinctada margaritifera* banned; size regulations on octopus and limpets (*Cellana* spp.)
New Caledonia	*Trochus* fishery controlled
Palau	*Trochus* fishery controlled
Vanuatu	*Trochus* fishery controlled. Minimum size limit of 20cm for collection of *Charonia tritonis*.
WESTERN ATLANTIC	
Bahamas	Fisheries Resources (Jurisdiction and Conservation) Regulations 1986. Collection and export of any marine products by non-Bahamians is prohibited. Management of conch fishery.
Belize	Legislation for management of conch fishery.
Bermuda	Fisheries (Protected Species) Order 1978 protects a number of species (*Stombus gigas, S. costatus, Conus bermudensis, Oliva reticularis, Pecten ziczac, Argopecten gibbus, Pinctada imbricata*, all Cassididae). Scuba divers may not collect; sale of marine animals taken within territorial waters permitted only if for human or animal consumption.
Cayman Is.	Marine Conservation Law (1978): controls on conch fishing; permit required for shell collecting.
Cuba	Legislation for management of conch fishery.
Netherlands Antilles	Marine Environment Ordinance (Bonaire) 1985; licence required for export of reef products.
St Lucia	Legislation for management of conch fishery.
Turks and Caicos	Legislation for management of conch fishery.
United States	Recreational shell collecting controlled by State legislation. Moratorium on commercial conch fishing in Florida; bag limit 10 specimens per recreational collector per day. Collection of live shells in California requires a permit and *bona fide* membership of an approved malacological organisation.
Venezuela	Legislation for management of conch fishery.

References

ABBOTT, R.T., 1980. *The Shell and Coral Trade in Florida.* Special Report 3, TRAFFIC (USA), Washington, D.C.

ADAMS, 1985. *In litt.* 7.2.85.

ANON., 1985. Cowrie shells endangered. *Traffic Bulletin* VI (5).

ANON., 1986. *Yearbook Of Fishery Statistics. Catches And Landings.* Vol. 60. FAO, Rome.

ANON., undated. *Sea Shells as Business.* Department of Business Development, Port Moresby, Papua New Guinea.

ANONUEVO, M.V., CABRERA, J., AND HIZON, M.Y. 1982. *A market study and catalogue of commercially viable seashells.* Final Report, December 1982. University of the Philippines.

BEALS, M., 1976. *Cypraea mauiensis* — an endangered species? *Hawaiian Shell News* 24 (1): 10.

BERG, C.J. AND OLSEN, D.A. 1988. Conservation and management of queen conch (*Strombus gigas*) fisheries in the Caribbean. In: Caddy, J.F. (Ed.), *Scientific Approaches to Management of Shellfish Resources.* John Wiley and Sons, New York.

BOUCHET, P., 1979. Coquillages de collection et protection des recifs. Report to ORSTOM, Centre de Noumea, New Caledonia.

BOUCHET, P. AND BOUR, W. 1980. The Trochus fishery in New Caledonia. The South Pacific Commission Fisheries Newsletter 20: 9-12.

BOUR, W. AND HOFFSCHIR, C., 1985. Evaluation et gestion de la resource en Trocas de Nouvelle Caledonie. Rapport final de Convention ORSTOM/Territoire de Nouvelle Caledonie et dependence, ORSTOM, Noumea.

BOUR, W., LOUBERSAC, L. AND RUAL, P. 1985. Reef thematic maps viewed through simulated data from the future SPOT Satellite. Application to the biotope of topshell (*Trochus niloticus*) on the Tetembia reef (New Caledonia). *Proceedings of the 5th International Coral Reef Congress, Tahiti* 4: 225-230.

CHOU, L.M. 1985. The coral reef environment of Singapore. In: *Proceedings of a conference on the biophysical environment of Singapore and neighbouring countries.* Singapore 3-5 May 1985.

CRAVEN, A., 1986. *In litt.*

DEVAMBEZ, L.C. 1959. Survey of *Trochus* reefs in the central and southern groups of the New Hebrides. South Pacific Commission. 7 pp.

ENDEAN, R. AND CAMERON. A.M. 1985. Ecocatastrophe on the Great Barrier Reef. *Proceedings of the 5th International Coral Reef Congress, Tahiti* 5: 309-314.

EVANS, S., KNOWLES, G., PYE-SMITH, C., AND SCOTT, R. 1977. Conserving shells in Kenya. *Oryx* XIII (5): 480-485.

GLUCKSMAN, J. AND LINDHOLM, R., 1982. A study of the commercial shell industry in Papua New Guinea since World War Two, with particular reference to village production of trochus (*Trochus niloticus*) and green snail (*Turbo marmoratus*). *Science New Guinea* 9: 1-10.

HEDLUND, S.E., 1977. The extent of coral, shell and algal harvesting in Guam waters. *University of Guam Marine Laboratory Technical Report* 37. 34 pp.

HEPPELL, D. 1987. *In litt.*

HESLINGA, G.A. AND HILLMAN, A. 1981. Hatchery culture of the commercial top shell *Trochus niloticus* in Palau, Caroline Islands. *Aquaculture* 22: 35-43.

HESLINGA, G.A., ORAK, O., AND NGIRAMENGIOR, M. 1984. Coral reef sanctuaries for Trochus shells. *Mar. Fish. Rev.* 46(4): 73-80.

KENDALL, B., 1985. The shell trade. *Swara* 8 (1).

LAMY, D. 1986. *Pterynotus phyllopterus* (Lamarck, 1822). Mollusque Muricidae des Antilles Françaises. Biologie, Ecologie et Elevage. These. Laboratoire de Biologie Marine et de Malacologie.

MCGOWAN, J.A., 1958. The *Trochus* fishery of the Trust Territory of the Pacific Islands. Report to the High Commissioner, U.S. Trust Territory of the Pacific Islands. Saipan, 46 pp.

MUNRO, J.L. 1988. Fisheries for giant clams (Tridacnidae: Bivalvia) and prospects for stock enhancement. In: Caddy, J.F. (Ed.). *Scientific approaches to management of shellfish resources.* John Wiley and Sons, New York.

MUNRO, J.L. AND HESLINGA, G.A. 1983. Prospects for the commercial cultivation of giant clams (Bivalvia: Tridacnidae). *Proceedings of the Gulf and Caribbean Fisheries Institute* 35: 122-134.

MUTHIGA, N.A. AND MCCLANAHAN, T.R., 1988. Population changes of a sea urchin (*Echinometra mathaei*) on an exploited fringing reef. *Afr. J. Ecol.* 24 pp.

PARKINSON, B.J. 1982. *The specimen shell resources of Fiji.* South Pacific Commission. 53 pp.

RABESANDRATANA, 1985. *In litt.*

RAO, H.S. 1937. On the habitat and habits of *Trochus niloticus* Linn. in the Andaman Sea. *Records of the Indian Museum Calcutta* 3 9: 47-82.

ROBERTS, R. 1977. Pêche et aquaculture a la Reunion. Collection 'des Travaux de Centre Universitaire de la Reunion.

SALM, R.V. 1978. Conservation of marine resources in Seychelles. Report for IUCN. 41 pp.

SALVAT, B., 1980. The living marine resources of the South Pacific past, present and future. In: UNESCO Population environment relations in tropical islands: the case of eastern Fiji. MAB Technical Notes 13: 131-148.

SARTI, N., 1983. Report to the Chief Fisheries Officer on a visit to Ashmore Reef. February 1983. Western Australian Department of Fisheries and Wildlife. Unpublished Report.

SHENOY, A., 1984. Non-edible marine products - a growing cottage industry in India. *Infofish Marketing Digest* 5: 35.

SIMS, N., 1985. The abundance, distribution and exploitation of *Trochus niloticus* L. in the Cook Islands. *Proceedings of the 5th International Coral Reef Congress, Tahiti.* 5 539-544.

UNEP/IUCN. 1988. *Coral Reefs of the World.* Volume 1: *Atlantic and Eastern Pacific.* Volume 2: *Indian Ocean, Red Sea, and Gulf.* UNEP Regional Seas Directories and Bibliographies. IUCN, Gland, Switzerland and Cambridge, U.K./UNEP, Nairobi.

USHER, G.F. 1984. Coral reef invertebrates in Indonesia: their exploitation and conservation needs. IUCN/WWF Report, Project 1688. 100 pp.

WELLS, S.M. 1981. *International trade in ornamental shells.* IUCN Conservation Monitoring Centre, Cambridge, U.K. 22 pp.

WELLS, S.M. 1982. Marine conservation in the Philippines and Papua New Guinea with special emphasis on the ornamental coral and shell trade. Unpublished Report to Winston Churchill Memorial Trust, London. 74 pp.

WELLS, S.M. 1988. Impacts of the precious shell harvest and trade: conservation of rare or fragile resources. In: Caddy, J. (Ed.) Scientific Approaches to Management of Shellfish Resources. John Wiley and Sons, N.Y.

WELLS, S.M. AND ALCALA, A.C. 1987. Collecting of shells and corals. In: Salvat, B. (Ed.) *Human Impacts on Coral Reefs: Facts and Recommendations.* Antenne Museum

WELLS, S.M., PYLE, R.M. AND COLLINS, N.M. 1983. The IUCN Invertebrate Red Data Book. IUCN Conservation Monitoring Centre, Cambridge.

WHATMORE, L., 1982. Mauritius is great but shelling's poor. *Hawaiian Shell News.* Feb.1982:8.

Chapter 5: Hug a slug - save a snail: a status report on molluscan diversity and a framework for action

E. Alison Kay

Department of Zoology, University of Hawaii, Honolulu, Hawaii, USA 96822

Preview

In the following account, I have attempted to provide additional information on the dramatic loss of animal and plant species worldwide which issue from governmental reports, IUCN and other conservation agencies by summarizing what we know about the status of one phylum, the Mollusca, around the world. Following an introduction which sets the stage with a discussion of interactions between humans and molluscs, the focus turns to the diversity of molluscs: the land snails of continents and islands, the molluscs of freshwaters, and the molluscs of coral reefs. The focus then changes to a discussion of molluscs as economic resources: mollusc fisheries, molluscs as alien species and molluscs as model systems. For each of these subjects I have tried to provide some history and some information on their present status, with the hope that they will provide background for actions that might be taken to ameliorate declining diversity. The required actions form the conclusion of this report.

Introduction

Molluscs and man

"No man is an island" wrote John Donne of human society; his words are equally descriptive of the web of animals and plants that is life on earth. That all forms of life are mutually dependent on each other is axiomatic. We also know that some organisms are more equal than others: plants because of our ultimate dependence on them, insects because there are so many of them, and vertebrates perhaps more because we too are vertebrates and we can relate to the soaring condor and the appealing panda.

Who among us counts the snail and its relatives as significant threads in the web of life and in human society? A reading of both history and science tells us that the Mollusca of the biologist — slugs, clams, pearl oysters, squid, coat-of-mail shells, tusk shells, and nautilus — play more roles in human life than does any other animal group of equivalent rank. From time immemorial molluscs have served as food, tools, currency, medicine, and sources of calcium carbonate. In addition to these practical roles, they also figure in legend and history, and as objects of art and worship, as items of adornment and decoration, and as musical instruments.

The shell middens of antiquity attest to the importance of molluscs as food throughout the world. The first tools, well before even a stone was chipped, were shells used as drills and scrapers. In the early years of the industrial age, when iron wheels became recalcitrant, someone discovered that the mucus of slugs was a satisfactory grease. Conchiolin, ground up bivalve shells, serves as the building blocks of houses in western Australia; in Louisiana it is the foundation for bayou roads. Cloaks woven from the byssus of the bivalve *Pinna* may have been the original golden fleece; tyrolian purple, the dye from a gastropod, was the symbol of royal rank. The sick have browsed through pharmacies in Hong Kong and Beijing for centuries in search of remedies derived from marine snails. Goods and brides were purchased for shells, the money cowrie in China, India, and Africa and the tusk shell on the west coast of the Americas. In China, money cowries were in use from about 1000 BC and the modern character for "precious" or "money" today incorporates the symbol for the money cowrie.

Botticelli's Venus, rising from the sea, was borne landward on a scallop shell; some Pacific islanders attribute the birth of their islands to the giant clam *Tridacna*. Whether history or legend, pearls from freshwater mussels are thought to have led the Romans to invade Britain in the 5th century BC. History also tells us that it was a mollusc which stimulated the initiation of products liability laws when a thirsty shopkeeper drank from a bottle of ginger beer only to find the decomposed remains of a snail therein (K. Brown 1980). Other molluscs have stopped trains and planes (helicid snails in North Africa) and sunk ships (the shipworm *Teredo*).

Molluscs retain many of their traditional roles in human life today. They have also gained new ones, among them recognition as useful animals for experimental studies of the nervous system and in behavior, as tools for the geneticist, and as sources of drugs, tranquilizers and antispasmodics for a variety of ills. Their most significant role may be only now emerging: the ability of bivalves to concentrate small particles and accumulate toxins and other pollutants is being utilized in programmes such as the 'Mussel Watch' (Anonymous 1980) to monitor changes in ocean water quality. Molluscs may well be the model group with which to develop and assess protocols which will tell us about the health of ecosystems in which occur vast numbers of invertebrates, if not vertebrates.

What is a mollusc?

What are these animals which play so many roles in human life? Their name, from the Greek, "mollos" means soft-bodied. That soft body, with a characteristic foot, head, and internal organs, has evolved into a myriad of shapes and forms that inhabit virtually every imaginable ecological niche on earth: in the ocean, on land, and in the freshwaters of lakes, rivers and wetlands.

The "snails" of land and sea are gastropods, meaning "stomach footed," because there is usually a coiled shell containing the viscera which is carried above a slug-like foot. Some gastropods, the "slugs," have either reduced shells or no shells. Clams, mussels and pearl oysters are termed the Bivalvia for the two shells which enclose the body. Bivalves lack a head as we know it in other animals and they feed as water containing food particles flows over their gills. They are found in both freshwater and the ocean. Five groups of molluscs are found only in the sea: the tusk shells or Scaphopoda burrow in soft sediments; the coat-of-mail shells or chitons (Polyplacophora) have a covering of eight interlocking shelly plates, reminiscent of medieval armor, and the Cephalopoda include the shelled pearly nautilus as well as squid and octopus which have no visible shell. The name, meaning "head foot," derives from the fact that they move by tentacles which form part of their heads. Two lesser known groups include fairly small animals (5 - 10 mm) which live at depths of more than 50m, the Monoplacophora and the Aplacophora.

Why save a snail?

Molluscs play essential roles in almost every known ecosystem on land and in the sea. Many molluscs are links in food chains, the pathways between green plants and the animals that are food for humans and other animals. On coral reefs in the Pacific, more than 20% of reef fishes feed on molluscs (Parrish, *et al.* 1985; Hiatt and Strasburg 1960); in turn, 70% of the meat diet of some Pacific islanders consists of reef fish (Marine Resources Management Division, Yap 1989). In all oceans, squid and octopus are the animals on which fishes, whales, dolphins, and sea birds feed. On European coastlines, the minute snail *Hydrobia ulvae* and the mussel *Mytilus edulis* are preyed on by shorebirds and estuarine fish such as flounders and gobies (Green 1968), and, during winter, the oyster catcher *Haematopus ostralegus* feeds on as many as 315 cockles (*Cardium*) a day (Thorson 1971). In South Africa, two species of the snake *Duberria* are so specialized they feed only on snails (van Bruggen 1978). There is also evidence that bivalves may be important to critical stages in the life history of certain food fishes, as the bivalve *Tellina* is to the juvenile plaice in Scottish inshore waters (Boyle 1981).

It has been suggested that the Pulmonata (land snails) alone bring the molluscs "into third place . . . in bioenergetic terms of animal turnover in terrestrial ecosystems" (Russell-Hunter 1983). That turnover results from the activities of land snails as they break down dead vegetation, produce soil and increase its fertility, and cycle nutrients. In Israel two species of lichen-eating snails that live on limestone rocks contribute significantly to weathering and soil formation in the rocky desert (Shachak, *et al.* 1987). Movement of the horn shell *Rhinoclavis* on reef flats in the Pacific alters bacterial and chlorophyll concentrations in the sand (Hansen and Skilleter 1988). Mussel beds of hundreds of thousands of individuals packed tightly together stabilize the river bottom and cleanse the river as the bivalves pump water through their bodies in the rivers of North America (Davis 1977).

In some circumstances, molluscs also outweigh both invertebrates and vertebrates in ecosystems: the polygyrid land snail *Mesodon thyroidus* with a density of 63,330 snails per hectare on a floodplain in Illinois and a standing tissue biomass of 26 kg per hectare, exceeded maximal fish biomass in the most productive river in the state (Emberton 1991); the biomass of the giant clam *Tridacna* and the pearl oyster *Pinctada* are more important than the corals in the lagoon at Reao in the Tuamotus (Salvat 1970); and in England in the River Thames at Reading, 80% of the biomass of benthic invertebrates is comprised of unionid mussels (Berrie and Boize 1992).

There is general agreement that the numbers of animal and plant species worldwide are declining at rates which far surpass those which have occurred in geological time. No one knows how many species now exist, but it is estimated that at current rates of extinction, 15-25% of the world's species could become extinct by the middle of the next century (Western and Pearl 1991). If that prediction is valid, the result can only lead to the disruption of major ecosystems worldwide, to widespread human suffering, and to alterations in the course of evolution. The preservation of species is critical to human welfare.

Not least among those animal species undergoing decline are molluscs. Of the perhaps 120,000 species of molluscs worldwide, a number second only to that of the arthropods in terms of species diversity, more than a thousand mollusc species can be found on local, national and international lists as recently extinct, rare, threatened, and endangered species (Kay, this volume). Fifteen percent of the more than 2,000 animals on the 1990 IUCN *Red List of Threatened Animals* are molluscs; 45% of the 272 invertebrate species in the IUCN *Invertebrate Red Data Book* (Wells *et al.* 1983) are molluscs; and more than 80 mollusc species are listed in CITES appendices I and II (CITES, 1990).

The following facts confer both urgency and direction to priorities in planning and implementation of a variety of measures designed to ameliorate rates of loss of molluscan diversity.

1) Although molluscs in all ecosystems appear on the lists of recently extinct, threatened and endangered species, terrestrial and freshwater mollusc species are particularly vulnerable to habitat destruction, over-collection, predation by alien species, and the spread of non-native vegetation into high elevation forests. All five species of an endemic subfamily (Neoplanorbinae) of ancylid pulmonate limpets and two genera of freshwater gastropods, *Tulatoma* (Viviperidae) and *Apella* (Pleuroceridae), have disappeared from the rivers of the United States in historic time (Basch 1962; Davis 1977), and more than 50% of the once exuberant molluscan fauna of North American rivers is now either extinct or endangered (Davis 1977). Virtually all of the land snails of St. Helena were extinct when Darwin visited the island in 1876; more than half of the 41 species of pulmonate tree snail *Achatinella* on the island of Oahu in Hawaii have become extinct since 1911 (Kondo 1970; Hadfield 1986a), and all seven endemic species of *Partula* on the island of Moorea in the Society Islands were extinguished between 1977 and 1987 (Murray *et al.* 1988).

Terrestrial and freshwater molluscs which are threatened account for 92% of the molluscs in the *IUCN Invertebrate Red Data Book* (Wells *et al.* 1983), 96% of the molluscs listed in the *IUCN Red List of Threatened Animals* (1990), and 95% of a world list of endangered mollusc species compiled by Kay (this volume).

These figures represent significant fractions of families and genera: 35% of the North American species in the freshwater mussel family Unionidae (United States Fish and Wildlife Service 1991), the remaining achatinelline snails on Oahu (United States Department of Interior 1986), and 15% of the land molluscs and 50% of the freshwater molluscs of central Europe (Ant 1976).

2) In contrast to the many historical terrestrial and freshwater mollusc extinctions, there is only one recorded extinction in history of a marine mollusc: a small Atlantic limpet (*Lottia alveus*), once abundant on eelgrass on the east coast of North America, is now extinct in the North Atlantic Ocean (Carlton *et al.* 1991). This may be the only historical extinction that is not apparently attributable to human agency (Vermeij 1989). Rather, the limpet was a victim of its own physiology (Gould 1991): its eelgrass host was subject to a massive die-off in the 1920's and 1930's, and, while remnants of the eelgrass populations survived in low salinity waters, the limpet, lacking the flexibility to survive reduced salinities or to move to another host plant, gradually died out.

Nor are the numbers of marine molluscs reported as threatened or endangered as great as those of terrestrial and freshwater molluscs, although marine molluscs are not immune to declining diversity. All seven species of the giant clams (family Tridacnidae) are listed in the *IUCN Red List of Threatened Animals* (Wells *et al.* 1983) as a result of over-exploitation in parts of their range (Yamaguchi 1977), and local extinctions have been recorded throughout the Pacific (Wells *et al.* 1983; Heslinga, *et al.* 1984; Munro 1989). The fishery figures for other marine molluscs which are intensively fished, although uncertain, relate to abalone, *Haliotis* worldwide (Shepherd *et al.* 1992); trochus, *Trochus niloticus* (Heslinga *et al.* 1985), and the green snail, *Turbo marmoratus*, in the Pacific (Yamaguchi and Kikutani 1989); the queen conch, *Strombus gigas*, in the Caribbean (Berg and Olsen 1989); and the loco (*Concholepas concholepas*) on Peruvian and Chilean coastlines (Castilla and Jerez 1986).

Mollusc diversity around the world

The land snails of continents

Every continent has its own land snails: *Bothriembryon* of Australia and the giant African snail *Achatina* of Africa are as typical of those countries as are the kangaroo and the lion. Land snail families and genera, however, may be represented on more than one continent because distribution is a reflection of geological history during which land masses have drifted and mountains have been uplifted. Continental molluscan faunas are, therefore, composed of elements representing different geographies and different histories.

The faunas of most islands are relatively well known; the faunas of continents, partly because of size and complexity, but partly also because we are dependent on 19th century records for much of what we do know, are not so well known. Thus we know very little for large parts of Africa and most of Asia and South America. Even relatively well known regions however, are sources of surprise: 1976-1977 field work in Western and Central Australia increased the number of valid camaenid species from about 40 to 125 (Solem 1979). In Europe and North America new species descriptions and reports of major range extensions are commonplace in each issue of malacological journals. The following account is disparate, but certain themes are repeated with that of destruction of habitat perhaps the most pervasive.

Africa

The fauna

The African continent south of the Sahara is part of the Ethiopian biogeographical region, with an estimated 6,000 land snail species (van Bruggen 1977).

The African land snails reflect the extraordinary geography and history of the continent and include both one of the smallest and the largest land snails in the world (the shell of *Punctum pallidum* measures 0.4 x 1.2 mm, that of *Achatina reticulata* measures 208 mm but with a giant 270 mm specimen of *Achatina achatina* recorded (Groh and Griffiths 1987)), a large number of carnivorous snails, and six endemic families. Two families, the giant African snails in the Achatinidae and the Urocyclidae may have evolved in an ancient equatorial forest belt and then spread south almost to the Cape of Good Hope (van Bruggen 1977). Both families show remarkable radiations: the Achatinidae are adapted to the extremes of desert and alpine conditions, the Urocyclidae include every type of gastropod from typical slugs to snails with large helicoid shells. Of the remaining four endemic families, two families are found in southern Africa, the carnivorous slugs in the Aperidae and the large-shelled (about 40 mm in length) Dorcasiidae which live in desert conditions and which are allied to the South American Strophocheilidae, and two families, the Thyrophorellidae and the Aillyidae, are restricted to West Africa (van Bruggen 1977).

In southern Africa, with perhaps 650 species, van Bruggen (1978) estimates there are about 20 species per 100,000 sq km. Six families account for more than 75% of the species (van Bruggen 1975): the Streptaxidae (>135 species), the Charopidae (>110 species), and the Subulinidae, Urocyclidae, Achatinidae and Enidae (each >100 species); and 90% of the species are endemic (van Bruggen 1978). Five families (Aperidae, Dorcasiidae, Corillidae, Charopidae, and Rhytididae), found only in southern Africa on the African continent, are sometimes called the Southern Relict Fauna because of their relationships with land snails in South America and Australia which suggest that they may have had their roots in Gondwanaland (van Bruggen 1980b).

Although only 0.2% of southern Africa is forested (van Bruggen 1978), most of the southern African land snails are forest dwellers, found on low vegetation and, especially, in litter; a few such as the operculate *Tropidophora* live on tree trunks. The shells of the forest snails are usually dark in colour and decorated with hairy protuberances. Savanna and deserts with low rainfall, high temperatures, and little food and shelter cover large parts of southern Africa and harbour fewer species (perhaps less than 150) than do the forests, but these desert snails are highly endemic and may appear in enormous numbers after rainfall.

The rich land snail fauna of east Africa (Kenya, Tanzania, and Uganda) of about 1,000 species (Verdcourt 1982), dates from at least the Miocene (Verdcourt 1984), and is about 75% endemic today. More than 70% of these land snails are forest dwellers, 13% occur in bushland, thicket and arid areas, and the remaining 5% are found at altitudes of more than 3,000 m (Verdcourt 1972). The dominant families are the Streptaxidae and Urocyclidae (Rodgers and Homewood 1982, Verdcourt 1972).

Status

Given the size of the continent, its extraordinary topography, the fact that it has the longest history of land use in the world, and its political complexity, a summary of the conservation status of the terrestrial molluscs is not possible. The taxonomy and distribution of the land snails of large areas of the continent remain inadequate. In Gabon, West Africa, for example, 75% of the species found in a study of rainforest litter are potentially undescribed (de Winter 1992).

Only one African land snail, the streptaxid *Gulella plantii*, is listed in the *IUCN Red List*, but there are indications of declining diversity. Van Bruggen (1969) notes, for example, that in Zululand "the flora and fauna have suffered less [in game reserves] than elsewhere." Unique habitats such as the fnbos of southern Cape Province with a mediterranean type of climate and about half of its 60 species of land snails endemic, is subject to veld fires that affect the molluscs (van Bruggen 1978). In the montane forest islands of the East Usambaras, the West Usambaras, and Kilimanjaro where there are unique assemblages of land snails known only from 19th century lists which indicate a rich endemic fauna, agricultural encroachment and timber operations have severely reduced forest area, and continuing encroachment puts the land snail fauna at risk (Rodgers and Homewood 1982; Wells *et al.* 1983).

There are ambitious programmes for national and state parks and refuges in Africa, and World Natural Heritage Sites and Biosphere Reserves have been recognized, but continuing incursions into tropical and montane forests by loggers, agricultural encroachment, soil erosion, mining, and the like continue to take a toll.

Asia: India

The fauna

Solem (1984) noted in the introduction to a recent volume on biogeographical studies on non-marine molluscs that "The absence of publications . . . on the Oriental Region . . . reflect the absence of current study." Biogeographers define the region as including all of Asia, that is, India, Sri Lanka, Burma, Thailand, the Malay peninsula, China with Hainan and Formosa, Japan, the Philippines and the Indo-Malayan archipelago to the Celebes and the Moluccas. But apart from the reviews of Solem himself (1959, 1961) on the New Hebrides and New Caledonia, and the 19th-mid-20th century compilations of such authors as van Bentham Jutting (1948, 1950, 1952) on the Indo-Malayan Archipelago (see under Islands below) and Gassies (1863-1880), Crosse (1894) and Franc (1957) on New Caledonia, there are no summaries of the non-marine molluscan faunas of the Oriental Region. On the Indian subcontinent, however, 19th and early 20th century British administrators, soldiers and surveyors such as Blanford, Godwin-Austen and Gude devoted years to the collection, dissection and study of Indian molluscs. Blanford and Godwin-Austin (1908) and Gude (1914, 1921) recorded about 1100 species of pulmonate and operculate land snails; a more recent figure of 1475 species, 525 operculates and 950 pulmonates (Winckworth 1950), has been reported.

The oldest elements in the Indian fauna are considered relicts of the Gondwanaland fauna (Mani 1974a) and are found in Peninsular India, considered by Indian biogeographers as *India vera* (Mani 1974b). Among the molluscs are a bivalve, the freshwater mussel *Mulleria* which is congeneric with a South American species, the streptaxids *Streptaxis* and *Ennea* which are shared with Madagascar and South Africa, and *Glessula* (Ferrusaciidae) which also occurs in South Africa.

Peninsular India also spawned some remarkable species radiations following the breakup of Gondwanaland, among them radiations in the pulmonate Helicarionidae listed with 39 genera and 427 species (Blanford and Godwin-Austin 1908); more recent malacologists recognize 25 genera and 200 species (Parkinson and Groh 1987). In the operculate family Cyclophoridae Gude (1921) lists 24 genera and 432 species.

The Indian land snails appear to be mostly ground-living forms with small ranges and with some very odd shells. In the family Succineidae, usually distinguished by thin, ovate shells, the shell is limpet-like in *Camptonyx* and absent in *Hyalimax*. The largest of the Indian land snails, the imperial snail of India, *Hemiplecta basiliens*, is endemic to the teak forests of the Western Ghats (Jairajpuri 1991). Most Indian land snails are very small, however, 1-2 mm in greatest dimension, and curiously shaped. In the operculate cyclophorids *Cyclotus* and *Pterocyclus* the aperture is twisted and upturned like a tube, a condition apparently occurring where there are strong seasonal fluctuations associated with monsoons, with the tubular aperture accommodating aestivation; in *Opisthostoma nilgirica*, the shell is shaped like a barrel, sculptured with fine axial ribs, and the aperture is like a miniature tuba. Hirsute "spines" and apertural armament are also common.

Status

The work of the early British conchologists can never be repeated as much of India no longer appears to support native terrestrial molluscan faunas. Centuries of habitation associated with massive deforestation have resulted in the disappearance of virtually all natural habitats. Mani (1974a) notes that the characteristic fauna of peninsular India has been virtually eliminated except for small but rapidly dwindling pockets; and there are virtually no land snails at all on the Indo-Gangetic plain, the most densely populated part of India. There is, however, a network of national parks, wildlife sanctuaries and multiple use management areas (Singh 1985) which may encompass tracts of native vegetation where native land molluscs still survive. The National Wildlife Action Plan adopted in 1983 provides for continuing creation of protected areas.

Australia

The fauna

The Australian land snail fauna is estimated at about 500 species (Smith 1984), but with Solem's (1988) report of "perhaps the greatest concentration of short range restricted endemic species found anywhere in the world" in the Ningbing Ranges and Jeremiah Hills of western Australia, earlier figures may be underestimates.

The several different elements in the land snail fauna reflect the complexities of the evolution of Australia itself from part of the continent of Gondwanaland to an island - continent moving north where it meets the islands of Indonesia. Several families are found worldwide (Succineidae, Pupillidae, and Vertiginidae); two families, the operculate Helicinidae and the Achatinellidae, are an old circum-Pacific element; the Camaenidae and Pupinidae are shared with the Indo-Malayan archipelago and Asia; and four families, the Rhytididae, Bulimulidae, Charopidae and the endemic family Caryodidae may be derivatives of the Gondwanaland fauna.

Australia is the flattest and driest of the continents: its highest mountain rises only 2,200 m, and more than half of the continent receives less than 25 cm of rain a year. The southwestern corner, one of the continent's major arid areas, is home to one of Australia's most remarkable land snails, *Bothriembryon*, an endemic genus related to the South American Bulimulidae. There are about 30 species which make up about half the taxa in the area (Smith 1984). They are well adapted to conditions where there is infrequent moisture: some of the snails secrete a mucous plug or epiphragm which enables them to survive for weeks to years until moisture recurs; others, with white shells, "glue" themselves to the trunks of trees or the substrate during drought conditions (Bishop 1981).

If one land snail family can be said to dominate the Australian fauna, it is the highly diversified Camaenidae with species which are adapted to desert conditions in the arid and semi-arid central portion of the continent and in Western Australia and to tropical rainforests in northeastern Queensland. Solem's analyses (1988 and references therein) of the post-Miocene speciation in these snails in the Kimberley district of Western Australia is a masterly account of an exuberant radiation which must represent only a fraction of what remains elsewhere in unexplored areas of the continent.

While deserts occupy a large proportion of Australia, the climate of Queensland and northern New South Wales is tropical to warm temperate and the accompanying rainforests and other vegetation support a molluscan fauna more like that of New Guinea and the Indo-Malayan archipelago than that of the rest of Australia. The fauna is dominated by camaenids such as *Sphaerospira*, *Xanthomelon* and *Meridolum*. Others of the land snails include the operculate prosobranchs such as the Helicinidae and Cyclophoridae. Among the endemics in Queensland are the camaeid *Hadra*, some with shells 60 mm in length, and the rainforest slugs Athoracophoridae and Rathouisiidae.

In temperate southeastern Australia and Tasmania 69% and 30% of the molluscan fauna respectively is endemic; many of these endemics are obligate inhabitants of the rainforest (Smith 1979, 1984). The Charopidae and Punctidae, with a host of species with minute shells and small distribution ranges, comprise 62% of the taxa in southeastern Australia.

Status

There are few areas in Australia that have not been affected by human activity. In New South Wales, more than two thirds of its forest cover has been removed since the time of first European settlement, nearly two thirds of the land in Victoria is privately owned with most cleared for agriculture, and there are estimates that the vegetation in 55% of the arid zone is degraded (Feller *et al*. 1979). Most Australian land snails are ground living snails and vulnerable to habitat alteration by fire and hoofed animals, while the land snails associated with temperate and tropical forests are susceptible to logging and other types of habitat disruption. Despite the apparent disruptions to habitat and other effects, only one Australian land snail is listed in the *IUCN Red List*, *Anoglypta launcestonensis*, an acavid from Tasmania. Thirty-four species from Australia and Tasmania, and another 90 species from the offshore islands, Lord Howe Island and Norfolk Island are listed as threatened or endangered (B.J. Smith pers. comm.,1987). Australia has in place a programme for the establishment of wildlife habitats, protected areas and reserves, and stringent regulations on introductions. There is provision for wilderness areas in national and state parks in the New South Wales National Parks and Wildlife Act of 1967 and the Victorian National Parks Act of 1975.

Europe

The fauna

Europe, extending north and east to Asia and south to the Mediterranean, and Africa north of the Sahara, is part of the biogeographical region termed the Palearctic. Waldén (1963) suggests a fauna of about 1500 species and 229 genera of which 124 are exclusively European. Numbers of species follow the north-south temperature gradient from the tropical southern Mediterranean-northern African sector with perhaps 800 species to northern taigas and tundra near the Arctic circle where there may be only 20 species (Likharev and Rammel'meier 1952). There are an estimated 16 species per 100,000 sq km (van Bruggen 1978).

The Helicidae is perhaps the most successful family in Europe in terms of numbers of species. It includes the edible snails *Helix* and *Otala*, other commonly occurring and often abundant snails such as the garden snail *Cepaea* and the sandhill snail *Theba pisana*, and a suite of lesser known species with restricted ranges. Other typical European families represented by generic and species radiations are the slugs, Arionidae and Limacidae; the grass snails Valloniidae, the whorl snails Vertiginidae, and the door snails, Clausiliidae.

No families of land molluscs are endemic to the European continent, but there is generic and specific endemism (Peake

1978). The speciation pattern reflects a complex geological history of the continent involving glaciation and changes in climate. In the northern lowlands which were repeatedly glaciated during the Pleistocene there are virtually no endemic species and most of the species are widely distributed, descended from immigrants from the south (Kerney and Cameron 1979). The mountainous south with different substrates and topographical relief has higher species diversity and large numbers of narrowly endemic species in the Alps, Carpathians, Albania, and northern Greece. In the Iberian Peninsula, the bridge between Europe and Africa, more than half of its land snail species are endemic (Puente and Prieto 1992); and in the Caucasus of eastern Europe more than 75% of the species of clausilids, limacids and helicids are endemic (Likharev and Rammel'meier 1952).

Status

Central European landscapes today are very different from the landscapes of pre-human times when vast areas of forests covered the land. Instead there are islands of woods and unwooded areas essentially controlled by human activity. In northern Europe, draining fens, forestry (in Sweden), farming practices dominated by monoculture, road construction, tourist facilities, and the effects of pollution and acid rain have changed the landscape and in so doing impact the molluscan faunas (Waldén this volume). In southern Europe major disruptions of habitat are due to forest fires, agriculture, and tourist development which destroys sensitive areas (that is, those areas with some forest cover) is also occurring at an alarming rate (Bouchet *in litt.*)

Documentation of mollusc distribution and conservation status in northern Europe has accelerated over the last decade with the development of mapping projects and publication of national Red Data books. The data indicate that there is an overall decline in diversity (Collins and Wells 1987) and that more than 200 non-marine molluscs endemic to single countries are now considered threatened in Europe (Wells and Chatfield 1992). The West German and Austrian Red Data books between them list well over 100 threatened and potentially threatened species (Blab *et al*. 1984; Gepp 1983); in Austria over 50% of the non-marine mollusc fauna is considered threatened; in Switzerland, 67% (Turner and Wuthrich 1985) and in the United Kingdom, about 13% (Kerney 1982; Foster 1983) of the terrestrial molluscs are of concern. In Belgium, ranges of some 50 species have declined since 1950 (van Goethem, *et al*. 1987). In France, Bouchet (1990) suggests that of the 53 endemic terrestrial molluscs occurring on French territory, most are restricted to small areas of the Maritime Alps, Corsica and Basque Country, 21 require immediate protection, and one slug species is reported as extinct.

Molluscs were added to the Berne Convention — the Convention on the Conservation of European Wildlife and Natural Habitats — in 1988; 23 species of molluscs are now listed among the more than 80 listed invertebrates. A recently issued Council of Europe directive specifically lists threatened species and habitats.

North America

The fauna

The estimated 750 species of land snails in North America (Solem 1984), which works out to about 5 species per 100,000 sq km (van Bruggen 1978), represents a relatively small fauna compared with that of other continents. There are two reasons for the depauperate fauna. One is geography: large areas of desert, taiga and tundra, short grass prairies and coniferous forest harbour relatively few species. The second reason is a matter of history: much of North America was glaciated in the Pleistocene, and, while this recently glaciated land has been re-colonized by land snails, there is little evidence for much speciation in these areas. About 80% of the indigenous species are therefore concentrated in two areas of the continent which were isolated by a major marine incursion during the Late Cretaceous and early Tertiary: (1) in the east from the plains bordering the eastern limit of the Rocky Mountains to the Atlantic, and (2) in the west from the Rocky Mountains and the Sierra Nevada to the Pacific. The eastern and western faunas merge in the north and south. In the north, where temperature limits distribution, a boreal area is inhabited mainly by circumpolar species; in the south, where a fringe of Texas and Florida borders the Caribbean, there are elements of a much larger Middle American fauna which also inhabits the West Indies, Bermuda, Central America and most of Mexico (Pilsbry 1948; Waldén 1963).

The eastern land snail fauna is dominated by the endemic family Polygyridae (Solem 1984; Walden 1963) with approximately 260 species (Emberton 1991) which are conspicuous in the invertebrate faunas of leaf-litter and floodplain habitats. In Florida, the tree snails *Liguus*, *Orthalicus* and *Drymaeus* are endemic, and other eastern endemics include genera in the Charopidae, Zonitidae and Pupillidae. Except for the Florida tree snails, the eastern land snails are ground-dwellers, in habitats from the Everglades to high altitude forests in the mountain states. The Florida Everglades harbour not only tree snails but endemic Pupillidae and Cerionidae and the operculate Helicinidae; a Cumberland province in the Blue Ridge and Cumberland Plateau is distinguished by several endemic genera of Zonitidae (Pilsbry 1948; Burch 1962); and the Driftless Area, a small area of southwestern Wisconsin harbours a relict Pleistocene fauna with the rare *Hendersonia occulta rubella* (Morrison 1929).

Western land snails are found from the high altitude forests of the northwest and the Rocky Mountains to the deserts of Colorado and the Mojave. Three families, the Helminthoglyptidae, Ammonitellidae and Oreohelicidae, and two subfamilies Thysanophorinae and Holospirinae (Solem 1984), are endemic to the region. In the northwest in Oregon, Washington, and Idaho, and in California, slugs such as *Ariolimax* and helminthoglyptids *Monadenia* and *Helminthoglytpa*, and the oreohelicid *Ammonitella* are characteristic. In the Rocky Mountains the predominant land snail is *Oreohelix* (Oreohelicidae) with perhaps 35 species (Pilsbry 1948). The southwest with its arid deserts is characterized by a number of distinctive genera in the Helminthoglyptidae: *Sonorella*, *Chaenaxis* and *Humboldtiana* with the largest of the southwest land snails, and, in the Polygyridae, *Ashmunella* with some 32 species (Bequaert and Miller 1973).

Many of the endemic polygyrids and helminthoglyptids are found in very small, restricted areas: *Helminthoglypta allynsmithi* is known only from a few rock slides in the canyon of the Merced River (Roth 1972). Speciation in the deserts of the southwest, where 68% of the species in Arizona alone are endemic, is also remarkable (Bequaert and Miller 1973), and parallels that in the deserts of southern Africa and in Australia.

Status

The major threats to land snail diversity in North America are habitat loss resulting from land clearing, logging, strip mining, fires, and continuing encroachment of urban centers into native ecosystems.

The centerpiece for the conservation of biodiversity in the United States is the Endangered Species Act of 1973 which authorized an official federal list of endangered and threatened wildlife which is not limited to the United States. Under the Act, species are proposed for listing. Recovery plans, which include habitat conservation and establishment of management and monitoring plans, are subsequently developed. Fifty-eight taxa of molluscs are presently on the federal list, 13 North American land snails and *Papuina pulcherrimus* from Manus Island, and 44 bivalves, 42 from North America and two from elsewhere.

Among the benefits to a listed species is protection from adverse effects of Federal activities, restrictions on take and trafficking, and authorization for the government to seek land purchases or exchanges for important habitat. Various federal agencies have responded to the Act by establishing research programmes, and many of the states have undertaken activities promoting the preservation of endangered biotas.

There is also an elaborate programme of national, state and local parks which provide habitats for some endangered species. The national park, refuge and reserve system includes 186 parks and nature reserves containing 2.2% of the continent (IUCN 1982).

South America

The fauna

The biotic resources of South America, which with Central America and the islands of the West Indies comprise the biogeographical region recognized as the neotropics, are among the richest in the world with 19% of the world's mammal species and one-third of the flowering plant species (Mares 1986). Jaeckel (1969) estimates 10,000 taxa (species, subspecies, races) of non-marine molluscs in South America; Parodiz (1957, 1980) lists just over 200 species of land molluscs (5 prosobranch families, 22 pulmonate families) in a catalogue of species from Argentina and bordering areas.

Charles Darwin, travelling from the coast of Chile to the Cordillera through "an uninhabited desert" in 1835 wrote that he " . . . saw traces of only one living animal in abundance, namely the shell of a small Bulimus [*Strophocheilus chilensis* (Sowerby)], which were collected together in extraordinary numbers on the driest spots. In the spring one humble little plant sends out a few leaves and on these the snails feed. As they are seen only very early in the morning, when the ground is slightly damp with dew, the Indians believe that they bred from it" (Darwin 1906). The small "Bulimus" is related to one of the few land shells which is considered a rarity (Dance 1972). *Sultana labeo*, the blubber-lip Bulimus, was discovered in a farmhouse at about 8,000 feet near Chachapoyas, Peru, in 1827; two other specimens were found alive but roasted and eaten by the finder's muleteer. The single shell was deposited in the museum of the Zoological Society of London but subsequently stolen and it was not until 1947 that someone revisiting the area procured additional specimens.

Darwin's small "Bulimus" also represents one of the oldest elements among the South American terrestrial molluscs for it is in the family Strophocheilidae, endemic to the continent but related to the Gondwanaland family Dorcasiidae in Africa. The carnivorous Streptaxidae and veronicellid slugs (Veronicellidae) are found both in South America and Africa. A third Gondwanaland family, the Bulimulidae which is the most widely distributed family in South America (Parodiz 1980), also occurs in Australia.

The continent can be divided into a northern tropical zone (Hylaea and the North) and a temperate Chaco-Pampean area which becomes much cooler in the south (Patagonia) (Parodiz 1980). The two areas have different geological histories, as indicated by both the recent and fossil freshwater mollusc faunas, and the land snail faunas appear to have different origins. In addition to the ancient stocks of South American molluscs, several families appear to have come from the north, among them the Pupillidae and Zonitidae. At least four families would appear to have arrived in South America via Middle America: the Helicidae, Urocoptidae, Oleacinidae and Cerionidae (Pilsbry 1896-1899; Parodiz 1980).

Status

Good data on the landsnails of South and Central America do not exist, and no South American species is listed in the IUCN Red Book. Pain (1981) noted that because of large-scale destruction of forests in certain areas of Brazil, some species of *Strophocheilus* have become scarce or possibly even extinct. The pampas, forests and mountains of South America have suffered fires, logging, erosion and extensive agriculture for centuries. There is an extensive system of parks and reserves: 218 parks and reserves include 2.7% of the continental land area (IUCN 1982), and there are systems of complex environmental laws that provide for the protection of habitats, plants and animals (Mares 1986). The Galapagos Islands, now a national park with conservation efforts supported by an international consortium, are a focal point for the conservation of molluscan biodiversity in South America (additional references under islands).

The land snails of islands

Island faunas

Charles Darwin first called attention to the importance of insular land shells in evolution: "Almost all oceanic islands, even the most isolated and smallest, are inhabited by land-shells, generally by endemic species . . . " (Darwin 1900). Solem (1984), analyzing land snail diversity worldwide, suggests that insular land snails represent " a significant, but unknown, portion of the world diversity of land snails . . . "

The terrestrial biotas of islands are indeed legendary among biologists for the diversity and novelty of their evolutionary products. Among the land shells, that diversity and novelty is represented by the peculiar acavids, 99 endemic species in five genera (Emberton 1990), some of them the size of tennis balls and with eggs 3 cm long from Madagascar; the earthworm-feeding *Paryphanta* from New Zealand; the large, green snail, *Papuina pulcherrima*, from Manus Island; the jewel-like tree snails *Achatinella* from Oahu in Hawaii; the multitudinous *Cerion* from islands in the West Indies; and the elongate, sinistral achatinid *Columna* from a tiny island in the Gulf of Guinea. Island land snails

are remarkable not only for species, but for entire families and subfamilies: three families and two subfamilies are endemic to the high islands of the Pacific alone, each taxonomic group with several genera and more species, each island with as many as 100 species of which 90% may be endemic.

The Malay Archipelago and the Philippines

The Malay archipelago was recognized by Alfred Russel Wallace (1872) as one of the world's great centers of animal and plant diversity. Many molluscan elements on islands in the archipelago reflect the fauna of India and Southeast Asia, among them cyclophorid operculates with their extraordinary apertures and protuberances, large helicarionid snails, rathouisiid slugs, and carnivorous streptaxids which reach their southern limits near the Celebes. The large, colourful, arboreal camaenid *Amphidromus* is also prominent on the islands in the archipelago.

The Philippines which are particularly rich in land snails are sometimes considered a separate province within the Indo-Malayan realm. Some of the most handsome land snails in the world are found on these islands, among them the endemic subfamily Helicostylinae (family Bradybaeindae) with nearly 300 species of large, colourful tree snails. The Camaenidae with many endemic species in *Obba* and the Helicarionidae with endemic genera *Lepidotrichia* and *Rhyssota* are also characteristic.

The West Indies

The biota of Middle America and the West Indies is usually included with that of South America in "Neotropica." Simpson (1894) described the land snails of the West Indies as so "astonishingly rich and diversified," that "no other area of the globe of equal extent can be compared with it." He counted 1600 species of land snails in 65 genera, "a number almost as great as that found on the mainland of the entire continent of America." Pilsbry (1948) agreed: "the Middle American fauna is fully equal in numbers of endemic families and genera . . . and equally entitled to stand as a primary region." In numbers of species, most of the major islands count species in the hundreds: Cuba 600, Jamaica over 500, Haiti 250, Puerto Rico 120. Not only do species numbers run high, but endemism is also high: 40 and 50% of the species are endemic to each island. The islands of the West Indies are also distinguished by the composition of the land snail fauna: there are perhaps 600 species of operculate prosobranchs (Helicinidae, Neocylidae, Annulariidae), a higher proportion than anywhere else. Six pulmonate families are also primary components of these remarkable species radiations. The Sagdidae, Cepoliinae (Helminthoglyptidae), and Cerionidae are endemic to the region. Specimens of *Cerion*, the only genus in the Cerionidae, are often so abundant as to completely cover the vegetation. There are also large numbers of species in the Urocoptidae, the carnivorous Oleacinidae and the orthalicine tree snails (Bulimulidae).

Status of island faunas

Island ecosystems are fragile, and island biotas are among the most vulnerable of all biotas to changing environmental conditions: island species, especially endemics, are virtually defenceless in the face of introduced alien species and manifest a rate of extinction far in excess of that of continental species (Atkinson 1989; Diamond 1984).

Islands have experienced profound changes in landscape since prehistoric time. In the Caribbean, land snail extinctions on Jamaica are attributed to habitat disturbance by humans during the last millennium (Goodfriend and Mitterer 1988). In the Pacific, on Tikopia in the Solomon Islands there are indications of severe human-induced soil erosion perhaps 3000 years ago (Kirch and Yen 1982); on Easter Island, there is evidence of extensive deforestation more than a thousand years ago (McCoy 1976); in Hawaii, extinctions of native land snails with settlements on Oahu began about 1500 BC (Christensen and Kirch 1986).

Change increased in pace in the 18th and 19th centuries as western voyagers explored the oceans. European explorers and settlers introduced hoofed mammals, rats and exotic plants. Darwin, describing St. Helena in 1836, noted that goats had been introduced by the Portuguese in the 16th century, and that a century afterwards "the evil was complete, . . . There can be little doubt that this great change in the vegetation affected . . . the land-shells, causing eight species to become extinct . . . " (Darwin 1906; and see Cronk 1989; Crowley and Pain 1977). Forests on Pacific islands were similarly destroyed and nearly the entire fauna of the family Endodontidae, a radiation of several hundred species, disappeared between 1900 and 1960 (Solem 1983). In New Zealand, introduced pigs and rats prey on the large endemic ground snails (*Paryphanta*, *Powelliphanta*, and *Placostylus*) and threaten their existence (Jeffs 1982, Lockley 1980, Ogle 1979, Meads *et al.* 1984). Many of the large, colourful tree snails in the endemic subfamily Helicostylinae in the Philippines are apparently extinct because of the destruction of their forest habitat (Abbott 1989).

Change continues today at an even greater rate as human populations on islands increase in numbers; urbanization affects land from the mountains to the sea; forest habitats are disrupted by encroaching agriculture, logging, roads and runways; tourism takes a toll on islands in the Mediterranean, Atlantic and Caribbean; sand for concrete and cement is removed from the strandline habitat of *Cerion* in the Caribbean; and introduced species decimate populations of indigenous land snails.

Several programmes for the management of protected areas on islands now exist: The Nature Conservancy (United States) purchased and manages large areas of native ecosystems in the Caribbean and Pacific. One of these areas in the Pacific serves as a study site for populations of native snails (Hadfield and Miller 1989). Plans for two national parks on Haiti include protected areas for endemic and potentially threatened land snails (Thompson 1986).

The status of land snails on several islands and island groups is listed in Table 5.1.

Freshwater molluscs

The fauna

There are perhaps 6000 species of gastropods and bivalves (Taylor 1988) which live in the freshwaters of lakes, rivers, hot springs, seeps, and seasonal ponds, habitats which are found on all the continents except Antarctica, in the Arctic, at high elevations, and on remote islands.

The freshwater mussels are perhaps the best known of freshwater molluscs, and, indeed, the pearl mussels *Margaritifera* in Europe may have been the first of the freshwater molluscs to have captured attention: enormous Neolithic shell mounds are evidence of their use as food throughout Europe, and their pearls were in demand for jewels. In the United States early naturalists were astonished at the diversity and abundance of the mussels: Rafinesque described 68 species in 12 genera in 1820 when all of the rivers of Europe had only 12 species (Stansbery 1971). More than 250 species in 47 genera are now recognized. Two families occur respectively in India, South America, Africa and Australia and are thought to represent relics of the Gondwanaland fauna.

Freshwater mussels are also known for their long lives: some of them live more than 100 years and they are both abundant and speciose. More than 1,000 named species of snails and mussels are known from the Ohio, Tennessee-Cumberland and Coosa-Alabama-Cahaba Rivers of eastern North America alone (Davis 1977). In the Mekong River Valley there is a highly diverse pomatiopsid snail fauna of three tribes, 13 genera and more than 100 species, only recently recognized (Davis 1979) as a major freshwater snail radiation of considerable evolutionary significance. The vast number of endemics in Lake Ohrid in the Balkans comprises half the freshwater molluscan fauna of Europe (Boss 1979; Radoman 1964), and an estimated 73% of the species of freshwater molluscs in Japan are found in Lake Biwa, of which 43% are endemic (Mori 1984). The snail faunas of other lakes such as Baikal in central Asia, Tanganyika in Africa, and Titicaca in South America are equally spectacular (see Boss 1979 for references).

Spring-fed aquatic environments also support remarkable radiations of freshwater molluscs, among them minute hydrobioid snails. In the "four marshes" of Cuatro Cienegas, Mexico, five genera and nine species of hydrobiids are endemic to the basin (Hershler 1985); a radiation of more than 30 species of hydrobioids has been described from springs and wetlands in Florida (Thompson 1968); and more than 40 species of hydrobioids are recognized in the Great Artesian Basin in Australia (Ponder and Clarke 1990; Ponder, this volume).

In contrast to riverine, deep lake, and spring-fed environments, seasonal ponds and wetlands support widely distributed snails: species of *Lymnaea*, *Physa* and *Ancylus* are found around the world.

Status

Rivers, lakes, and springs are like islands in their isolation and vulnerability to habitat destruction. Rivers have also been exploited for their faunas, and polluted. Indeed it has been asserted that every river system in the world today has been affected in some way by humans (Davies and Walker 1986). Ortmann described the impact in western Pennsylvania as early as 1909: "pollution by . . . sewage . . . coal mines . . . oil wells . . . chemical factories . . . [and] . . . finally damming up certain rivers." The impact of human activities is reflected in the faunas: five species of an endemic subfamily (Neoplanorbinae) of ancylid pulmonate limpets (Basch 1962), two genera of freshwater gastropods, *Tulatoma* (Viviparidae) and *Apella* (Pleuroceridae) (Davis 1977) and 35% of 297 taxa of freshwater mussels are listed as extinct, endangered or candidates for listing as endangered in the United States (United States Fish and Wildlife Service 1991). Populations of the pearl mussels (*Unio crassus* and *Margaritifera margaritifera*) are also seriously declining, and are locally extinct in Europe and the United Kingdom (Jungbluth this volume; Bauer 1988; Woodward 1990), and there is but one remaining population of *Margaratifera auricaria* (Altaba 1990).

Lake Baikal, isolated in central Asia, with a unique fauna not only of molluscs but of crustaceans, fish, and seals (Khozov 1963), is threatened by logging of neighboring forests and1 effluent from pulp mills. Nearly 4% of Lake Biwa has been filled to create rice fields and recreation areas in the last 50 years and water quality continues to deteriorate (Okuda 1984). De-watering of springs destroys essential habitat of dozens of unique snails. More than half these habitats have disappeared in Florida (Thompson 1968); others are disappearing in Europe as springs dry up and there is physical disruption of the landscape. The immediate danger to Cuatro Cienegas in Mexico is from the effects of canals which drain marshes and lower water level in the springs (Taylor and Minckley 1966). Protection for the mound springs of the Great Artesian Basin is now being discussed (Ponder this volume).

The molluscs of coral reefs

The fauna

Coral reefs, although restricted to the tropics between 30°N and 30°S of the equator and to ocean depths of less than about 30m, cover about 0.1% of the surface of the earth. Thirty percent lie in the area of the Indo-Malayan Archipelago, bounded by Indonesia on the west, northern Australia on the south, the Philippines in the east, and mainland Asia in the north; another 30% occur in the Indian Ocean and Red Sea; 13% are found in the south Pacific; 12% occur in the western Pacific; 14% occur in the Caribbean and north Atlantic; and 1% is found in the south Atlantic (Smith 1978).

The molluscs of coral reefs have long been celebrated for their beauty, diversity, and utility. Among the famous shells of coral reefs are the golden cowrie, *Lyncina aurantium*, and a host of other cowries, cone shells and miters. The giant clams *Tridacna*, pearl oysters *Pinctada*, pearl button shell *Trochus niloticus* and turbinid *Turbo marmoratus* were utilized throughout the pre-western Pacific and form well known fisheries today. Still others of coral reef molluscs, among them the strombids (*Strombus*) and clams such as *Anadara*, remain central to subsistence diets in the Pacific and Indian oceans, and in the Caribbean.

Molluscs also play important roles in coral reefs. As reef builders, bivalves such as the giant clam (*Tridacna*), *Spondylus* and *Chama* and the gastropod wormshells (family Vermetidae) contribute to the framework of the reef and to sediments; and boring bivalves such as the mytilid "stone eater" *Lithophaga* and grazing gastropods, littorines, nerites and chitons remove quantities of limestone (see for example, Taylor and Way 1976) and are key elements in the bioerosion of the reef framework. Molluscs also play essential roles in community structure in food chains and as deposit feeders. The numbers and biomass of molluscs associated with reefs attest to their importance: in the Tuamotus in French Polynesia, molluscs are more important than staghorn coral (*Acropora*) and other corals in the biomass of lagoons (Salvat 1970).

Status

Reefs, which in the past supported human populations because their products were used only for subsistence while waste products were returned to nutrient cycles, are today increasingly degraded by human activity: shells and corals are collected for export, and fishing with poison and dynamite rather than net or spear destroys reefs, as do dredging and blasting channels through the reef to provide for small marinas.

The impact of reef destruction on molluscs is clearly visible: the molluscs of reefs which are destroyed by dynamite or sediment disappear as quickly as do the corals (personal observation). The impact of exploitation is poorly documented (Pointer and Catterall 1988) and is not so clear. While fisheries such as those for *Tridacna*, *Pinctada*, *Trochus*, and *Turbo marmoratus* show fluctuating or declining stocks (see below), the strombid *Strombus luhuanus* which is central to subsistence food resources in the Pacific, and the money cowrie *Monetaria moneta* of which millions were exchanged in the 19th century, continue to occur in very large numbers on reef flats through the Pacific. Pointer and Catterall(1988) provide both explanation and model: *Strombus luhuanus* is apparently resilient to gathering practices by traditional methods because of its size-dependent burying habit and partly subtidal distribution which provides refugia from human predation. At Bootless Islet near Port Moresby, Papua-New Guinea, where it has been continuously exploited for more than 500 years (Allen 1977), and at Yule Island in the Gulf of Papua, Papua-New Guinea, where as many as 5 million strombs may be collected in a year (Hinton 1982) there is no evidence of declining stocks. In the Caribbean, however, another strombid species, *S. gigas*, with similar habits, is now being exploited with new fishing technologies such as SCUBA and dredging, and the stock is being overfished (May 1984).

Marine sanctuaries or protected areas are now widespread, the largest is the 200,000 sq. km sanctuary established in 1975 on the Great Barrier Reef in Australia. In the United States there are some 14 sanctuaries off the coasts of nine states and American Samoa. Other protected marine areas include Sandy Bay Marine Preserve in Honduras, Shimomi Marine Park in Kenya, Pemba Island off the coast of Tanzania in East Africa, Tunku Abdul Rahman National Park in Malaysia, and Tubbatataba Reef in the Philippines.

Molluscs as economic resources

Mollusc fisheries

Facts and Figures. Molluscs comprised 8.2% of the world's fisheries catch in 1990 (FAO 1990), exclusive of local subsistence collection. More than 95% of the mollusc fisheries are from marine waters, and more than half of world production is from the north Pacific. Bivalves, primarily oysters, mussels, and scallops, make up 51% of the mollusc fishery, cephalopods 35% and gastropods less than 2% of the catch. Abalone (*Haliotis*) comprises the major gastropod fishery. Nearly all the freshwater catch of molluscs is in Asia (Japan, Korea, Philippines and Indonesia), and is composed largely of freshwater clams (*Corbicula* spp.) (FAO 1990).

Artisanal and recreational fisheries are also sources of molluscs for consumption. Indeed, these fisheries in the Pacific provide native populations with the major portion of their protein for subsistence (Chapman 1987, Cook 1976). Evidence from anthropological and sociological studies indicates that substantial amounts of molluscs are involved: 10-30% of the weight of animal flesh and 6% to 17% of the calories of some Aborigines in Arnhem Land (Meehan 1977).

Declining stocks

That increasing consumer demand for shellfish and squid coupled with limited standing stocks leads to precipitous declines in wild stocks was recognized as early as 1850. In Britain one of the most highly productive oyster fisheries in the 18th century was in the Firth of Forth but annual harvests of more than 20 millions failed before the end of the century (Fullerton 1960). A fishery for green snail (*Turbo marmoratus*) initiated in the Ryukyu islands in the early 1880's collapsed in less than 20 years because of overfishing (Yamaguchi and Kikutani 1989). More recent records of declines include those of abalone world-wide (Shepherd *et al.* 1992); mussel landings world-wide (Lutz 1985); wild stocks of the soft-shell clam (*Mya arenaria*) (Beal 1990) and bay quahogs (*Mercenaria mercenaria*) (Bourne 1989) in the United States; and the oceanic squid fishery for *Todaropsis* in Japanese waters in the 1970's (Okutani 1977). The loco (*Concholepas concholepas*) from the coastlines of Chile and Peru, which made up more than 25% of the gastropod catch in the 1980's with a high of 21,236 mt in 1987 was not listed in the FAO fisheries statistics in 1989, and reported at only 227 mt in 1990 (FAO 1990).

The data indicate that many mollusc fisheries populations tend to fluctuate, but, as Roper and Rathjen (1991) suggest for cephalopod fisheries, there remain many unknowns, " . . . stocks can be significantly affected by normal annual or cyclical environmental fluctuations, [and] analyses of population statistics by several national fishery agencies are inadequate to provide dependable assessments of predictable harvestable stocks . . . ". Artisanal fisheries also suffer from declining yields. Consumption of shellfish in the intertidal zones on the Transkei coast of South Africa (Branch 1975; Hockey and Bosman 1986), in the Canaries and Azores (Bouchet in litt.), in Costa Rica (Ortega 1987), and in Hawaii (Kay *et al.* 1982) has affected populations of limpets resulting in smaller mean sizes.

The cropping of marine production entails competition with bottom feeding fishes such as cod and halibut and with whales and pelagic fishes which feed on squid and octopus, as well as causing disruption of bottom communities by dredges and trawls. These detrimental effects along with declining and unpredictable fisheries stocks have provided much of the stimulus for the development of mariculture which is more and more recognized as a viable means of providing for direct production, of generating income, of re-seeding through hatcheries, and of avoiding overharvest and depletion of wild stocks. Mollusc culture accounts for 72% of shelled molluscs marketed and 53% of all marketed molluscs (John Bardach pers. comm., 1991). Culture of abalone in Japan, the United States, Mexico, and New Zealand has now reached a point where Shepherd *et al.* (1992) predict that "the culture of abalone will expand to production levels that will eventually rival or exceed production from wild stocks."

There remains, however, need for the establishment of production-oriented hatcheries around the world to meet expanding regional demands for seedstock. Hatcheries for production and re-seeding can be successful. In the tropical Pacific, hatcheries for the giant clam (*Tridacna*) provide for local conservation, subsistence food production, and large-scale commercial enterprises which generate employment opportunities and export revenue (Heslinga and Fitt 1987). There is a substantial market demand in Taiwan, Hong Kong, Singapore and Japan, and the clams continue to be a subsistence food in the Pacific. Hatcheries in Palau now have the capacity to produce 22,000-55,000 of one of the giant clams (*Tridacna derasa*) on a five-month cycle (Heslinga and Watson 1985). Other commercially important molluscs for which there are also hatcheries in the Pacific include trochus (*Trochus niloticus*) (Heslinga and Hillmann 1981), the green mussel (*Perna viridis*) (Heslinga *et al.* 1985), and the cockle (*Anadara granosa*) (Broome 1985).

The shell trade

The shell trade — collectors items, commercial shell, jewelry, mother-of-pearl, the ornamental trade, shellcraft, and the like — involves thousands of tonnes of shells annually (Wood and Wells this volume). Except for the freshwater pearl mussel, the shells of which are harvested for seed pearls, the bulk of the shell trade involves marine molluscs, primarily pearl oysters (*Pinctada* spp.), trochus, (*Trochus niloticus*), the chank (*Turbinella*), and the green snail (*Turbo marmoratus*).

Marine mollusc fisheries

Pearl oyster beds in the Red Sea were the source of pearls in early Egyptian times and by the beginning of the Christian era pearl fishing was an established industry in the Persian Gulf and the Indian Ocean. Other famous pearl beds occur in the Gulf of Manar, off Trincomalee (Sri Lanka), in north-western Australia, and in the Caribbean. Pearls from French Polynesia were first exported to Valparaiso in 1810, and more than 100,000 tonnes of the pearl oyster (*Pinctada*) have been exported from atolls in the Tuamotus since then (Salvat 1981). The first local extinction of a pearl oyster bed was noted in the Tuamotus in 1827 (Cuming 1827-1828); by the 1850s there was a general depletion of the pearl oyster beds in the Tuamotus (Salvat 1981) and in the Indian Ocean (Thomas

1884). Japanese culture of pearls beginning in 1898 relieved some of the pressures on pearl oyster beds, but between 1900 and 1960 the pearl oyster beds of seven atolls in the Tuamotus had been exhausted, and pearl oysters had disappeared in the Hawaiian Islands (Galtsoff 1933), in Madagascar (Wood and Wells this volume), and in parts of the Indian Ocean.

Ironically it was the decline of pearl oyster populations that led to the exploitation of another marine mollusc in the 20th century. The soft parts of trochus (*Trochus niloticus*) were used by Pacific islanders for food, and the shell cut as bracelets and fish hooks (Hedley 1917). Elsewhere trochus was known only to malacologists until about 1910 when former supplies of pearl shell were depleted and a search began for new sources of mother-of-pearl. The thick, nacreous shell of trochus was ideal for button making and was soon exploited by manufacturers. Vessels formerly engaged in gathering pearl shell were diverted to the work of collecting trochus shell on the Great Barrier Reef from Torres Strait to Port Mackay (Hedley 1917), in the Philippines (Seale 1916), and in New Guinea, the Solomon Islands and Fiji (Hedley 1917). Concerns about over-fishing were almost immediately expressed. Fishery companies licensed in 1926 to fish trochus in the Andaman and Nicobar Islands in the Indian Ocean gathered 500 tonnes of shells in three months, but after three seasons of fishing, quantities of shell fished per season were reduced to less than 40 tonnes, and the rate of collection per diver per hour fell from more than 20 in 1933 to 2-3 in 1935 (Rao 1937). The trend has continued, and local stocks have been fished to near economic extinction in Palau, Yap, Truk, Helen's Reef, New Caledonia, New Hebrides, the Philippines, etc. (Heslinga and Hillmann 1981).

Conventional regulatory methods have not been particularly effective on Pacific islands because there is little capability of enforcement. In these areas, reseeding of selected reefs with hatchery cultured trochus juveniles may be an appropriate means of conserving the resource, and hatcheries are now set up in Palau, Pohnpei, and New Caledonia (Heslinga and Hillmann 1981).

Freshwater mollusc fisheries

The freshwater mussels, the Unionidae in the United States and the Margaritiferidae in Europe and the United Kingdom, have been over-exploited for the pearl button and pearl industry since the turn of the century (Woodward 1990), and continue to be subject to over-exploitation as they are harvested for pearls and for use in the cultured pearl industry. Unionids from the United States currently provide the sole seed material for the world's cultured pearl industry and 5,000 to 6,000 tonnes of raw shell are exported each year, primarily to Japan (Brautigam 1990).

Land snail utilization

Land snails are also utilized for food: *Achatina* in Africa and *Bulimulus* in South America have been eaten for generations, as has the edible snail *Helix pomatia* in Europe. The Romans introduced "escogartiers" to western Europe, snail gardens in which snails were fed on aromatic herbs such as thyme and marjoram (Boyle 1981). The practice of raising land snails for food continues today in France, the United Kingdom, Australia, Taiwan, etc. (Mead 1979, Simpson 1992). Land shells, sewn into necklaces, bracelets and hat bands, also serve as economic resources, often for the tourist industry.

Molluscs as alien species

Alien species have travelled with humans since prehistoric time, and are often so common that they are not recognized for what they are. Virtually every slug found on a garden plant in eastern North America was accidentally imported from Europe (Solem 1974), and the most familiar snails in southern Australia, the common garden snail, *Helix aspersa* and the conical snail *Otala lactea*, were also introduced from Europe (Smith 1981).

The tale of two snails

It has long been recognized that animal and plant introductions into new habitats result in disrupted ecosystems, exterminations of native species and create major environmental and resource management problems. Two snails, the giant African snail, *Achatina fulica*, and the carnivorous *Euglandina rosea* from Florida, provide classic examples of what happens when alien species invade new territories and when biological control goes astray.

The giant African snail's journey from its African homeland through the Indian Ocean, into Asia, and across the Pacific to Hawaii, with occasional forays onto the North American continent, has been chronicled by Mead (1961, 1979). The snail was introduced from South Africa to Mauritius about 1800, and subsequently to Réunion and the Seychelles. It was purposefully carried to Calcutta, India in 1847; by 1900 it was in Ceylon; in 1931 it was in China; during the 1930's the Japanese introduced it to several islands in the western Pacific; and it arrived in Hawaii in 1936. In each new location there was a population explosion within a few months of its arrival and it quickly became an agricultural pest. In the Pacific the giant African snail not only decimates domestic gardens, but is a carrier of the parasite for eosinophilic meningitis (Wallace and Rosen 1969). No effective methods of control have been found, and attempts at biological control have caused more problems than they have solved (Hadfield and Kay 1989).

A carnivorous tree snail from Florida, *Euglandina rosea*, was introduced in Hawaii in 1952 in an attempt to control the giant African snail. There is no evidence that *Euglandina* successfully controls *Achatina* (Hadfield and Kay 1981; Tillier and Clarke 1983); there is incontrovertible evidence that it has caused the extinction of a population of an endemic tree snail (*Achatinella mustelina*) in Hawaii (Hadfield and Mountain 1981; Hadfield 1986a; Hadfield and Miller 1992). *E. rosea* has now been introduced at more than 20 sites on oceanic islands in the Pacific and Indian Oceans and in the Caribbean in attempts to control the giant African snail. On Moorea in French Polynesia it is responsible for the extinction of seven species of the endemic land snail, *Partula* (Murray, *et al.* 1988).

Freshwater introductions

During the last ten years, newspaper headlines have heralded the unwanted arrival of several freshwater molluscs in such distant locations as Southeast Asia, Hawaii, and North America. The apple snails, the ampullarids *Pila* from Asia and *Pomacea* from tropical and subtropical America and the Caribbean, and the viviparid *Cipangopaludina* from Asia, are the most recent of the introductions, found now in rice paddies in Southeast Asia (Mochida 1991) and taro patches in Hawaii (Cowie 1992b). In 1990 the headlines heralded the zebra mussel (*Dreissena polymorpha*) which had arrived in the Great Lakes from Europe (Hebert et al. 1989; Haurwitz 1990). In 1980 the Asian clam (*Corbicula*) invaded an Arkansas power plant (Pool and McCullough 1979).

These molluscs have much in common: each accidentally arrived from a point of origin thousands of miles from its present location; in each of the new environments massive populations built up in very short periods of time; and in each of the new environments the snails are disrupting native ecosystems or long-domesticated agricultural systems and wreaking massive economic damage.

The zebra mussel has the longest history of the molluscs as an introduced species. It came originally from the basins of the Black and Caspian Seas, spreading in the late 18th century across Europe and reaching British waters in 1824 (Kew 1893). It occurs in very large numbers, blocking pipes and channels of domestic and industrial water supply systems (Morton 1969). It probably arrived in the Great Lakes of North America about 1986, and began to build up massive populations with densities of 700,000 per square meter (Roberts 1990). The mussels affect the ecosystems both by disrupting native mussels and other fisheries because of their settlement habit, and, because they are filter feeders, taking in quantities of water and phytoplankton which will eventually disrupt the lower food web with effects reverberating up the food chain (Roberts 1990). The zebra mussel is now moving south through the rivers of the eastern United States.

Another bivalve, *Corbicula fluminea*, was introduced to North America at the end of the 19th century from Asia and was first reported alive from the mouth of the Columbia River between Washington and Oregon in 1938 (McMahon 1982). It moved south through the waterways of California in the 1940's, and then between 1950 and late 1980 was recorded in the waterways of 14 eastern states, from Texas to New York and Florida. Like the zebra mussel, it outcompetes native unionid and sphaeriid bivalves, damages water systems, and clogs irrigation scheme pipelines (McMahon 1982, Clarke 1986).

The mystery snails and apple snails are represented by at least five species of Ampullariidae which were deliberately introduced from their native habitats in the tropics of the Americas and the Caribbean. They were taken to Southeast Asia for culture as food (Mochida 1991), and to Hawaii for culture and as aquarium snails. In Southeast Asia these snails cause serious damage to rice paddies; in Hawaii they damage the taro crop (Cowie pers. comm., 1992)

Other recent freshwater introductions include *Biomphalaria* from South America which, with its parasites, is now found in China and Hong Kong (Dudgeon and Yipp 1983), and the Chinese mussel *Anodonta woodiana* which is now in France and Hungary (Kiss and Petro 1992).

Marine introductions

The introduction of alien marine molluscs along world coastlines is less well documented than are introductions on land and in waterways. The earliest marine introductions were most probably molluscs and barnacles accidentally carried on the wooden hulls of sailing ships. There is increasing evidence that marine species transported deliberately or accidentally by humans to areas where those species did not previously occur are negatively affecting the ecology of marine communities (Carlton 1987, 1989; Carlton, *et al.* 1990).

Nearly forty years ago, Charles Elton (1958) remarked that oysters presented an ever-increasing means for the dispersal of fouling organisms. That observation has been confirmed (Carlton 1987, 1989; Brown 1991). One of the most effective agencies in the transport of alien marine molluscs has been the Japanese oyster (*Crassostrea gigas*), preferentially cultivated because it grows faster and is thus marketable sooner. As a result of transport of this species, the Pacific coast of the United States now supports some 40 non-native molluscan species (Brown 1991), among them the Japanese oyster drill (*Ocenebra japonica*) which feeds on both native and foreign oysters (Hanna 1966).

Ship fouling and ballast also provide transport for marine organisms from one port to another. In the United States, the Asian clam (*Potamocorbula amurensis*) may have been introduced into San Francisco Bay by ballast water about 1986. The bivalve has spread dramatically and is now dominant in some areas (Carlton *et al.* 1990, Nichols *et al.* 1990). Carlton *et al.* (1990) predict it will cause major alterations in the San Francisco Bay ecosystem. A nudibranch introduced into New Zealand waters probably by one of these modes is an opportunist, preempting food and space and is inimical to local faunas (Willan 1987).

Controlling alien species

Control methods for alien terrestrial and freshwater molluscs include chemical (chlorine) and thermal agents (for the control of *Corbicula* in the United States and of the viviparids and apple snails) (Cheng 1989), biological control (for the control of the garden pest *Helix aspersa* in California by the decollate snail *Rumina decollata*) (Anonymous 1989) (but see the discussion of *Euglandina* as an agent of biological control), and construction of fences around areas to keep out alien predators in areas of suitable habitat (for populations of *Powelliphanta* in New Zealand (Jeffs 1982)). Surveillance and import/export regulations are widely used in the Pacific and in Europe. In the Pacific, governmental agricultural agencies have recently increased surveillance on all islands to prevent the further spread of the giant African snail (*Achatina fulica*). As most marine molluscs have planktonic larvae, there is no way of preventing the spread of these invaders to adjacent areas along a coastline, although species with non-planktonic larval forms may not be so liable to dispersal.

Molluscs as model systems

Mendel's pea plants and Morgan's *Drosophila* are legendary for their roles as model systems from which have stemmed the science of genetics. Molluscs also rank high as particularly useful models from which insights into basic biological principles have emerged. Second only to arthropods in diversity of species, molluscs may be second to none in terms of their distribution in space and time and their versatility in field and laboratory: most molluscs are small enough that they are amenable to experiment; their shells can be marked and are traceable in the field; they can be cultured in terraria and aquaria; many of them are extraordinarily fecund and have short generation times permitting statistical and genetic analyses; and various of their organ systems are easily dissectable.

The molluscan shell

Historians read and interpret history from documents. The molluscan shell is similarly an historical document, on which are recorded time and events. Charles Lyell used them to date the Tertiary because their fossils were particularly numerous and distinct in Tertiary strata. Others have interpreted features of the shell such as coiling (Trueman 1922) and sculpture (Williamson 1981) in attempts to demonstrate lineages of evolving fossils, the coils of the former representing an unbroken lineage, the sculpture of the latter providing the gross differences required by punctuated evolution. Stephen J. Gould (1969), interested in the evolution of form, uses the extraordinarily variable shells of *Cerion* to focus on the question of how the varying shapes of an individual's growth can serve as a source of evolutionary change.

The title of Darwin's *The Origin of Species* included the phrase "by means of Natural Selection;" but the modern view of species formation holds that there are actually two processes, first, geographic isolation of a subpopulation, and subsequently the process of selection. The genesis of the concept of isolation as a mechanism in species formation also lies with mollusc shells but in this case with the colours and colour patterns of shells which can be used in distinguishing species. John Thomas Gulick (1832-1923), a missionary's son in Hawaii, amassed a large collection of the colourful tree shells *Achatinella* on Oahu, and, about 1870, began to question the role of natural selection in the formation of species: "The conditions under which they live are so completely similar . . . The vegetation is much the same; the bird and insect enemies, so far as they have any, are the same, . ." (Gulick 1872). His view (see Gulick 1905 for references), that geographical isolation is an essential in the process has come to prevail (Carson 1987).

Natural selection is, however, a critical factor in preserving variability, especially in cases of balanced polymorphism such as is known in the English garden snail *Cepaea*. These snails exhibit a wide range of colours and banding patterns. The most common colours are yellow and pink, and shells of either colour may be unbanded or may have as many as five bands differing in intensity. The maintenance of different frequencies of the various polymorphic forms is largely due to selective predation by thrushes: banded snails on mottled backgrounds are less visible than unbanded snails and preyed on less frequently; unbanded snails have a survival advantage where the background is fairly uniform. The now classic studies of Cain and Shepperd (see White 1978 for a review) are among the best analyzed in ecological genetics and have set the stage for continuing work utilizing molecular markers.

In the early years of the 20th century when Darwinian theory was under intense scrutiny, one of the first questions asked was that of the relative values of congenital and "environmental" factors of organic structure, the "nature versus nurture" question. Henry Crampton (1925) writes of his interest in the subject as early as 1906 and of his search for "a series of related forms" with which to try to answer the question. He decided on *Partula*, a genus of Pacific island land snails, on which he would employ "the methods of biometry and genetics." Crampton's classic studies laid the foundation for a research programme which today addresses questions of the genetics of speciation, of shell colours and banding, the matter of gene frequencies in the wild, the genetics of coiling, the possibilities of character displacement, and which allows the possibility of molecular analysis of DNA (Murray and Clarke 1980; Johnson, *et al.* 1990; Murray, *et al.* 1991; Cowie 1992a).

Molluscs in communities

Tropical coral reefs are well known for the enormous numbers of species which are associated with them. At the same time, a fundamental starting point in the quest for an understanding of the structure of communities is the principle of competitive exclusion: in equilibrium communities no two species occupy the same niche. This concept was modified by Evelyn Hutchinson who suggested that large numbers of closely related species that appeared to occur in a restricted environment might be explained by resource partitioning. Kohn (1959) in a now classic paper demonstrated that indeed the adult ecological niche of each of some 12 to 14 species of the gastropod *Conus* on solution benches in Hawaii differ significantly with respect to at least two characteristics: the nature of the food, the nature of and relations to the substratum, and their distribution with respect to the ocean. This work has served as the foundation for a host of studies focusing on questions about the historical - geographic, ecologic and evolutionary patterns which account for the high species richness of tropical coral reefs.

The quick and the slow

Except for the cephalopods, some of which have speeds of up to 20 knots, molluscs are usually thought of as slow-moving and rather unexciting. Both the quick and the slow of the molluscs, however, are among the chief players in research in neurobiology.

Squid are known for their active swimming in the surface waters of the open ocean. The stellate nerves contain the giant axons which were used in all the early studies of the nerve impulse. The giant axons innervate muscles in the wall of the mantle. Powerful contractions of those muscles result in the rapid expulsion of water from the mantle cavity and the squid escapes potential predators by jet propulsion. The giant axons, some 650 m in diameter, accommodate microelectrodes from which are recorded the electrophysiological activities associated with a nerve impulse. From these studies have come our understanding of the electrical properties of nerve fibers and those of the cell membrane itself, and a series of discoveries of very wide significance in biology and medicine.

The octopus is different in form from the sleek-bodied squid. It is a visual and tactile animal like ourselves, and, indeed has a nervous system that does many of the things are own does, including learning. It has provided much insight into the structure and function of the brain (Wells 1962) because the octopus brain is far less complicated than that of vertebrates.

As informative as cephalopods are, the slow-moving sea hare, *Aplysia*, may be neurobiology's most celebrated invertebrate today. The sea hare has the advantage of simplicity: there are perhaps a trillion neurons in the human brain and most nerve cell bodies measure only 10-20 m in diameter. *Aplysia* possesses the largest nerve cells in the animal kingdom, cells which can be easily located and identified, cells into which microelectrodes can be inserted allowing both chemical manipulation and electrophysiological measurement (see Audeskirk and Audeskirk 1985 for a review), and cells which are now known to control complex orientation responses, feeding movements and activity rhythms by precisely known motor pathways and networks.

Kandel *et al.* (1983) have traced the neural circuitry involved in behavior involving three forms of learning, habituation, sensitization and classical conditioning. Another opisthobranch, the nudibranch *Hermissenda*, has been trained by classical conditioning and the molecular basis of learning in that animal is being explored (Alkon *et al.* 1985).

Marine gastropods play yet another role for the neurobiologist. Natural toxins from dinoflagellates and venomous snakes have been used in the study of ion channels, the channels through which ions pass into and out of nerve and muscle cells, for many years. The discovery that each species of the marine genus *Conus* has its own small toxic peptides, some of which block the flow of sodium, potassium and calcium ions across membranes, others specific inhibitors of acetylcholine receptors (Olivera *et al.* 1990), has been called "the biggest recent gold mine," in the field in recent years (Barinaga 1990).

A question of age

There are many aspects of life about which we can be uncertain. There is one which is invariant: all animals, including most vertebrates with determinate life histories, age and die. All that is, except for a mollusc in which the developmental programme can be suspended. Gerontologists have traditionally relied on laboratory mice and rats to study the ageing process. The sea slug *Phestilla sibogae* may change all that. *Phestilla*, which is found on coral reefs in the Pacific, lives, feeds and reproduces on a specific coral. It normally spends about three days as a free-swimming larva after hatching, then settles on to the coral and metamorphoses into an adult slug. For the next 60 days it eats the coral and produces eggs; then it dies (Miller and Hadfield 1990). If, however, the slugs are kept swimming in a water column without the coral on which they normally occur, they can live an additional 30 days in a state of almost suspended animation. When they are given their usual coral home, they metamorphose and live their full reproductive span of time.

There are other features of metamorphosis in *Phestilla* which are providing insight into fundamental biological processes. The field of cellular embryology was pioneered by E.G. Conklin's work on another marine gastropod, *Crepidula*, in which he attempted to trace the origin of the organs of the embryo and larva to specific cells in the dividing egg. What perhaps Conklin did not realize was that there is a process which provides in one organism in a brief time span nearly all of the developmental processes which occur in embryology from molecular through tissue transformation (Hadfield pers. comm., 1992). In *Phestilla* in which large numbers of larvae are produced and easily reared, metamorphosis is externally controlled, triggered by a chemical from its prey coral. These features and others provide means for the exploration of a host of the phenomena involved in metamorphosis (Hadfield 1986b, unpublished): the nature of the chemical that induces metamorphosis; the internally signalling pathway of the morphagen; the role of neurotransmitters in metamorphosis; and the occurrence of genes coding for a known family of transmembrane chemoreceptors.

Mussel watch

As canaries once warned miners of "bad air" so are molluscs indicators of "bad water". More than 80 years ago Ortmann (1909) realized that streams in North America without freshwater mussels had something wrong with them, and pointed out the effects of pollutants and river degradation on mussel beds. Bivalves are well known to concentrate small particles and accumulate a variety of toxins. Marine gastropods show the effects of toxins such as mercury by dwarfed and twisted shells, and various physiological abnormalities. In 1976, the Mussel Watch (Goldberg *et al.* 1978), a scheme calling for coordinated and standardized measurement of pollutants in four species of bivalve, including two species of *Mytilus*, *Crassostrea virginica* and *Ostrea equestris*, was set up at more than 100 sample sites on the coast of North America. The bivalves are analyzed for heavy metals, radionuclides, halogenated hydrocarbons, and petroleum hydrocarbons. The scheme has produced useful data on baseline levels of these substances, and may well be the model with which to develop and assess protocols which tell us about the health of ecosystems worldwide.

Actions required for the conservation of molluscan diversity

E. Alison Kay

Department of Zoology, University of Hawaii, Honolulu, Hawaii, U.S.A. 96822

I. Acquire and manage threatened habitats on islands, in aquatic ecosystems, on continents and on coral reefs for the conservation and protection of the native molluscan biota.

Implementation:

1) Identify suitable areas where there are significantly diverse molluscan populations for protected status and establish such areas as refuges, sanctuaries and the like.

Islands

Despite the immensity of habitat destruction on islands, there remain fragments of lowland forest and relatively untouched highland areas where remnants of native biota survive. Some of these may still host viable populations of invertebrates. There are also entire islands, for example, Henderson Island in the Pacific and Aldabra in the Indian Ocean, on which there remain virtually untouched biotas. Programmes for the management of protected areas on islands are feasible, and, indeed, entire islands and groups of islands such as the Northwestern Hawaiian Islands, which are administered as the Hawaiian Islands National Wildlife Refuge by the United States Fish and Wildlife Service, and the Galapagos Islands which are a National Park, have been afforded protection. An initiative for protection of entire islands would recognize the precarious position and the significance of insular biotas.

Continents

The molluscan faunas of Asia, South America, and parts of Africa are not well known, but assuming that greatest diversity of these faunas is associated with forests, as it is in parts of Africa and in Europe and North America, and, given the enormous rate of destruction of forests worldwide, identification of areas where there are significantly diverse molluscan populations for protected status and establishment of such areas as refuges is of highest priority. Molluscs with wide distributional ranges will often fall under the protective custody of national and state parks; species with restricted ranges, known perhaps from a single locality, are highly vulnerable to extinction and would appropriately be identified in a quest for more protected areas.

Freshwater ecosystems

The rate of destruction and disruption of aquatic ecosystems rivals that of the destruction of forests. Identification of, recommendations and support for, and establishment of, protected areas for rivers with significant naiad and freshwater pearl mussel populations, and lakes and springs with diverse radiations of other aquatic molluscs is a priority.

The management of coral reefs

Coral reefs are increasingly impacted by nutrient enrichment (sewage, agriculture), exploitation (overfishing, coral mining), and sedimentation and turbidity. Reef management, however, must operate on a large scale, involve both interaction with fisheries and protected area management teams, and involve regulation of both areas and species. Marine parks and sanctuaries are examples of area regulation; they are designed as reservoirs from which larvae can recruit to damaged and over-exploited reef areas. Randall (1982) estimates that if only five percent of a reef environment is protected, the larvae of marine organisms in the preserves are sufficient to seed adjacent protected areas. Species regulation takes the form of legislation now enacted by many countries to conserve their marine resources, and, indeed, more than 50 species of molluscs are now regulated by individual countries.

II. Develop the data base necessary for knowledge of molluscan diversity.

Implementation

1. Establish biological monitoring programs at the local level to aid in the assessment of the current status of regional molluscan diversity. Monitoring programmed are multipurpose management tools which will provide for:

   1) data on the biotic and abiotic characteristics of the environment which identify regions of greatest molluscan diversity;

   2) immediate warning of non-acceptable impacts of human activities and their waste products on the environment;

   3) a longterm data base to evaluate and forecast natural changes and impacts of human activities;

   4) identification of endangered habitats and species;

   5) identification of stocks of molluscs of potential use in fisheries, the shell trade, and biomedical research.

2. Establish baselines from distributional information now available in systematic works and unpublished information in museum collections to produce base maps of species distributions. Computerize museum records for species/localities through time and establish mechanisms to effect cooperation and networking internationally.

3. Establish priorities for taxa to be added to the database by coordinated action groups for land snails, unionids, marine gastropods, marine bivalves, insular biotas, and freshwater

gastropods; maintain a central data base at a satellite database center to record level of progress.

4. Update and evaluate a world list of extinct (human-caused extinction) and threatened molluscan species. A world list of threatened and recently extinct molluscs serves as a resource for summarizing conservation problems with respect to molluscs, and for material which can be used for purposes of education and publicity. Lists of molluscs for the IUCN Red List, the Invertebrate Red Data Book, CITES, and the Berne Convention have been developed from a data base at the World Conservation Monitoring Centre (WCMC), Cambridge, and a world list has been compiled at the University of Hawaii, Honolulu, Hawaii. However the databases are far from complete, need critical analysis, and require maintenance.

5. Ensure sources of funding for systematics, life history and demographic studies of molluscs, especially those in fragmented and disturbed habitats, threatened and endangered species and those which provide major stocks for mollusc fisheries and the shell trade by supporting molluscan systematics and taxonomy in university programs, museums and conservation management programs.

Are molluscan systematists an endangered species?

No matter how much public education is undertaken, no matter how much legal habitat protection is put in place, and no matter how many alien species are removed, there is no substitute for comprehensive biological knowledge of a fauna. The skills of systematists and taxonomists are pivotal for reliable species identifications, knowledge of life history, and demographics. These are all essential for conservation biology and to agricultural, health, environmental, customs and other agencies which must respond to accidental introductions of pest species, health problems caused by molluscan-borne diseases or the ingestion of molluscs, declining populations, and importations of shells and shell products. Unfortunately, a recent newspaper headline, "Scientists who study endangered species are themselves in danger of extinction" (Connor 1992) summarizes a widely recognized trend: the numbers of expert systematists and taxonomists in all fields are declining (Oliver 1988, Wilson 1985), and financial and organizational support for systematics, the study of biological diversity, has declined at alarming rates in universities and museums worldwide (Wilson 1985).

What we need to know

Much of the necessary data on biology, life history, demographics, and systematics are lacking for the molluscs which are of most concern. More than 300 names for the renowned, jewel-like achatinelline tree snails of Hawaii have been proposed, but the first data on growth rates, size and age at maturity, and fecundity did not appear until 1981, and even now there are data on only two species (Hadfield and Mountain 1981; Hadfield and Miller 1989). There are few published data on the endangered New Zealand flax snail (*Placostylus*), none on the Manus green snail (*Papuina*). Nor is there a strong data base on age at maturity and fecundity of common alien and pest species such as the giant African snail or

the carnivorous Florida snail. Worldwide there are an estimated 20,000 undescribed species of mollusc, and problems in identifying sibling and cryptic species. Demographic, biological and life history studies are essentials in captive breeding programs, and, indeed, the success of the program for captive breeding of *Partula* depends on an intimate knowledge of the life style parameters of those snails (Bloxam and Tonge 1986), while a small scale captive breeding program for Hawaiian achatinelline snails in Hawaii results from the detailed life history studies which served as the basis for designing the program, the successful culture of the fungus on which the snails feed, and the availability of substrate from the native habitat (Hadfield pers. comm., 1990). All exploitation is intimately bound up with fundamental population ecology and reports on virtually every shell fishery note the lack of information on life history, population dynamics, recruitment processes and the like [see for example Harrison 1986 on the Australian abalone; Roper and Rathjen 1991 on cephalopod fisheries; Castilla and Jerez 1986 on the loco (*Concholepas*)].

Hard data are necessary to effect policy and develop funded programs. The results provide knowledge of localities and areas of high species diversity and immediately show what is rare, potentially endangered, and potentially extinct. Decision makers are thereby provided with the information necessary to evaluate issues, and priorities can be established to determine the courses of action needed, that is, whether protection by habitat, cessation of fishing pressure, control of predators, etc.

6. Educate national and governmental agencies such as park services, natural resource conservation agencies, and fisheries on the values of identifying diversity; establish a coordinating committee to provide leadership to stimulate funding internationally.

III. Prevent the introduction of alien species that have negative impacts on native mollusc species and control and eradicate these exotic species where such introductions have already occurred.

Implementation

1. Prohibit worldwide the introduction of alien species without appropriate research into long-range effects of these organisms on native ecosystems. Establish and implement stringent quarantine regulations at all ports of entry.

2. Control and eradicate exotic species such as *Euglandina rosea* where such introductions have already occurred. Circulate among government agencies the strongly worded IUCN position statement "Translocation of Living Organisms" (IUCN 1987b) which cautions against the introduction of species to natural habitats and islands; support and cooperate with government quarantine, agriculture and health departments in monitoring and identifying possible noxious species that arrive accidentally.

IV. Establish self-sustaining captive populations of endangered mollusc species and support their eventual re-introduction into their native habitats.

Implementation

"Habitat protection alone is not sufficient to achieve the goal of the World Conservation Strategy, if the maintenance of biotic diversity, is to be achieved. Establishment of self-sustaining captive populations and other supportive intervention will be needed to avoid the loss of many species, especially those at high risk in greatly reduced, highly fragmented and disturbed habitats. Captive breeding programs need to be established before species are reduced to critically low numbers, and thereafter need to be coordinated internationally according to sound biological principles, with a view to the maintenance or re-establishment of viable populations in the wild" (IUCN 1987a).

Captive breeding programs should not detract from the immediate concern of protecting molluscan faunas in the wild, but they are a cost-effective way of dealing with rare species (Wilson 1987; Wells this volume), and the publicity generated by a few carefully selected projects can enhance public awareness of mollusc conservation issues. Laboratory reared populations provide information on species which can be applied to their conservation in nature, for example by providing estimates of genetic diversity in small populations and of the numbers needed to sustain viable populations.

A captive breeding program involving the Pacific land snail *Partula* has been underway for several years (see, for example, Bloxam and Tonge 1986), and six species of *Partula* from Moorea survive today only in the laboratory and in zoos. The program demonstrates that genetic stocks can survive, even though, as in this case, all seven Moorean species of *Partula* in the wild are apparently extinct (Murray *et al.* 1988). Other threatened non-marine molluscs currently bred in captivity include *Powelliphanta* in New Zealand, *Geomalacus maculosus* in Europe, and *Partulina* in Hawaii.

V. Promote public awareness and concern for molluscan conservation programmed.

Implementation:

1. Create and develop public awareness through education programmed of the importance of molluscs to humans in culture, agriculture and ecosystems and as part of the natural heritage as natural resources.

Molluscs neither soar like the condor, nor are they cuddly like the panda. Pleas to "save a snail" or "hug a slug" rarely convince the shell collector to leave a shell behind or attract funds for research from the conservation community or the public. Indeed, in the western world, snails and slugs are seemingly more often seen as pests and carriers of disease than recognized for their utility. Some molluscs do cause damage to agricultural crops and ornamental gardens; some molluscs are intermediate hosts for diseases such as those caused by the human blood fluke, cattle liver fluke and the rat lungworm. For the most part, however, molluscs are agricultural pests where they are alien intruders in ecosystems (Godan 1983). In India, with more than 1500 species of native land snails, seven mollusc species (<1%) are known to cause some damage to agricultural and horticultural gardens, but only one, the giant African snail (*Achatina fulica*), an introduced species, is considered serious. The spread of disease by snails can also be attributed in many instances to human-induced changes in ecosystems: the high incidence of blood fluke in Egypt has been associated with the introduction of perennial irrigation (van der Schalie 1973).

2. Establish training workshops in molluscan taxonomy and systematics for field workers. At the local "field" level, particularly where there are mollusc fisheries and mariculture and in shell importing and exporting countries, taxonomic skills are essential for identification purposes and necessary for the implementation of management techniques and for conservation in general. Workshops involving teams of experts in molluscan systematics and taxonomy could provide the expertise to workers in the field, giving them needed knowledge and confidence.

3. Adopt and encourage the utilization of the deep knowledge of marine life possessed by traditionally trained "master fishermen" on Pacific islands by establishing cooperative work units of western-trained conservation officers to better manage insular biotas and reefs.

Acknowledgements

I am indebted to a great many people for their contributions to this report. The members of the first Mollusc Specialist Group of the Species Survival Commission provided input and criticism on three drafts: Philippe Bouchet, Dolf van Bruggen, John Burch, Michael G. Hadfield, Winston Ponder, Henrik Waldén, Susan Wells, and Fred Woodward. I also thank Arthur Bogan, George Davis, Robert Cowie, Michael G. Hadfield and Dick Willan for a variety of suggestions, and Fred Naggs and John Peake for their substantive criticism and insight which gave the report its final form.

Table 1

The status of terrestrial molluscs on islands for which data are available.

Atlantic and Mediterranean

Aegean Islands

14 families, 60 genera, 40-50% species endemic. Human influence since the 3rd century: agriculture, goat raising, fire, urbanization. Local extinctions in historic time caused by human activity. Reference: Mylonas 1984.

Azores

67 land snail species, 41.8% endemic. Zonitidae show most radiation. References: Waldén 1983, 1984.

Canary Islands

157 land snail species. 78% endemic, 49% of endemic taxa in *Hemicycla* and *Napaeus*. References: Waldén: 1983, 1984.

Cape Verde Islands

21 land snail species, 43% endemic. References: Waldén 1983, 1984.

Madeira

261 land snail species, 74% endemic, more than half endemics in helicid subfamily Geobirinae. 17 species extinct or near extinction, 22 rare and endangered, 19 rare. References: Cook, *et al*. 1972; Waldén 1983, 1984, 1986.

St. Helena

Ca. 100 species associated with forests; virtually all presumed extinct. Goats introduced by the Portuguese in 1513; original vegetation replaced as a result of browsing, grazing, erosion, cutting for timber and fuel, introduction of alien plants, clearing for cultivation, plantations, pasture. References: Crowley and Paine 1977; Cronk 1989; Solem 1977; Woodward 1991.

São Tomé and Principe

Several unusual taxa endemic to these islands: monotypic achatinid *Atopolcochlis*, *Lignus alabaster*, sinistral *Columna*; and in the monotypic Thyrophorellidae, the sinistral *T. thomensis*. References: Groh and Griffiths 1987; Naggs 1992.

Caribbean

Puerto Rico

Ca. 85 species. Natural vegetation drastically altered with arrival of European colonists 500 years ago: by 1912 >80% of island deforested by clearing for agriculture, grazing, timber; introduction of goats and cattle. <1% remained pristine. Reference: Densmore 1986.

West Indies: Jamaica

500 land snail species, more than 50% operculates; generic and species endemism. Radiations of Sagdidae and Urocoptidae. Local extinctions from habitat destruction before European arrival; continuing destruction of forests; north coast almost completely denuded. References: Goodfriend and Mitterer 1988; Groh and Parkinson 1987; Simpson 1894.

Indian Ocean

Madagascar

400 land snail species, 98% endemism. The Gondwanaland family Acavidae with 99 nominal species dominant; *Trophidophora* with 50 species. *Achatina fulica* and *Euglandina rosea* introduced. Threats: virtual complete deforestation with severe soil erosion. References: van Bruggen 1980a; Emberton 1990; Groh and Griffiths 1987; Solem 1984.

Mauritius

130 land snail species, 64% endemic. The carnivorous Streptaxidae dominant; speciation also in *Tropidophora* and Helicarionidae. *Achatina fulica* and *Euglandina rosea* introduced. Extinct: the streptaxid *Gibbus lyonetianus*, other streptaxids and most operculates. Threats: *Euglandina* implicated in extinction of native species; extensive deforestation with ebony forest replaced by sugar cane. References: Griffiths *et al* 1993; Groh and Griffiths 1987; Walden 1984.

Reunion

48 land snail species, 42% endemic. *Achatina fulica* and *Euglandina rosea* introduced. Extensive deforestation. Reference: Walden 1984.

Seychelles

41 land shell species, 15 freshwater species, 41% endemic. Land shells probably disappeared prior to 1869 with the nearly complete destruction by fire and timber cutting of the original flora; most of granitic island species now found only in summit relict forests where "they barely survive." Recent extinctions: three species not traced recently; on St. Anne 30 endemic species at risk. *Achatina fulica*, *Euglandina rosea*, *Gonaxis quadrilateris* introduced. Aldabra, an elevated reef, with virtually undisturbed land snails. References: Gerlach 1987; Griffiths et al. 1993; Lionnet 1984; Nevill 1869.

Pacific Ocean

American Samoa. Tutuila and Manua Islands

>50 species, many single island endemics. *Achatina fulica*, *Euglandina rosea*, and *Gonaxis kibweziensis* introduced. Endangered: *Samoana conica*, *S. abbreviata*, *Trocomorpha aria*, *Eua zebrina*. Recent extinctions: Ofu - 1 endodontoid; Ta'u - 3 Charopidae, 1 endodontoid presumed extinct; Tutuila - 2 Charopidae, 1 Helicarionidae. Threats: introduced *Euglandina* and *Gonaxis*, upper elevation forest lost to agriculture and hurricanes, rat predation. References: Clench 1949; Miller, *et al*. 1993; Solem 1975, 1983.

Austral Islands: Rapa

100 species listed; estimated 200 species; 98% endemic. Tornatellinidae and Endodontidae dominant, with several radiations. 50% extinct 1934-1960; small fossil locality distant from remaining patches of native forest with large numbers of zonitids, partulids, endodontoids today restricted to the remaining forest. One-fifth of native forest remains of the once entirely forested island. Introduced feral cattle and goats causing extensive destruction by uprooting and extensive erosion. References: Cooke 1935; Paulay 1985; Solem 1976, 1983, 1984.

Fiji: Viti Levu

15 families, 58 species, including 2 endemic charopid genera, one endemic genus in Cyclophoridae. *Lau Archipelago*. 39 species from three islands, 27 endemic, 9 introduced by Polynesian voyagers and European commercial activities; endemic taxa and introduced species not competing. References: Garrett 1887a; Germain 1932; Solem 1978, 1983, 1990.

Galapagos Islands

90 land snail species, most single island endemics; fauna dominated by *Bulimulus*. Endangered: 30 bulimulid species. Local extinctions from habitat destruction before arrival of Europeans. Recent extinctions: *B. nux* once abundant on San Cristobal and Floreana (two subspecies remain). Threats: introduced fire ants and black rat; destruction of native vegetation by clearing, grazing, exotic plants. References: Chambers and Steadman 1986; Coppois 1984, 1986; Coppois and Glowacki 1983; Coppois and Wells 1987; Dall 1896; A. Smith 1966.

Hawaiian Islands

Ca. 1,000 land snail species, >90% endemic, most single island endemics. Spectacular radiations in tree snails *Achatinella* on Oahu, and in ground-living Amastridae *Carelia* on Kauai. Local extinctions from habitat destruction before arrival of Europeans; overcollection of tree snails in the 19th century. Recent extinctions: 20 species of Achatinellines; *Carelia* and other ground-living amastrids. *Achatinella* registered as an endangered genus under Endangered Species Act. *Achatina fulica* and *Euglandina rosea* introduced. Threats: habitat loss caused by agriculture, deforestation, urban development and the introduction of hoofed mammals; predation by the introduced *Euglandina rosea*, triclad *Platydemus manokwari*. References: Christensen and Kirch 1986; Hadfield 1986a; Hadfield and Miller 1989; Hadfield and Mountain 1981; Kondo 1970.

Lord Howe Island and Norfolk Island

Lord Howe: >50 endemic species. Several extinctions recorded among them the freshwater snail *Posticobia norfolkensis* for Norfolk Island. Threats: clearing of native vegetation; land degraded by introduced species. References: Ponder 1981, personal communication; Solem 1983; Turner, *et al.* 1968

Mangareva

33 species including 3 endemic genera of Endodontidae. In 1934 nearly all the islands had been continuously burned over, ridges were bare of trees, and the endemic forest had disappeared. A fossil bed produced several endodontid species. All but one or two native species presumed extinct. References: Cooke 1935; Solem 1976, 1990.

Mariana Islands. Guam:

5 species *Partula*; 6 species Charopidae. *Achatina fulica*, *Euglandina rosea*, *Gonaxis kibweziensis*, *G. quadrilateralis* introduced. *Euglandina* possibly contributed to decline of 3 endemic species of *Partula* and extinction of one species. Terrestrial triclad *Platydemus manokwari* effective in control of giant African snail but contributes to decline of *Partula*. Threats: habitat destruction and fragmentation; effects of *Euglandina*. References: Griffiths et al. 1993; Mead 1979; Smith and Hopper 1992.

Marquesas Islands

88 land snail species, about 50% of potential fauna; 78% endemic, mostly single island endemics. Speciation in Zonitidae (28 spp.), Endodontidae (12 spp.), Pupillidae (6 spp.) Partulidae (18 spp.) Tornatellinidae (11 spp.) Succineidae (2 spp.), Helicinidae (8 spp.). Extinct: lowland species collected by Garrett in 1880's. Threats: flora below 608 m profoundly altered by humans, native vegetation destroyed by introduced grazing animals and grass *Paspalum*; goats have destroyed flora of steep slopes; continuing burning. References: Adamson 1935, 1936; Garrett 1887b; Solem 1976.

New Caledonia

300-400 endemic land snail species, most restricted to small areas of the island; 10% derive from Indo-Malayan archipelago, others show Gondwanaland affinities; 80% represent a monophyletic radiation of the Charopidae, 10% a radiation of the Rhytididae which prey on the Charopidae. *Achatina fulica* and *Euglandina rosea* introduced. Threats: habitat destruction with all endemic species at risk, especially the Charopidae in Mt. Koghi hills. References: Griffith *et al.* 1993; Mead 1979; Solem 1961, 1984; Tillier and Clarke 1983.

New Hebrides

73 land snail species, 57 endemic, 10 widespread Pacific species, 5 species are "tropical tramps." Most of the endemic species are in the Charopidae (9), Bulimulidae (9), Rhytididae (5) and Partulidae (5). Threats: continuing deforestation and habitat disruption. Reference: Solem 1959.

New Zealand

About 1000 species of land snails, 99.5% endemic. Distinguishing elements include the leaf-veined slugs Athoracophoridae; large, earthworm eating snails in the Rhytididae; minute snails in the Charopidae; and the Bulimulidae. North Island snails display the highest sympatric diversity in the world. Endangered: Rhytididae, small scattered populations of Bulimulidae, Placostylus, Paryphanta. Threats: introduced mammals such as rats; habitat disruption. References: Climo, et al. 1986; Jeffs 1982; Lockley 1980; Powell 1979; Solem 1984; Solem et al. 1981.

Papua New Guinea and Irian Jaya

Numbers of land snail species vary from 198 (Iredale) to >500 for Irian Jaya (van Bentham Jutting). Dominants include the Camaenidae (*Papuina*), Helicarionidae, Cyclophoridae. *Papustyla pulcherrima* from Manus Island listed in *Red Data Book* and under U.S. Endangered Species Act. References: van Bentham Jutting 1965; Iredale 1941.

Philippines

Estimates of 1100-3000 species; extraordinarily high diversity. Extinct: many endemic species assumed extinct or seriously endangered. Threats: deforestation. References: Parkinson, *et al.* 1987; van Bruggen 1989, personal communication.

Pitcairn Islands: Henderson Island

14 land snail species (Christensen), 8 with 100% endemicity (Paulay). Evidence of Polynesian habitation but the island is relatively undisturbed; in 1934 the fauna lacked most of the exotics introduced to other Pacific islands. *Pitcairn Island*: limited areas of vegetation remaining. References: Christensen 1983; Cooke and Kondo 1960; Paulay 1991.

Society Islands: Tahiti

80 land snail species. *Achatina fulica* and *Euglandina rosea* introduced. 9 species *Partula* extinct. References: Clarke *et al.* 1984; Crampton 1916, 1932; Garrett 1884; Kondo 1970; Mead 1979; Murray and Clarke 1980; Solem 1984, 1990; Tillier and Clarke 1983.

References

ABBOTT, R.T. 1989. *Compendium of landshells*. Burlington: American Malacologists.

ADAMSON, A.M. 1935. Marquesan insects. M.S. thesis, Univ. of Hawaii.

ADAMSON, A.M. 1936. Marquesan insects: environment. *Bernice P. Bishop Museum Bull*. 139.

ALKON, D., M. SAKAKIBARA, R. FORMAN, J. HARRIGAN, I.LDERHENDLER, J. FARLEY. 1985. Reduction of two voltage dependent K$^+$ currents mediates retention of a learned association. *Behav. Neural Biol*. 44: 278.

ALLEN, J. 1977. Fishing for wallabies: trade as a mechanism for social interaction, integration and elaboration on the Central Papuan coast. In: Friedman, J. and M.J. Rowlands, eds. *The evolution of social systems*. London: Duckworth Publications. pp. 419-456.

ALTABA, C.R. 1990. The last known population of the freshwater mussel *Margaritifera auricularia* (Bivalvia, Unionida): a conservation priority. *Biol. Conserv*. 52: 271-286.

ANONYMOUS. 1980. *The International Mussel Watch*. National Academy of Sciences, Washington, D.C.

ANONYMOUS, 1989. *Sunset Magazine*. Oct.: 28.

ANT, A. 1976. Areal vesandenungen und gegenwaragei stand der Gefahrdung mitteleuropaische Land und Susswassermollusken. *Schrift. fur vegetationsk*. 10: 309-339.

ATKINSON, I. 1989. Introduced animals and extinctions. In: D. Western and M.C. Pearl, eds. *Conservation for the 21st century*. New York: Oxford University Press. pp. 54-75.

AUDESKIRK, T. AND G. AUDESKIRK 1985. Behavior of gastropod mollusks. In: Willow, A.O.D., ed. *The Mollusca* Vol. 8 *Neuro-biology and Behavior* Part 1. New York: Academic Pres.

BARINAGA, M. 1990. Science digests the secrets of voracious killer snails. *Science* 249: 250-251.

BASCH, P.F. 1962. Radulae of North American ancylid snails. II. Subfamily Planorbinae. *The Nautilus* 75: 145-149.

BAUER. G. 1988. Threats to the freshwater pearl mussel *Margaritifera margaritifera* L. in central Europe. *Biol. Cons*. 45: 239-253.

BEAL, B. 1990. NCRI sponsors soft-shell clam (*Mya arenaria*) hatchery/management program. *NCRI News* (National Coastal Research and Development Institute 5 (1): 1,3.

van BENTHAM JUTTING, T. 1948. Systematic studies on the non-marine Mollusca of the Indo-Australian Archipelago. I. Critical revision of the Javanese operculate land-shells of the families Hydrocenidae, Helicinidae, Cyclophoridae, Pupinidae and Cochlostomatidae. *Treubia* 19: 539-604.

van BENTHAM JUTTING, T. 1950. Systematic studies on the non-marine Mollusca of the Indo-Australian Archipelago. II. Critical revision of the Javanese pulmonate land-shells of the families Helicarionidae, Pleurodontidae, Fruticicolidae and Streptaxidae. *Treubia* 20: 381-505.

van BENTHAM JUTTING, T. 1952. Systematic studies of the non-marine Mollusca of the Indo-Australia Archipelago. III. Critical revision of the Javanese pulmonate land-shells of the families Ellobiidae to Limacidae, with an appendix on Helicarionidae. *Treubia* 21: 19-73.

van BENTHAM JUTTING, W.S.S. 1965. Non-marine Mollusca of west New Guinea. Part 4, Pulmonata, 2. *Nova Guinea* (Zool.) 32: 205-304.

BEQUAERT, J.C. AND W.B. MILLER. 1973. *The mollusks of the arid southwest*. Tucson: The University of Arizona Press.

BERG, C.J. and D.A. OLSEN. 1989. Conservation and management of queen conch (*Strombus gigas*) fisheries in the Caribbean. In: Caddy, J.F. (Ed.). *Marine invertebrate fisheries: their assessment and management*. New York: John Wiley & Sons.

BERRIE, A.D. and B.J. BOIZE. 1992. Host utilization by glochidia of *Anodonta anatina* and *Pseudanodonta complanata* in the River Thames, England. In: F. Giusti and G. Manganelli, eds. Abstracts 11th International Malacological Congress, Siena: 13.

BISHOP, M.J. 1981. The biogeography and evolution of Australian land snails. In: Keast, A., ed. *Ecological biogeography of Australia*. The Hague: Junk.

BLAB, J., E. NOWAK, W. TRAUTMANN, and H. SUKOPP. 1984. *Rote Liste der gefahrdeten Tiere und Pflanzen in der Budesrepublik Deutschland*. Naturschutz Aktuell Nr. 1.

BLANFORD, W.T. and H.H. GODWIN-AUSTEN. 1908. *The fauna of British India*. Mollusca. Testacellidae and Zonitidae. London: Taylor and Francis.

BLOXAM, Q.M.C. and S. TONGE. 1986. Breeding programmes for reptiles and snails at Jersey Zoo — an appraisal. *Int. Zoo Yb*. 24/25: 49-56.

BOSS, K.J. 1979. On the evolution of gastroods in ancient lakes. In: V. Fretter and J. Peake (eds.), *Pulmonates* Vol. 2A, pp. 385-428. London: Academic Press.

BOUCHET, P. 1990a. La malacofaune Francaise: endemisme, patrimoine naturel et protection. *Rev. Ecol. (Terre Vie)* 45: 259- 283.

BOUCHET, P. 1990b. *In litt*.

BOURNE, N. 1989. Clam fisheries and culture in Canada. In: J.J. Manzi and M. Castagna, eds. *Clam mariculture in North America*. New York: Elsevier.

BOYLE, P.R. 1981. *Molluscs and man*. Institute of Biology Studies in Biology No. 134. London: Edward Arnold.

BRANCH, G.M. 1975. Notes on the ecology of *Patella concolor* and and *Cellana capensis*, and the effects of human consumption on limpet populations. *Zoologica Africana* 10: 75-85.

BRAUTIGAM, A. 1990. Trade in Unionids from the United States for the cultured pearl industry. *Tentacle* 2: 1-2.

BROOME, M.J. 1985. The biology and culture of marine bivalve molluscs of the genus *Anadara*. ICLARM, Manila, Philippines.

BROWN, A.C. 1991. Introduced species. In: Talbot, F.H. and R.E. Stevenson, eds. *The Encyclopedia of the earth. Oceans and Islands*. New York: Smithmark. pp. 218-220.

BROWN, K. 1980. The snail that changed the law. Strandloper No. 204: 2.

BRUGGEN, A.C. VAN. 1969. Notes on the distribution of terrestrial molluscs in southern Africa. *Malacologia* 9: 256-258.

BRUGGEN, A.C. VAN. 1975. Studies on the land molluscs of Zululand. *Zool. Verhandl*. 103: 1-116.

BRUGGEN, A.C. VAN. 1977. A preliminary analysis of African non-marine Gastropoda. Euthyneura Families. *Malacologia* 16: 75-80.

BRUGGEN, A.C. VAN. 1978. Land molluscs. In: M.J.A. Werger, ed. *Biogeography and ecology of southern Africa*. Monographiae Biologicae. The Hague: Junk. pp. 877-923.

BRUGGEN, A.C. VAN. 1980a. A preliminary checklist of the terrestrial molluscs of Madagascar. *Achatina* 8: 147-164.

BRUGGEN, A.C. VAN. 1980b. Gondwanaland connections in the terrestrial molluscs of Africa and Australia. *Malac. Soc. Australia*. 4: 215-222.

BRUGGEN, A.C. VAN. 1989. Personal communication.

BURCH, J.B. 1962. *How to know the eastern land snails*. Dubuque: Wm. C. Brown Company.

CARLTON, J. 1987. Patterns of transoceanic marine biological invasions in the Pacific Ocean. *Bull. Mar. Sci.* 41: 452-465.

CARLTON, J. 1989. Man's role in changing the face of the ocean: biological invasions and implications for conservation of near-shore environments. *Conserv. Biol.* 3: 265-273.

CARLTON, J., J.K. THOMPSON, L.E. SCHEMEL, and F.H. NICHOLS. 1990. Remarkable invasion of San Francisco Bay (California, USA) by the Asian clam *Potamocorbula amurensis*. I. Introduction and dispersal. *Mar. Ecol. Prog. Ser.* 66: 81-94.

CARLTON, J., G.J. VERMEIJ, D.R. LINDBERG and E.C. DUDLEY. 1991. The first historical extinction of a marine invertebrate in an ocean basin. *Biol. Bull.* 180: 72-80.

CARSON, H.L. 1987. The process whereby species originate. *Bioscience* 37: 715-720.

CASTILLA, J.C. and G. JEREZ. 1986. Artisanal fishery and development of a data base for managing the loco, *Concholepas concholepas* resource in Chile. In: G.S. Jamieson and N. Bourne, eds. *North Pacific Workshop on Stock Assessment and Management of Invertebrates. Can. Spec. Publ. Fish. andAquatic Sci.* 92: 57-74.

CHAMBERS, S.M. and D.W. STEADMAN. 1986. Holocene terrestrial gastropod faunas from Isla Santa Cruz and Isla Floreana, Galapagos: evidence for late Holocene declines. *Trans. San Diego Soc. Nat. Hist.* 21: 89-110.

CHAPMAN, M.D. 1987. Women's fishing in Oceania. *Human Ecol.* 15:267-288.

CHENG, E.Y. 1989. Control strategy for the introduced snail, *Pomacea lineata*. on rice paddy. *British Crop Protection Council Monograph* 41: 69-75.

CHRISTENSEN, C.C. 1983. *In litt.*

CHRISTENSEN, C.C. and P.V. KIRCH. 1986. Nonmarine mollusks and ecological change at Barbers Point, O'ahu, Hawai'i. *Bishop Mus. Occ. Pap.* 26: 52-80.

CITES. 1990. Appendices I, II. Convention on International Trade in Endangered Species of Wild Fauna and Flora. IUCN.

CLARKE, A. 1986. Competitive exclusion of *Canthyria* (Unionidae) by *Corbicula fluminea* (Muller). *Malacology Data Net* (Ecosearch Ser.) 1: 58-65.

CLARKE, B.C., J. MURRAY, and M.S. JOHNSON. 1984. The extinction of endemic species by a program of biological control. *Pacif. Sci.* 38: 97-104.

CLENCH, W.J. 1949. Cyclophoridae and Pupinidae of Caroline, Fijian, and Samoan Islands. *B.P. Bishop Mus. Bull.* 196:1-52.

CLIMO, F.M., D.J. ROSCOE, and K.J. WALKER. 1986. Research on land snails in New Zealand. Wildlife Research Liaison Group, Wellington, New Zealand.

COLLINS, N.M. and S.M. WELLS. 1987. Invertebrates in special need of protection in Europe. Nature and Environment Series No. 35, Council of Europe, Strasbourg. 170 pp.

CONNOR, S. 1992. Research on rare species 'may soon become extinct.' *Independent* Jan. 1992.

COOK, J.M. 1976. Farmers and fishermen of Tubuai: changing subsistence patterns in French Polynesia. PhD. thesis University of Kansas.

COOK, L.M., T. JACK, and C.W.A. PETTITT. 1972. The distribution of land molluscs in the Madeiran archipelago. *Bol. Mus. Mun. Funchal* 26: 5-30.

COOKE, C.M. Jr. 1935. In: H.E. Gregory, Report of the Director. *B.P. Bishop Mus. Bull.* 133: 36-55.

COOKE, C.M. Jr. and Y. KONDO. 1960. Revision of Tornatellinidae and Achatinellidae (Gastropoda, Pulmonata). *B.P. Bishop Mus. Bull.* 221.

COPPOIS, G. 1984. Distribution of bulimulid land snails on the north slope of Santa Cruz Island, Galapagos. *Biol. Journ. Linn. Soc.* 21: 217-227.

COPPOIS, G. 1986. Threatened Galapagos bulimulid land snails:an update. Abstracts. Ninth International Malacological Congress Edinburgh, Scotland:18.

COPPOIS, G. and C. GLOWACKI. 1983. Bulimulid land snails from the Galapagos. 1. Factor analysis of Santa Cruz Island species. *Malacologia* 23: 209-219.

COPPOIS, G. and S. Wells. 1987. Threatened Galapagos snails. *Oryx* 21: 236-241.

COWIE, R.H. 1992a. Evolution and extinction of Partulidae, endemic Pacific island land snails. *Phil. Trans. R. Soc. Lond. B.* 335: 167-191.

COWIE, R.H. 1992b. Introduced ampullariid and viviparid snails in Hawaii. *Pacif. Sci.* 46: 397.

CRAMPTON, H.E. 1916. Studies on the variation, distribution, and evolution of the genus *Partula*. The species inhabiting Tahiti. *Carnegie Instn. Wash. Publ.* 228: 1-313.

CRAMPTON, H.E. 1925. Contemporaneous organic differentiation in the species of *Partula* living in Moorea, Society Islands. *Am. Nat.* 59: 5-35.

CRAMPTON, H.E. 1932. Studies on the variation, distribution, and evolution of the genus *Partula*. The species inhabiting Moorea. *Carnegie Inst. Wash. Publ.* 410: 1-335.

CRONK, Q.C.B. 1989. The past and present vegetation of St. Helena. *Journ. Biogeogr.* 16: 47-64.

CROSSE, H. 1894. Faune malacologique terrestre et fluviatile de la Nouvelle-Caledonie et ses dependences. *Jour. de Conchy.* 42: 161-473.

CROWLEY, T.E. and T. PAIN. 1977. Le faune terrestre del'ile de Sainte-Helene. *Ann. Mus. Roy. de L'Afrique Centrale*, Ser. 8 Sciences Zoologiques 220: 534-575.

CUMING, H. 1827-1828. Journal of a voyage from Valparaiso to the Society and the adjacent islands performed in the schooner *Discoverer* Samuel Grimwood Master in the years 1827 and 1828. Manuscript. Mitchell Library, Sydney.

DALL, W.H. 1896. Insular land shell faunas, especially as illustrated by the data obtained by D.G. Baur in the Galapagos Islands. *Proc. Acad. Nat. Sci. Philadelphia*, 1896: 395-459.

DANCE, S.P. 1972. *Shells and shell collecting*. London: Hamlyn.

DARWIN, C.R. 1900. *The origin of species*. 6th edition. London: John Murray.

DARWIN, C.R. 1906. *Journal of researches into the geology and natural history of the various countries visited during the voyage of H.M.S. Beagle*. London: J.M. Dent & Co.

DAVIES, B.R. and K.F. WALKER. 1986. The ecology of river systems. In: Davies, B.R. and K.F. Walker, eds. *River systems as ecological units. An introduction to the ecology of river systems*. Dordecht: Dr. W. Junk.

DAVIS, G.M. 1977. Rare and endangered species: a dilemma. *Frontiers* 41: 12-14.

DAVIS, G.M. 1979. The origin and evolution of the gastropod family Pomatiopsidae, with emphasis on the Mekong River Triculinae. *Acad. of Nat. Sci. Philadelphia Monogr.* 20. 120 p.

DENSMORE, D. 1986. Endangered plants of our Caribbean islands: a unique flora faces unique problems. *Endangered Species Techn. Bull.* 11: 3-4.

DIAMOND, J.M. 1984. Historic extinctions. A Rosetta stone for understanding prehistoric extinctions. In: P.S. Martin and R.G. Klein, eds. *Quaternary Extinctions, a Prehistoric Revolution*. Tucson: University of Arizona Press. pp. 824-862.

DUDGEON, D. and M.Y. YIPP. 1983. A report on the gastropod fauna of aquarium fish farms in Hong Kong, with special reference to an introduced human schistosome host species: *Biomphalaria straminea* (Pulmonata: Planorbidae). *Malac. Rev.* 16: 93-94.

ELTON, C.S. 1958. *The ecology of invasions*. London: Chapman and Hall.

EMBERTON, K.C. 1990. Acavid land snails of Madagascar subgeneric revision based on published data (Gastropoda: Pulmonata: Stylommatophora). *Proc. Acad. Nat. Sci. Philadelphia* 142: 101-117.

EMBERTON, K.C. 1991. The genitalic, allozymic and conchologica evolution of the tribe Mesodontini (Pulmonata: Stylommatophora: Polygyridae). *Malacologia* 33: 71-178.

FAO. 1990. Yearbook. Fishery statistics. Catches and landings. Vol. 71, Food and Agriculture Organization of the United Nations, Rome.

FELLER, M., D. HOOKER, T. DREHER, I. EAST, and R. JUNG. 1979. Wilderness in Victoria: an inventory. Monash Publications in Geography No. 21.

FOSTER, A. 1983. National review of non-marine Mollusca. Invertebrate Site Register Report 4. N.C.C., Chief Scientist Team.

FRANC, A. 1957. Mollusques terrestres et fluviatiles de l'Archipel Neo-Caledonien. *Mem. Mus. Hist. Nat. Paris*, n.s., ser. A, Zool., 13, 200 pp.

FULLERTON, J.H. 1960. In: C.M. Yonge, *Oysters*. Collins: London.

GALTSOFF, P.S. 1933. Pearl and Hermes Reef, Hawaii, hydrological and biological observations. *B.P. Bishop Mus. Bull.* 107.

GARRETT, A. 1884. The terrestrial Mollusca inhabiting the Society Islands. *Journ. Acad. Nat. Sci. Philadelphia* (2) 9: 17-114.

GARRETT, A. 1887a. On the terrestrial mollusks of the Viti Islands, Part I. *Proc. Zool. Soc. London*: 164-189.

GARRETT, A. 1887b. Mollusques terrestres des Iles Marquises (Polynesie). *Bull Soc. Malac. France* 4: 1-48.

GASSIES, J.b. 1863-1880. Faune conchyliologique terrestre et fluvio-lacustre de la Nouvelle-Caledonie. *Act. Soc. Linn.* Bordeaux, 24: 211-330 (Part 1), 28: 1-212 (Part 2), 34: 1-107 (part 3).

GEPP, J. 1983. *Rote Listen Gefahrdeter Tiers Osterreichs*. Bundesministeriums fur Gesundheit und Umweltschutz. Vienna. 242 pp.

GERLACH, J. 1987. *The land snails of the Seychelles*. Northhamptonshire: Gerlach.

GERMAIN, LOUIS. 1932. La faune malacologique des iles Fidji. *Ann. Inst. Oceanogr.* n.s. 12: 39-63.

GODAN, D. 1983. *Pest slugs and snails*. Berlin: Springer.

GOETHEM, J.L. van, R. MARQUET, and J.J. de WILDE. 1987. Quelques conclusions au sujet de l'Atlas Provisoire des Gasteropodes Terrestres de la Belgique. *Apex* 2: 85-97.

GOLDBERG, E.E., V.T. BOWEN, J.W. FARRINGTON, G. HARVEY, J.H. MARTIN, P.L. PARKER, R.W. RISEBROUGH, W. ROBERTSON, E. SCHNEIDER, E. GAMBLE. 1978. The mussel watch. *Envir. Conserv.* 5: 101-126.

GOODFRIEND, G.A. and R.M. MITTERER. 1988. Late Quaternary land snails from the north coast of Jamaica: local extinctions and climatic change. *Palaeogeogr., Palaeoclimat., and Palaeont.* 63: 293-311.

GOULD, S.J. 1969. An evolutionary microcosm: Pleistocene and recent history of the land snail P. (*Poecilozonites*) in Bermuda. *Bull. Mus. Comp. Zool.* Harvard 138: 406-531.

GOULD, S.J. 1991. On the loss of a limpet. *Natural History* June: 22-27.

GREEN, J. 1968. *The biology of estuarine animals*. London: Sidgwick and Jackson.

GRIFFITHS, O., A. Cook and S.M. Wells. 1993. The diet of the introduced carnivorous snail *Euglandina rosea* in Mauritius and its implications for threatened island gastropod faunas. *J. Zool., Lond.* 229: 79-89.

GROH, K. and O. GRIFFITHS. 1987. Africa and adjacent islands. In: Parkinson, B., with J. Hemmen and K. Groh. *Tropical Landshells of the world*. Wiesbaden: Verlag Christa Hemmen.

GROH, K. and B. PARKINSON. 1987. Florida-Caribbean. In: Parkinson B., with J. Hemmen and K. Groh. *Tropical Landshells of the world*. Wiesbaden: Verlag Christa Hemmen.

GUDE, G.K. 1914. *The fauna of British India. Mollusca II. Trochomorphidae and Janellidae*. London: Taylor and Francis.

GUDE, G.K. 1921. *The fauna of British India. Mollusca-III. Land Operculates*. London: Taylor and Francis.

GULICK, J.T. 1872. On the variation of species as related to their geographical distribution, illustrated by the Achatinellinae. *Nature* 6: 222-224.

GULICK, J.T. 1905. *Evolution, Racial and Habitudinal*. Washington, D.C.: Carnegie Institution.

HADFIELD, M.G. 1986a. Extinction in Hawaiian achatinelline snails. *Malacologia* 27: 67-81.

HADFIELD, M.G. 1986b. Settlement and recruitment of marine invertebrates: a perspective and some proposals. *Bull. Mar. Sci.* 39: 418-425.

HADFIELD, M.G. and E.A. KAY. 1981. The multiple villainies of *Euglandina rosea*. *Hawaiian Shell News* 29 (4): 5.

HADFIELD, M.G. and S.E. MILLER. 1989. Demographic studies of *Partulina proxima*. *Pacif. Sci.* 43: 1-16.

HADFIELD, M.G. and S.E. MILLER. 1992. Alien predators and decimation of endemic Hawaiian tree snails. *Pacif. Sci.* 46: 395.

HADFIELD, M.G. and B.S. MOUNTAIN. 1981 [for 1980]. A field study of a vanishing species, *Achatinella mustelina* (Gastropoda, Pulmonata), in the Waianae mountains of Oahu. *Pacif. Sci.* 34: 345-358.

HANNA, G.D. 1966. Introduced mollusks of western North America. *Occ. Pap. Calif. Acad. Sci.* 48: 1-108.

HANSEN, J.A. and G.M. SKILLETER. 1988. Effects of deposit feeding by the gastropod *Rhinoclavis aspera*, on microbial abundance and production in coral reef sediments. *Abstracts. 8th Internatl. Coral Reef Symp.* Aug. 1988. Townsville, Australia. No. 161.

HARRISON, A.J. 1986. Gastropod fisheries in the Pacific with particular reference to Australian abalone. *Can. Spec. Publ. Fish. Aquat. Sci.* 92: 14-22.

HAURWITZ, R. 1990. Marauding mussels may migrate here from Lake Erie. *The Pittsburg Press*. Sunday Oct. 25 1989. In: *AMU News* 21: 11.

HEBERT, P.D.N., B.W. Muncaster, and G.L. Mackie. 1989. Ecological and genetic studies on *Dreissena polymorpha* (Pallas): a new mollusc in the Great Lakes. *Can. J. Fish.* Aquat. Sci. 46: 1587-1591.

HEDLEY, C. 1917. The economics of *Trochus niloticus*. *Austr. Zool.* 1: 69-73.

HERSHLER, R. 1985. Systematic revision of the Hydrobiidae (Gastropoda: Rissoacea) of the Cuatro Cienegas Basin, Coahuila, Mexico. *Malacologia* 26: 31-123.

HESLINGA, G.A. and W.K. FITT. 1987. The domestication of reef-dwelling clams. *Bioscience* 37: 332-339.

HESLINGA, G.A. and A. HILLMANN. 1981. Hatchery culture of the commercial top snail *Trochus niloticus* in Palau, Caroline Islands. *Aquáculture* 22: 35-43.

HESLINGA, G.A. and T.C. WATSON. 1985. Recent advances in giant clam culture. *Proc. 5th Int. Coral Reef Symp.* 5: 531-538.

HESLINGA, G., O. ORAK, and M. NGIRAMENGIOR. 1985. Coral reef sanctuaries for *Trochus* shells. *South Pacific Comm. Fish*. Newsletter No. 35: 17-20.

HESLINGA, G.A., F.E. PERRON and O. ORAK. 1984. Mass culture of giant clams (f. Tridacnidae) in Palau. *Aquaculture* 39: 197-215.

HIATT, R.W. and D.E. STRASBURG. 1960. Ecological relationships of the fish fauna on coral reefs in the Marshall Islands. *Ecol. Monogr*. 30: 65-127.

HINTON, A. 1982. Conservation in perspective. *Keppel Bay Tidings*. Oct.-Nov.

HOCKEY, P.A.R. and A.L. BOSMAN. 1986. Man as an intertidal predator in Transkei: disturbance, community convergence and management of a natural food resource. *Oikos* 46: 3-14.

IREDALE, T. 1941. A basic list of the land Mollusca of Papua. *Austr. Zool*. 10: 51-94.

IUCN. 1982. Directory of neotropical protected areas. Dublin: Tycooly International Publications.

IUCN. 1987a. The IUCN Policy Statement on Captive Breeding. SSC Captive Breeding Specialist Group. IUCN. 3 pp.

IUCN. 1987b. The IUCN Position Statement on Translocation of Living Organisms. Species Survival Commission. IUCN. 20 pp.

IUCN. 1990. *Red List of Threatened Animals*. International Union for Conservation of Nature and Natural Resources. 105

JAECKEL, S.G.A., JR. 1969. Die Mollusken Sudamerikas. In: E. J. Fittkau, J. Illies, H. Klinge, G.H. Schwabe, H. Sioli, eds. *Biogeography and ecology in South America*, vol. 2. Monographie Biologica vol. 19. Junk: The Hague. pp. 794-827.

JAIRAJPURI, M.S. 1991. *Animal resources of India Protozoa to Mammalia*. Zoological Survey of India.

JEFFS, A. 1982. Endemic snail species close to extinction. *Forest and Bird* 14: 9.

JOHNSON, M.S., MURRAY, J. and B. CLARKE. 1990. The coil polymorphism in *Partula suturata* does not favour sympatric speciation. *Evolution* 44: 459-464.

KANDEL, E., T. ABRAMS, L. BERNIER, T. CAREW, R. HAWKINS, J. SCHWARTZ. 1983. Classical conditioning and sensitization share aspects of the same molecular cascade in *Aplysia*. *Cold Spring Harbor Symp. Quant. Biol*. 47: 821-830.

KAY, E.A., CORPUZ, G. and W. MAGRUDER. 1982. Opihi. Their biology and culture. Aquaculture Development Program. State of Hawaii Dept. of Land and Natural Resources.

KERNEY, M.P. 1982. The mapping of non-marine Mollusca. *Malacologia* 22: 403-407.

KERNEY, M.P. and R.D. CAMERON. 1979. *A field guide to the land snails of Britain and Northwest Europe*. London: Collins.

KEW, H.W. 1893. *The dispersal of shells*. International Science Series 75.

KHOZOV, M. 1963. *Lake Baikal and its life*. Monographie Biologicae. The Hague: Junk.

KIRCH, P.V. and D.E. YEN. 1982. Tikopia: the prehistory and ecology of a Polynesian outlier. Honolulu: *B.P. Bishop Mus. Bull*. 238.

KISS, A. and E. PETRO. 1992. Distribution and biomass of some Chinese mussel *Anodonta woodiana* Lea, 1834 Bivalvia: Unionacea)

Population in Hungary. In: Giusti, F. and G. Manganelli, eds. *Abstr. 11th Intern. Malacol. Congr. Siena* 1992: 31-33.

KOHN, A.J. 1959. The ecology of *Conus* in Hawaii. *Ecol. Monogr*. 29: 47-90.

KONDO, Y. 1970. Extinct land molluscan species. Colloquium on Endangered Species of Hawaii. Mimeo. B.P. Bishop Museum, Honolulu, Hawaii.

LIKHAREV, I.M. and (1952). Terrestrial mollusks of the U.S.S.R. 1962 translation. Israel Program for Scientific Translation, Jerusalem.

LIONNET, G. 1984. Terrestrial testaceous molluscs of the Seychelles. In: Stoddart, D.R., ed. *Biogeography and ecology of the Seychelles Islands*. Monographiae Biologicae. The Hague: Junk.

LOCKLEY, R.M. 1980. *New Zealand endangered species*. New Zealand: Cassell.

LUTZ, R.A. 1985. Mussel aquaculture in the United States. In: Huner, J.V. and E.E. Brown, Eds. *Crustacean and mollusk aquaculture in the United States*. Cincinnati: Avi Publishing Co.

MANI, M.S. 1974a. Biogeography of the Peninsula. In: Mani, M.S., ed. *Biogeography of India*. Monographiae Biologicae. The Hague: W. Junk. pp. 614-647.

MANI, M.S. 1974b. Biogeography of the eastern borderlands. In: Mani, M.S., ed. *Biogeography of India*. Monographiae Biologicae. The Hague: W. Junk. pp. 648-663.

MARES, M.A. 1986. Conservation in South America: problems, consequences, and solutions. *Science* 233: 734-739.

MARINE RESOURCES MANAGEMENT DIVISION. 1987. FY-1987 Annual Re- port. Yap State Dept. of Resources and Development, Colonia, Yap.

MAY, R.M. 1984. Introduction. In: May, R.M., ed. *Exploitation of marine communities*. Kahlem Konferenzen 1984. New York: Springer Verlag. pp. 1-10.

MCCOY, P. 1976. *Easter Island settlement patterns in the late prehistoric and protohistoric periods*. New York: Easter Island Committee, International Fund for Monuments.

MCMAHON, R.F. 1982. Ecology of an invasive pest bivalve, *Corbicula*. In: Russell-Hunter, W.D., Ed. *The Mollusca*. Vol 6. Ecology. San Diego: Academic Press. pp. 505-561.

MEAD, A.R. 1961. *The giant African snail. A problem in economic malacology*. Chicago: University of Chicago Press. 257 pp.

MEAD, A.R. 1979. *Pulmonates* 2B. *Economic malacology with particular reference to Achatina fulica*. In: Fretter, V. and J. Peake. New York: Academic Press.

MEADS, M.J., K.J. WALKER, G.P. ELLIOTT. 1984. Status, conservation, and management of the land snails of the genus *Powelliphanta* (Mollusca: Pulmonata). *New Zealand Journ. of Zool*. 11: 277-307.

MEEHAN, B. 1977. Man does not live by calories alone: the role of shellfish in a coastal cuisine. In: Allen, J., J. Golson and R. Jones, eds. *Sunda and Sahul. Prehistoric studies in* Southeast Asia, Melanesia and Australia. New York: Academic Press.

MILLER, S.E. and M.G. HADFIELD. 1990. Developmental arrrest during larval life and life-span extension in a marine mollusk. *Science* 248: 356-358.

MILLER, S.E., R. COWIE, B. SMITH and N. ROJEK. 1993. The decline of partulid snail populations in American Samoa. *Species* 20: 65.

MOCHIDA, O. 1991. Spread of freshwater *Pomacea* snails (Pilidae, Mollusca) from Argentina to Asia. *Micronesica Suppl*. 3:51-62.

MORI, S. 1984. Molluscs. In: S. Horie, ed. *Lake Biwa*. Monographiae Biologicae. Vol. 54. The Hague: Junk. pp.331-337.

MORRISON, J.P.E. 1929. On the occurrence of *Hendersonia* in Crawford County, Wisconsin. *Nautilus* 43: 41-45.E.

MORTON, B.S. 1969. Studies on the biology of *Dreissena polymorpha* Pall. 4. Habits, habitats, distribution and control. *Water Treatment and Examination* 18: 233-240.

MUNRO, J.L. 1989. Fisheries for giant clams (Tridacnidae: Bivalvia) and prospects for stock enhancement. In: Caddy, J.F. (Ed.). *Marine invertebrate fisheries: their assessment and management*. New York: John Wiley & Sons.

MURRAY, J. and B. CLARKE. 1980. The genus *Partula* on Moorea: speciation in progress. *Proc. R. Soc. Lond.* B. 211: 83-117.

MURRAY, J., E. MURRAY, M.S. JOHNSON, and B. CLARKE. 1988. The extinction of *Partula* on Moorea. *Pacif. Sci.* 42: 150-153.

MURRAY, J., STINE, O.C., and M.S. JOHNSON. 1991. The evolution of mitochondrial DNA in *Partula. Heredity, Lond.* 66: 93-104.

MYLONAS, M. 1984. The influence of man: a special problem in the study of zoogeography of terrestrial molluscs on the Aegean Islands, Greece. In: Solem, A. and A.C. van Bruggen, eds. *World-wide snails*. pp. 249-259. Leiden: E.J. Brill.

NEVILL, G. 1869. Additional notes on land-shells of the Seychelles Islands. *Proc. Zool. Soc. London*: 61-62.

NICHOLS, F.H., J.K. THOMPSON, and L.E. SCHEMEL. 1990. Remarkable invasion of San Francisco Bay (California, U.S.A.) by the Asian clam *Potamocorbula amurensis*. Displacement of a former community. *Mar. Ecol. Progr. Ser.* 66: 95-101.

OGLE, C.C. 1979. Critical status of *Placostylus* and *Paryphanta* land snails in the far north. Fauna Survey Unit report 14. New Zealand Wildlife Service.

OKUDA, S. 1984. The influence of human activities on Lake Biwa. In: S. Horie, ed. *Lake Biwa*. Monographie Biologicae. The Hague: Junk. pp. 635-641.

OKUTANI, T. 1977. Stock assessment of cephalopod resources fished by Japan. FAO Fisheries Technical Paper No. 173.

OLIVER, J.H., JR. 1988. Crisis in biosystematics of arthropods. *Science* 240: 967.

OLIVERA, B.M., J. RIVIER, C. CLARK, C.A. RAMILO, G.P. CORPUZ, FE C. ABOGADIE, E.E. MENA, S.R. WOODWARD, D.R. HILLYARD, L.J. CRUZ. 1990. Diversity of *Conus* neuropeptides. *Science* 249: 257-263.

ORTEGA, S. 1987. The effect of human predation on the size distribution of *Siphonaria gigas* (Mollusca: Pulmonata) on the Pacific coast of Costa Rica. *Veliger* 29: 251-255.

ORTMANN, A.E. 1909. The destruction of the fresh-water fauna in western Pennsylvania. *Proc. Amer. Philosph. Soc.* 48: 90-110.

PAIN, T. 1981. Meet the Strophocheilidae. *Hawaiian Shell News* 29 (8): 1,6.

PARKINSON, B. and K. GROH. 1987. Tropical Asia. In: Parkinson, B., J. Hemmen and K. Groh. *Tropical landshells of the world*. Wiesbaden: Christa Hemmen.

PARODIZ, J.J. 1957. Catalogue of the land Mollusca of Argentina. *Nautilus* 70: 122-135; 71: 22-30, 63-67.

PARODIZ, J.J. 1980. Distribution and origin of the continental South American malacofauna. *Malacologia* 22: 421-425.

PARRISH, J.D., M.W. CALLAHAN and J.E. NORRIS. 1985. Fish trophic relationships that structure reef communities. *Proc. Fifth Internatl. Coral Reef Congress, Tahiti*, vol. 4: 73-78.

PAULAY, G. 1985. Adaptive radiation on an isolated oceanic island: the Cryptorhynchinae (Curculionidae) of Rapa revisited. *Biol. Journ. Linn. Soc.* 26: 95-187.

PAULAY, G. 1991. Henderson Island: biogeography and evolution at the edge of the Pacific Plate. In: Dudley, E.C., ed. *The Unity of Evolutionary Biology. The Proceedings of the Fourth International Congress of Systematic and Evolutionary Biology*. Vol. 1: 304-313. Portland: Dioscoroides Press.

PEAKE, J. 1978. Distribution and ecology of the Stylommatophora. In: V. Fretter and J. Peake, eds. *Pulmonates* Vol. 2A. New York: Academic Press. pp. 429.-526.

PILSBRY, H.A. 1896-1899. Non-Marine Mollusca of Patagonia. *Rep. Princeton Univ. Exped. Patagonia* 3 (Zoology) (5): 513-633.

PILSBRY, H.A. 1948. Land Mollusca of North America (North of Mexico). *Acad. Nat. Sci. Philadelphia*, Monograph No. 3, Vol. 2, Pt. 2: i-xlvii + 521-1113.

POINER, I.R. and C.P. CATTERALL. 1988. The effects of traditional gathering on populations of the marine gastropod *Strombus luhuanus* Linne 1758, in southern Papua, New Guinea. *Oecologia* 76: 191-199.

PONDER, W.F. and G.A. CLARKE. 1990. A radiation of hydrobiid snails in threatened artesian springs in western Queensland. *Rec. Australian Mus.* 42: 301-363.

POOL, D. and J.D. MCCULLOUGH 1979. The Asiatic clam *Corbicula manilensis* from two reservoirs in eastern Texas. *The Nautilus* 93: 37.

POWELL, A.W.B. 1979. *New Zealand Mollusca*. Auckland: Collins.

PUENTE, A.I. AND C.E. PRIETO. 1992. Endemic Helicoidea species of the Iberian peninsula (Pulmonata). In: Giusti, F. and G. Magnelli, eds. *Abstr. 11th Intern. Malacol. Congr. Siena*: 94-95.

RADOMAN, P. 1964. Nove Ohridske Hidrobide (III). *Arh. Biol. Nauka* 15: 101-119.

RANDALL, J.E. 1982. Tropical marine sanctuaries and their significance in reef fisheries research. In: G.R. Huntsman, W.R. Nicholson, and W.W. Fox, Jr. *The Biological Bases for Reef Fishery Management*. NOAA Technical Memorandum NMFS-SEFC-80. pp. 167-178.

RAO, H.S. 1937. On the habitat and habits of *Trochus niloticus* Linn. in the Andaman Seas. *Rec. Ind. Mus.* 39: 47-82.

ROBERTS, L. 1990. Zebra mussel invasion threatens U.S. waters. *Science* 265: 1370-1372.

RODGERS, W.A. and K.M. HOMEWOOD. 1982. Species richness and endemism in the Usambara mountain forests, Tanzania. *Biol. J. Linn. Soc.* 18: 197-242.

ROPER, C.F.E. and W. RATHJEN. 1991. World-wide squid fisheries: a summary of landings and capture techniques. *Journ. Cephalopod Biol.* 2: 51-63.

ROTH, B. 1972. Native mollusks — little known and little loved. *Sierra Club Bull.* 57 (6): 5-7.

RUSSELL-HUNTER, W.D. 1983. Overview: Planetary distribution of and ecological constraints upon the Mollusca. In: Russell-Hunter, W.D., ed. *The Mollusca* Vol. 6. New York: Academic Press. pp. 1-27.

SALVAT, B. 1970. II. Importance Biologique et sedimentologique de la faune malacologique dans les atolls Polynesiens. *Cah. Pacif.* 14: 8-53.

SALVAT, B. 1981. Preservation of coral reefs: scientific whim or economic necessity? Past, present and future. *Proc. Fourth Int. Coral Reef Symp. Manila* 1: 225-229.

SHACHAK, M., C.G. JONES and Y. GRANOT. 1987. Herbivory in rocks and the weathering of a desert. *Science* 236: 1098-1099.

van der SCHALIE, H. 1973. Damn(n) large rivers — then what? *The Biologist* 55: 29-35. Seale, A. 1916. Sea products of Mindanao and Sulu II: pearls, pearl shells, and button shells. *Phil. J. Sci.* D. 11: 245-264.

SHEPHERD, S.A., M. J. TEGNER, and S.A.G. DEL PROO. 1992. *Abalone of the world*. Oxford: Fishing News Books.

SIMPSON, C.T. 1894. Distribution of the land and freshwater mollusks of the West Indian Region, and their evidence with regard to past changes of land and sea. *Proc. U.S. Natl. Mus.* 17: 423-429.

SIMPSON, R.D. 1992. The status of the market and production of edible snails in Australia. F. Giusti and G. Manganelli, eds. *Abstr. 11th Intern. Malacol.* Congr., Siena.

SINGH, S. 1985. Protected areas in India. In: Conserving Asia's Natural Heritage. In: J.W. Thorsell, ed. Proc. 25th Working Session of IUCN's Commission on National Parks and Protected Areas, pp. 11-18.

SMITH, A.G. 1966. Land snails of the Galapagos. In: Bowman, R.I.,ed. *The Galapagos*. Berkeley: University of California Press.

SMITH, B. and D. HOPPER. 1992. The status of tree snails (Gastropoda: Partulidae) on Guam, with a resurvey of sites studied by H.E. Crampton in 1920. *Pacif. Sci.* 46: 77-85.

SMITH, B.J. 1979. Survey of non-marine molluscs of south-eastern Australia. *Malacologia* 18: 103-105.

SMITH, B.J. 1981. Introduced non-marine molluscs in Australia. *Victorian Nat.* 98: 24-26.

SMITH, B.J. 1984. Regional endemism of the south-eastern Australian land mollusc fauna (Gastropoda: Pulmonata). In: A. Solem and A.C. van Bruggen, eds. *World-wide snails*. Leiden: E.J. Brill/W. Backhuys.

SMITH, S.V. 1978. Coral reef area and contributions of reefs to processes and resources of the world's oceans. *Nature* 273 (5659): 225-226.

SOLEM, A. 1959. Systematics and zoogeography of the land and fresh-water Mollusca of the New Hebrides. *Fieldiana: Zool.* 43: 1-359.

SOLEM, A. 1961. New Caledonian land and fresh-water snails. *Fieldiana: Zoology.* 41: 413-501.

SOLEM, A. 1974. *The Shell Makers. Introducing Mollusks*. New York: Wiley Interscience.

SOLEM, A. 1975. Final Report. OES 14-16—0008-873. Upolu. Office of Endangered Species, Washington D.C.

SOLEM, A. 1976. *Endodontoid land snails from Pacific islands. (Mollusca: Pulmonata: Sigmurethra). Part I. Family Endodontidae.* Illinois: Field Museum of Natural History, Chicago. 508 pp.

SOLEM, A. 1977. Fam. Charopidae. La faune terrestre de l'ile de Sainte-Helene. 4th Pt. *Ann. Mus. Roy. de l'Afrique Centrale.* 220: 521-533.

SOLEM, A. 1978. Land snails from Mothe, Lakemba, and Karoni Islands, Lau Archipelago, Fiji. *Pacif. Sci.* 32: 39-45.

SOLEM, A. 1979. A theory of land snail biogeographic patterns through time. In: Van der Spoel, S., A.C. van Bruggen, and J. Lever, eds. *Pathways in Malacology*. Utrecht: Bohn, Scheltema and Holkema. pp. 225-249.

SOLEM, A. 1983. *Endodontoid land snails from Pacific islands. (Mollusca: Pulmonata: Sigmurethra). Part II. Families Punctidae and Charopidae, Zoogeography.* Illinois: Field Museum of Natural History, Chicago. 336 pp.

SOLEM, A. 1984. A world model of land snail diversity and abundance. In: Solem, A. and A.C. van Bruggen (Eds). *World-wide snails*. Leiden: E.J. Brill/W. Backhuys.

SOLEM, A. 1988. Maximum in the minimum: biogeography of land snails from the Ningbing Ranges and Jeremiah Hills, northern Kimberley, Western Australia. *J. Malac. Soc. Aust.* 9: 59-113.

SOLEM, A. 1990. Limitations of equilibrium theory in relation to land snails. *Atti dei Convengni Lincei* 85: 97-116.

SOLEM, A., F.M. CLIMO, and E.J. ROSCOE. 1981. Sympatric species diversity of New Zealand land snails. *N.Z. J. Zool.* 8: 453-485.

STANSBERY, D.H. 1971. Rare and endangered mollusks in the eastern United States. In: Jorgensen, S.E. and R.W. Sharp, eds. *Proc. Symp. rare and endangered mollusks (naiads) of the United States.* Unted States Fish and Wildlife Service.

TAYLOR, D.W. 1988. Aspects of freshwater mollusc ecological biogeography. *Palaeogeogr., Palaeoclimatol., Palaeoecol.* 62: 511-576.

TAYLOR, D.W. and W.L. MINCKLEY, 1966. New world for biologists. *Pacific Discovery* 19: 18-22.

TAYLOR, J.D. and K. WAY. 1976. Erosive activities of chitons at Aldabra Atoll. *Journ. Sedim. Petrol.* 46: 974-977.

THOMAS, H.S. 1884. A report on pearl fisheries and chank fisheries, 1884. Madras: The Government Press.

THOMPSON, F.G. 1968. *The aquatic snails of the family Hydrobiidae of Peninsular Florida*. Gainesville: University of Florida Press.

THOMPSON, F.G. 1986. Land mollusks of the proposed National Parks of Haiti. Report.

THORSON, G. 1971. *Life in the sea*. New York: McGraw Hill.

TILLIER, S. and B.C. CLARKE. 1983. Lutte biologique et destruction du patrimonine genetique: le cas des mollusques gasteropodes pulmones dans les territoires francais du Pacifique. *Genet. Sel. Evol.* 15: 559-566.

TRUEMAN, A.E. 1922. On the use of *Gryphaea* in the correlation of the Lower Lias. *Geol. Mag.* 59: 256-268.

TURNER, H. and M. WUTHRICH. 1985. *Systematic catalogue of Swiss Mollusca.* Swiss Federal Institute of Forestry Research, Birmensdorf, Switzerland. 2nd edition.

TURNER, J.S., C.N. SMITHERS, and R.D. HOOGLAND. 1968. The conservation of Norfolk Island. *Austr. Conserv. Found., Spec. Publ.* 1, 41 pp.

UNITED STATES DEPARTMENT OF THE INTERIOR. 1986. Endangered and threatened wildlife and plants. January 1, 1986. 50 CFR 17.11 and 17.12.

UNITED STATES FISH AND WILDLIFE SERVICE. 1991. Endangered and threatened wildlife and plants. 50 CFR 17.11 and 17.12. July 15.

VERDCOURT, B. 1972. The zoogeography of non-marine Mollusca of East Africa. *Journ. of Conch.* 27: 291-307.

VERDCOURT, B. 1982. In: W.A. Rodgers and K.M. Homewood, Species richness and endemism in the Usambara mountain forests, Tanzania. *Biol. J. Linn. Soc.* 18: 197-242.

VERDCOURT, B. 1984. Discontinuities in the distribution of some East African land snails. In: Solem, A. and A.C. va Bruggen, eds. *World-wide snails*. Leiden: E.J. Brill/W. Backhuys.

VERMEIJ, G.J. 1989. Saving the sea: what we know and what we need to know. *Conserv. Biol.* 3: 240-241.

WALDEN, H.W. 1963. Historical and taxonomical aspects of the land Gastropoda in the North Atlantic region. In: A. Love and D. Love, Eds. *North Atlantic Biota and their History*. New York: Pergamon Press. pp. 153-171.

WALDEN, H.W. 1983. Systematic and biogeographical studies of the terrestrial Gastropoda of Madeira. With an annotated check- list. *Ann. Zool. Fennici* 20: 255-275.

WALDEN, H.W. 1984. On the origin, affinities, and evolution of the land Mollusca of the mid-Atlantic islands, with special reference to Madeira. *Bol. Mus. Mun. Funchal* 36: 51-82. Walden, H.W. 1986. Endangered land mollusc species in Sweden and on Madeira. In: *Abstracts Ninth International Malacol. Congr. Edinburgh Scotland.*

WALLACE, A.R. 1872. *The Malay Archipelago.* London: MacMillan and Co.

WALLACE, G.D. and L. ROSEN. 1969. Studies on eosinophilic meningitis. V. Molluscan hosts of *Angiostrongylus cantonensis* on Pacific islands. *Am. J. Trop. Med. Hyg.* 18: 206-216.

WELLS, M.J. 1962. *Brain and behaviour in cephalopods.* London: Heinemann.

WELLS, S.M. and J.E. CHATFIELD. 1992. Conservation priorities for European non-marine molluscs. In: Giusti, F. and G. Magnelli, eds. *Abstr. 11th Intern. Malacol. Congr. Siena*: 203-204.

WELLS, S.M., R.M. PYLE and N.M. COLLINS. 1983. *The IUCN Invertebrate Red Data Book.* Cambridge, UK: IUCN

WESTERN, D. and M.C. PEARL, eds. 1991. *Conservation in the 21st century.* New York: Oxford University Press.

WHITE, M.J.D. 1978. *Modes of speciation.* San Francisco: Freeman.

WILLAN, R.C. 1987. The mussel *Musculista senhousia* in Australasia; another aggressive alien highlights the need for quarantine at ports. *Bull. of Mar. Sci.* 41: 475-489.

WILLIAMSON, P.G. 1981. Palaeontological documentation of speciation in Cenozoic molluscs from Turkana Basin. *Nature* 293: 699-702.

WILSON, E.O. 1985. Time to revive systematics. *Science* 230: 1227.

WILSON, E.O. 1987. The little things that run the world. (The importance and conservation of invertebrates). *Conserv Biol.* 1: 344-346.

WINCKWORTH, R. 1950. In: Jairapjpuri, M.S. 1991 *Animal resources of India Protozoa to Mammalia.* Zoological Survey of India.

de WINTER, A.J. 1992. Gastropod diversity in a rain forest in Gabon, West Africa. In: Giust, F. and G. Magnelli, eds. *Abstr. 11th Intern. Malacol. Congr. Siena*: 172-173.

WOODWARD, F.R. 1990. *Margaritifera margaritifera.* European Invertebrate Survey.

WOODWARD, F.R. 1991. Dr. William B. Lorrain and St. Helena's endemic land shells. *Hawaiian Shell News* 39 (11): 1,4.

YAMAGUCHI, M. 1977. Conservation and cultivation of giant clams in the tropical Pacific. *Biol. Conserv.* 11: 13-20.

YAMAGUCHI, M. and K.-I. KIKUTANI. 1989. Feasibility study of green snail transplantation to the Federated States of Micronesia. South Pacific Aquaculture Development Project, Food and Agricultura Organization of the United Nations. Suva, Fiji. 25 pp.

Appendix 1.

Members of the Mollusc Specialist Group of the IUCN Species Survival Commission as at March 1995

Mr Quentin M.C. BLOXHAM
Curator of Herpetology
Jersey Wildlife Preservation Trust
Les Augres Manor Trinity
Jersey JE3 5BF
CHANNEL ISLANDS
Tel:44/534/864666
Fax:44/534/865161

Dr Arthur E. BOGAN
Freshwater Molluscan Research
36 Venus Way
Sewell NJ 08080
U S A
Tel:1/609/5829113
Fax:1/215/2991130

Dr Philippe BOUCHET
Museum Nat. d'Histoire Naturelle
URA 699 - CNRS 55 Rue Buffon
Paris 75005
FRANCE
Tel:33/1/40793107
Fax:33/1/40793089
e-mail:bouche@mnhn

Dr A. C. van BRUGGEN
Senior Principal Scientific Officer
Leiden University, Systematic Zoology
Section Rijksmuseum
van Natuurlikje Hostorie
P.O.Box 9517
Leiden 2300 RA
NETHERLANDS
Tel:31/71/143844
Fax:31/71/274900

Dr Guy COPPOIS
Assistant
Lab.de Zoologie Systematique et Ecol.
Animale Universite Libre de Bruxelles
50 av. F.D. Roosevelt
Bruxelles 1050
BELGIUM
Tel:32/2/6502260
Fax:32/2/6502231

Dr Robert COWIE
Associate Malacologist
The State Museum of Natural and Cultural History

1525 Bernie Street
P.O. Box 19000A
Honolulu 96817-0916 Hawaii
U S A
Tel:1/808/847/3511
Fax:1/808/841/8968

Dr Maria Christina DREHER MANSUR
Museu de Ciencias Naturais
Av. Salvador Franca,
1427 Caixa Postal - 1188
Porto Alegre - RS 90.690.000
BRAZIL

Dr Ken EMBERTON
Assist. Curator,
Dept. of Malacology
Academy of Natural Sciences
of Philadelphia
1900 Benjamin Franklin Parkway
Philadelphia PA 19103-1195
U S A
Tel:1/215/2991131
Fax:1/215/2991170

Dr Jackie Van GOETHEM
Institute Royal des Sciences naturelles de Bélgiqu
Rue Vautier 29
Bruxelles 1040
BELGIUM

Dr Ph. Sci. Victor N. GORYACHEV
Lab. of Global Climate Change
All-Russian Inst. of Nature Conserv.
VNII prioroda
Vilar
113628 Moscow
RUSSIAN FEDERATION
Tel:7/095/4509420
Fax:7/095/4232322

Dr Michael G. HADFIELD
Professor of Zoology
University of Hawaii
Kewalo Marine Laboratory
41 Ajui Street
Honolulu HI 96813
U S A
Tel:1/808/5397319
Fax:1/808/5994817

Dr E. Alison KAY
Professor of Zoology
University of Hawaii
Department of Zoology
2538 The Mall
Honolulu 96822 Hawai
U S A
Tel:1/808/9568620
Fax:1/808/9569812

Dr Maria Christina MANSUR
Museu de Ciencias Naturais
Fundacao Zoobotanica
Av. Salvador Franca 1427
Porto Alegre - RS 90.690.000
BRAZIL

Prof. Brian MORTON
Director
University of Hong Kong
The Swire Marine Lab.
Cape d'Aguilar
Hong Kong
HONG KONG
Tel:852/8092179
Fax:852/8092197

Dr Beata M. POKRYSZKO
Collection Curator
Museum of Natural History
Wroclaw University
Sienkiewicza 21
Wroclaw PL-50-335
POLAND
Tel:48/71/225041
Fax:48/71/402800

Dr Winston F. PONDER
Principal Research Scientist
Australian Museum
6-8 College Street
Sydney NSW 2000
AUSTRALIA
Tel:61/2/3398120
Fax:61/2/3604350

Mr Theo RIPKEN
Volunteer Assistant
Nationaal Natuurhistorisches Museum
Afda. Mollusca
Postbus 9517
Leiden 2300 RA
NETHERLANDS
Dr Mary Barbara SEDDON
Curator (Terrestrial Mollusca)
National Museum of Wales
Dept. of Zoology
Cathays Park

Cardiff CF1 3NP
UNITED KINGDOM
Tel:44/1222/397951
Fax:44/1222/239009
e-mail:seddonm@cf.ac.uk.

Dr Greg SHERLEY
Research Scientist
NZ Dept. of Cons.,
Science & Rech.ch Div.
Box 10420
Wellington
NEW ZEALAND
Tel:64/4/4710726
Fax:64/4/4713279

Dr Fred G. THOMPSON
Curator of Malacology
Florida Museum of Natural History
Univ. of Florida
Gainesville 32611-2035 Florida
U S A
Tel:1/904/3921721
Fax:1/904/3928783

Dr Henrik W. WALDEN
Curator
Natural History Museum
Goteborg S-40235
SWEDEN

Ms Susan M. WELLS
Coral Cay Cons. Univ.
College of Belize University
Drive West Landiver
P.O. Box 990
Belize City
BELIZE
Tel:501/2/32787
Fax:501/2/32787
e-mail:coral@ucb.edu.bz

Mr Frederick Richard WOODWARD
Depute Keeper
Natural History Art Gallery
and Museum Kelvingrove
Glasgow G3 8AG
Scotland
UNITED KINGDOM
Tel:44/41/3573929
Fax:44/41/3574537